FERNS
of the
SOUTHEASTERN STATES

FERNS

of the

SOUTHEASTERN STATES

Descriptions of the fern-plants growing
naturally in the States south of the
Virginia-Kentucky State line and east of
the Mississippi River

(Illustrated)

By

JOHN KUNKEL SMALL

Drawings by
RUTH SINCLAIR GEORGE

Facsimile of the edition of 1938

HAFNER PUBLISHING COMPANY

New York   London

1964

REPRINTED BY ARRANGEMENT

Printed and Published by
Hafner Publishing Company, Inc.
31 East 10th Street
New York, N.Y. 10003

Library of Congress Catalog Card Number: 63-16480

Lithographed in the U.S.A.
by NOBLE OFFSET PRINTERS, INC.
New York, N. Y. 10003

JOHN KUNKEL SMALL—AN APPRECIATION
January 31, 1869–January 20, 1938

No section of the continental United States surpasses the region commonly referred to as the southeastern states in the abundance of its vegetation, the variety of its flora, or the number of its plant species. Soil, topography, climate, all combine in making it an unusual floral region. It has attracted the attention of botanists, plantsmen and collectors. Here came in earlier days Catesby, Ellis, Walter, the Frasers, the Bartrams, the Michauxs, Drummond, and others, in search of medicinal plants and garden materials. The labors of all these enriched the gardens of other lands. Here lived and worked such men as Chapman, Mohr, and Tracy, who, through their studies and collections, added greatly to the botanical knowledge of this vast area. Yet all these left the region only partially explored and known. Much of it during their day and time was difficult or well nigh impossible of access. Much of it had never known the footsteps of botanist or collector and in consequence knowledge of the plants of the region was incomplete.

About the beginning of the twentieth century Dr. John K. Small, connected with the then recently established New York Botanical Garden, turned his attention to the botany of the southeastern states. His first trip into North Carolina in student days was in 1891, and into Florida in 1901, and from the latter date down to his death, January 20, 1938, his interest in the area and the plants peculiar to it never ceased. One or more trips annually were generally made. He brought to the work to which he had set himself thorough training, a retentive memory, keen discernment of form and color, unswerving devotion to his undertaking, and physical stamina such as few possess. No journey was too difficult, no road too hard, no morass too deep to stop him. These but challenged his powers, mental and physical. He wrote of his journeys and the plants he found in more than ninety papers. To read them is to realize how intimately he knew his subject and in what great measure he was able to take his reader with him. Doctor Small's interest centered not only in the herbarium material that he procured, but more definitely in the living plants he met. Had it not been for this latter interest, it is doubtful whether he would have been able to establish a satisfactory basis for many of the classifications he made. Above all else he was a field worker.

In 1903 his "Flora of the Southeastern United States" came from the press,—a huge volume of 1370 pages—and a second edition was published in 1913. These volumes embraced the areas included not only in the southeastern states but extended well over into Texas. When his "Manual of the Southeastern Flora" was issued in 1933, the area was reduced to that portion of the United States lying east of the Mississippi River and northward to include Tennessee and North Carolina, and, though this volume appears smaller in size because of thinner paper, it has a total of 1554 pages and describes more than 5500 species. Many plants new to botanical science were described and new genera established in his floras and in smaller books and papers. As a result of his labors, the foundations for botanical knowledge of the southeastern plants have been placed upon a basis that possibly would not have been established otherwise except after the lapse of many years.

From the very beginning Doctor Small was interested in ferns and these formed the subject of several distinct publications. Five papers attest his interest; the first of these was published in 1918. Two books, "The Ferns of Florida," 1932, and "Ferns of the Vicinity of New York," 1935, have come from his pen. The third with its excellent drawings is presented herewith.

Doctor Small was absorbed in his botanical studies: otherwise it would have been impossible for him to cover the widespread field that he did. His absorption resulted in his being known only to a limited circle of workers with a common interest. These were wholeheartedly his friends. They appreciated the ability, the integrity, and above all the comradeship of the man who gave of himself so generously in the furtherance of the science that interested him. Because of that centered interest the botany of the southeastern states has been advanced many decades. He found a limited scattered plant knowledge, he expanded it, segregated it, made it available for a vast area. His name will always be associated with the plants he loved so much.

H. HAROLD HUME

University of Florida,
  Gainesville, Florida,
    May 1, 1938.

FERNS

of the

SOUTHEASTERN STATES

CONTENTS

CONTENTS

PREFACE

The southeastern corner of the United States was the first part of the New World mainland to attract the adventurer and the investigator. The lust for gold and silver was the chief incentive. However, among the hordes of early expeditioners were a few who observed generally, or were interested in, other things. The wealth of novel vegetation could not escape attention, and attempts at description. Thus, early records of the plants of the Coastal Plain resulted, even though more or less indefinite. After the mass-expeditionary period had come to an end, the individualist period began with the usual better and more abundant results.

Although botany in North America was cradled in the far southeast, it reached maturity in the northeast. Only when the individual collectors traversed the southeastern region—the botanical pioneers from Great Britain and the Continent, from the American colonies and later from the states—did the true nature and magnitude of its flora become manifest. As a result of the evidence gathered by these pioneers and by subsequent collectors and students, the ferns of the southeastern flora are now generally understood. The low rolling country, more easy of access, yielded its genera and species earliest; the rugged mountains, for the most part difficult of access, yielded next. The part with least relief, but latest to be populated by the white man, peninsular Florida, yielded last, and its harvest was large.

Up to the beginning of the present century fern collecting and studies in Florida were largely incidental to travelling botanists or to special attention in quite circumscribed areas. In the first decade of this century the hidden fern treasures in hammocks of the Pleistocene Everglade Keys and vicinity at the southern end of the Florida peninsula were tapped by the writer and his associates in exploration. This region was up to that time quite difficult of access. Beginning with the third decade the last region to be thoroughly explored for ferns—the ancient tropical Oligocene Island region in the upper part of the peninsula—was made the object of an intensive fern study by Edward P. St. John and Robert P. St. John. The results of these remarkable explorations

5

and studies are recorded on the following pages, especially under the genera *Trichomanes, Thelypteris,* and *Ophioglossum.*

Notwithstanding the progress made during these various explorations it is probable that fern discoveries of importance can still be made in the southeastern states. One mountainous section of North Carolina remains botanically almost unknown. The unusual flora and plant associates of the nearly unexplored Big Cypress west of Deep Lake in southern Florida gives promise of additional fern novelties. The lakes, marshes, and water courses which cover a large part of the Peninsular State furnish habitats for vast numbers of isoetes and aquatic allies. Whether these plants and those of contiguous territory are representatives of a few or of several species is undetermined. The discovery of a large fern at Goulds, a few miles south of Miami, is evidence that even the conspicuous ferns have not all been reported from this range.

During several revisions of the preliminary manuscript information and destructive and constructive criticism was forthcoming from such fern students as Edgar T. Wherry, Edward P. St. John, and Wm. A. Knight. These students also read the final copy and the proof. To Robert P. St. John, in particular, thanks are due for constant aid extending through several years. The proof was also read by John Hendley Barnhart and by Bertha Pickering who also made the index. The chapter on "The Cultivation of Native Southeastern Ferns" was contributed by Wm. A. Knight. The "Taxonomic List with Citations" and the "Authorities City in This Work" were compiled by John Hendley Barnhart.

The figures on the following pages are from drawings made by Ruth Sinclair George. A three-centimeter rule accompanies figures that have been reduced from natural size. The preparation of the manuscript was made possible by the cooperation of the Board of Managers of The New York Botanical Garden through the late Director, Marshall A. Howe, and the drawings through the cooperation of Jules Van Item, Supervisor of W. P. A. projects.

JOHN KUNKEL SMALL

THE NEW YORK BOTANICAL GARDEN

INTRODUCTION

A region in the eastern United States made up, geologically, of the oldest and the newest formations with several intermediate ones, is bound both to harbor a large number of plants and to reflect interesting problems in all groups of plants.

The area involved is relatively not large, but the great age of a considerable part of it and the altitudinal vacillation in that past geologic time, and the vast expanse of very recent formations result in an extensive flora and complicated floristics in various branches of the plant kingdom.

The problems of an ancient plant group—the Pteridophyta, ferns and fern-allies—as this is developed in the region under consideration, are very intriguing. This volume is the result, in part, of the writer's studies in the ferns[1] of eastern North America during a half century.

When one, even the botanist, speaks of the southeastern United States, he usually does not realize that he is considering not only the most densely populated plant area in North America, but also the most ferny one.

From fern-clad mountain peaks over 6000 feet high down to still more extensively fern-clad hammocks, swamps, marshes, and ponds, at or near sea-level, as well as all kinds of rock exposures, there are afforded altitudes and habitats suitable for almost any genus or species of fern capable of growing in eastern North America. The diversity and number of the ferns from the states south of the Virginia-Kentucky line and east of the Mississippi River that are represented in the larger herbaria is evidence of the truth of this observation.

The boreal region of the southeast (southern mountains, Blue Ridge in particular) and the tropical (southern Florida) contribute to the list many ferns that naturally are lacking from the intermediate altitudes. References to the list on the following pages will demonstrate the validity of the above statements.

[1] In this volume the word fern is used in a broad sense to cover the groups of fern-allies as well as the true ferns.

There were at least two major plant reservoirs that supplied the ancestors of the ferns that now populate the southeastern United States: First, the crest of the Blue Ridge, which held vegetation in reserve when a large part of the southeast was submerged under the sea; Second, the Caribbean islands lying south of the continental shelf upon which peninsular Florida and the Keys now stand, which held vegetation in reserve for Florida, until its relatively recent elevation above the sea.

The nomenclatural (though scarcely the taxonomic) foundation, in fern literature, of the present work is the "Species Plantarum" of Linnaeus, published in 1753. This early treatment of the ferns is, of course, incomplete, in the matter of both genera and of species, and is also decidedly unorganized. Indeed, Linnaeus[1] knew of but 45 of our 189 species of native ferns. He grouped them under twelve ill-defined generic headings. Moreover, Linnaeus knew comparatively few of these 45 species from the region under consideration, his plants and information having come mainly from insular and continental tropical America. It was subsequent exploration that discovered the many tropical American species this side of the Gulf Stream.

The following list shows the Linnaean interpretation of our fern-plants, and also their present-day generic equivalents:

Onoclea sensibilis L.
Ophioglossum vulgatum L.
Ophioglossum palmatum L. = Cheiroglossa palmata (L.) Presl.
Osmunda virginiana L. = Osmundopteris virginiana (L.) Small.
Osmunda regalis L.

[1] Carl Linnaeus was born 13/14 May, 1707, at Rashult, Smoland, Sweden. His interest in botany dated from his youth. At twenty he began his university studies at Lund, going to Upsala in the following year. In 1732 he traveled in Lapland, under the auspices of the Upsala Academy and during the next few years visited various parts of Sweden, Denmark, Germany, Holland, and England. In 1735 he received the degree of doctor of medicine in Holland, and made his home in that country for several years. It was while there that he published the details of his artificial "sexual system" of plant classification, which soon made his reputation world-wide, and was used exclusively by nearly all botanists for almost a hundred years. In 1738 he returned to Sweden, and became a practicing physician in Stockholm; from 1741 he was a professor in the University of Upsala, where he remained until his death, 10 January, 1778, publishing meanwhile numerous works, botanical and zoological; the most famous is his "Species Plantarum," 1753, which is now accepted as the starting-point of modern botanical nomenclature.—JOHN HENDLEY BARNHART.

Osmunda cinnamomea L.
Osmunda adiantifolia L. = Anemia adiantifolia (L.) Sw.
Acrostichum polypodioides L. = Marginaria polypodioides (L.) Tidestrom.
Acrostichum areolatum L. = Lorinseria areolata (L.) Presl.
Acrostichum platyneuron L. = Asplenium platyneuron (L.) Oakes.
Acrostichum ilvense L. = Woodsia ilvensis (L.) R.Br.
Acrostichum Thelypteris L. = Thelypteris Thelypteris (L.) Nieuwl.
Pteris lanceolata L. = Paltonium lanceolatum (L.) Presl.
Pteris caudata L.
Pteris lineata L. = Vittaria lineata (L.) J. E. Smith.
Pteris atropurpurea L. = Pellaea atropurpurea (L.) Link.
Blechnum occidentale L.
Lonchites repens L. = Hypolepis repens (L.) Presl.
Asplenium rhizophylla L. = Camptosorus rhizophyllus (L.) Link.
Asplenium Scolopendrium L. = Phyllitis Scolopendrium (L.) Newm.
Asplenium serratum L.
Asplenium Trichomanes L.
Asplenium Trichomanes dentatum L. = Asplenium dentatum L.
Polypodium heterophyllum L. = Phymatodes heterophyllum (L.) Small.
Polypodium Phyllitidis L. = Campyloneurum Phyllitidis (L.) Presl.
Polypodium virginianum L.
Polypodium pectinatum L.
Polypodium aureum L. = Phlebodium aureum (L.) R.Br.
Polypodium Phegopteris L. = Phegopteris Phegopteris (L.) Keyserl.
Polypodium noveboracense L.=Thelypteris noveboracensis (L.) Nieuwl.
Polypodium marginale L. = Dryopteris marginalis (L.) A. Gray.
Polypodium fragile L. = Cystopteris fragilis (L.) Bernh.
Polypodium bulbiferum L. = Cystopteris bulbifera (L.) Bernh.
Adiantum pedatum L.
Adiantum Capillus-Veneris L.
Adiantum clavatum L. = Sphenomeris clavata (L.) Maxon.
Lycopodium nudum L. = Psilotum nudum (L.) Griseb.
Lycopodium clavatum L.
Lycopodium rupestre L. = Selaginella rupestris (L.) Spring.
Lycopodium alopecuroides L.
Lycopodium Selago L.
Lycopodium obscurum L.
Lycopodium cernuum L.
Lycopodium carolinianum L.
Lycopodium apodum L. = Diplostachyum apodum (L.) Small.

After the Linnaean period many ferns and groups of ferns were removed from their earlier generic associations and classed in more natural, or, at least, less complex groups. Curiously enough, after a lapse of nearly two centuries, untidy and confusing genera are still maintained in the classifications of some fern students. This uneven division of the ferns, *i.e.,* into simple or natural groups, and complex or unnatural groups under generic headings, is confusing to the amateur. Accordingly, in this text an attempt has been made to interpret the fern-plants involved in more simple or natural generic concepts.

PLANT PROVINCES

Fortunately for the botanist the fundamental geologic and physiographic structure of the southeast is comparatively simple. Six major plant areas are involved. They coincide with certain groups of geological formations. The four older areas lie in sub-parallel bands (Piedmont, Blue Ridge, Appalachian Valley, and Appalachian Plateaus) and are flanked by a younger formation (the Coastal Plain) on the east, south, and southwest; and on the west by the Interior Low Plateaus.

The plant provinces comprise two main kinds of geologic formations, (a) igneous and metamorphic (recrystallized) and (b) sedimentary. Starting with the present most elevated provinces, the Blue Ridge and adjoining Piedmont, we find igneous and metamorphic rocks. The next formations in respect to age lie to the westward, namely the Appalachian Valley, the Appalachian Plateaus, and the Interior Low Plateaus. These are consolidated sedimentary rocks composed largely of detritus eroded from the older formations.

The oldest vegetation of our area was wholly wiped out ages ago, and so were its direct descendants. The oldest highland vegetation populated the Piedmont and the Blue Ridge, whence it spread as new formations appeared. How many waves of vegetation there were we do not know. In the final adjustment we scarcely know which flora is the older—that of the Coastal Plain or that of the Appalachian and Interior Low Plateaus provinces. The beginnings of these floras, indeed, may have been coincident, that of the former starting with elements from the tropics, that of the latter with elements from the highlands.

Outstanding Features

Throughout our area are many minor plant regions, all interesting and some celebrated as fern localities. Watersheds and river valleys are in all of the provinces.

In the Blue Ridge are mountain ranges, ridges, and peaks, gorges, waterfalls, and high plateaus. The Blue Ridge represents the most elevated country east of the Rocky Mountains. There are many peaks over 6000 feet in altitude. According to present available figures the twin Black Brothers represent the maximum altitude, the higher peak registering 6690 feet above sea-level. Clingman's Dome is 6642 feet and Mt. Mitchell is 6684 feet. The differences in elevation furnish different fern habitats. The lower peaks are clothed with deciduous forests and their moist places are mainly along streams; the high peaks, mostly above 5000 feet, are clothed with coniferous growth and are frequently cloud-capped and consequently very moist.

In the Piedmont the outstanding areas are the outcrops of igneous and metamorphic rocks. Dunn's Mountain in North Carolina and Stone Mountain in Georgia are well known granite domes. Stone Mountain is the original and only known locality for the fern-relative *Isoetes melanospora*. Two other very prominent isolated elevations, with a maximum altitude of 1705 feet, should be mentioned, King's Mountain, and Crowder's Mountain, which rise out of the plain near Gastonia, North Carolina; also Kenesaw and other mountains in Georgia. The fall-line along the inner edge of the Coastal Plain has special features. Also, back of the fall-line there are deep valleys cut by the rivers, with the steep rocky sides often facing north. The altitude of the Piedmont increases inland and southward, and points fully 1800 feet above sea-level are reached in North Carolina and Georgia.

In topography the Appalachian Valley, the Appalachian Plateaus, and the Interior Low Plateaus have some things in common, but there are also unique features in each.

In the Appalachian Valley there is a series of parallel longitudinal valleys and mountain ridges all of which result in a trellised drainage system with large streams and deep valleys, and much limestone which many ferns like. There are steep river bluffs and rock cliffs in some places. The sharp included ridges with a maximum altitude of about 3000 feet have the cliffs facing both eastward and westward. The hills in some places are rock-capped. It is near the southern end of this province that *Phyllitis Scolopendrium,* far removed from its center of abundance, first appears south of New York State.

In the Appalachian Plateaus with the features of a dissected plateau there are horizontal strata and the drainage is decidedly dendritic, which helps to keep the wood and swamp ferns more evenly distributed. The escarpments permit of waterfalls, rapids, and coves. There are many cliffs, chiefly of sandstone but locally of limestone. Gorges are also present. The varied rock formations and various degrees of moisture form suitable habitats for rock-loving ferns. The interesting fern *Asplenium Bradleyi* was discovered on Walden's Ridge, at the southern end of this province. Altitudes range from 500 to 3000 feet above sea-level.

In the Interior Low Plateaus dendritic drainage also obtains. There are rich woods and swamps. In some places there are steep bluffs along the rivers. Extensive outcrops of limestone have been eroded by the action of the weather and by flowing water. Large and small caverns are also present where interesting ferns may be found. It was in this province that *Cheilanthes alabamensis* was discovered.

In the Coastal Plain, the lowest and flattest province, but very diversified in soil, the outstanding minor plant habitats are river courses, springs, swamps, savannahs, lakes; and there are major areas, such as pine-woods, deciduous woods, including some hammocks, and in Florida outcrops of limestone strata in the form of cliffs, grottoes, and caves. It is in the southern parts of this province that ferns are represented by the greatest number of genera and species.

Two areas in the Florida Peninsula are outstanding features in the Coastal Plain—the one geologically very old, lying in the temperate part of the State, the other much less ancient and lying in the tropical and subtropical part of the State. The area

referred to on the following pages as Oligocene Island region is
the remnant of an ancient island of Oligocene times which has
continuously remained above the sea since then. It has an oval
outline, the length extending from and including the Gainesville
region at the north and the Tampa region at the south; the width
includes the western half of the peninsula thereabouts. In this
ancient area are stranded about a score of native tropical ferns
not known elsewhere in the State. This fern assemblage represents the remains of a very early plant invasion from the American
tropics.[1]

The second outstanding feature in the Florida Coastal Plain is
part of the Pleistocene area of the southern portion of the peninsula and the Keys, representing an assemblage of tropical and
subtropical plants. The invasion of ferns during Pleistocene times
and later has left us not less than thirty native tropical ferns,
mainly in the hammocks, south of the latitude of Lake Okeechobee.

Although there is considerable altitude in the whole southeastern
area, with mountains well over 6000 feet high, as a result of the
southern latitude, of over 2000 miles of seacoast, and of the
proximity to the tropics of parts of the region, the tropical elements are dominant in numbers.

Our record shows one hundred and eighty-nine species of ferns
and fern-allies growing naturally in the southeastern continental
United States. The great majority of these are native plants.
One less than a dozen are naturalized. However, these exotics
have adapted themselves so well to the habitats of their native relatives and associates that in the following notes no distinction
beween natives and exotics need be mentioned.

The southeastern flora has had a long history. In its area are
embraced the oldest and the youngest geologic formations. Its
fern content has been derived from two main sources; a vast and
productive tropical reservoir on the south and a limited temperate-
boreal reservoir on the north. The accumulation of the present
extensive fern population naturally was a gradual process. However, there are definite migrations indicated: several from the

[1] See Am. Fern Jour. **26** : 41–50. 1936.

tropics into the lowlands, and one from the north along the highlands. The latter so generously supplied the lower part of the contiguous states with ferns that the Blue Ridge province can claim only about six species as peculiar to itself. The Antillean tropics have been even more generous with their rich store-house by making the most recent extensive geological feature of the United States—peninsular Florida—the richest fern area, both in the number of species and the number of plants, in continental North America north of Mexico. The fern assemblage of the southeast represents well over fifty per cent of that of the United States and Canada.

JOHN K. SMALL

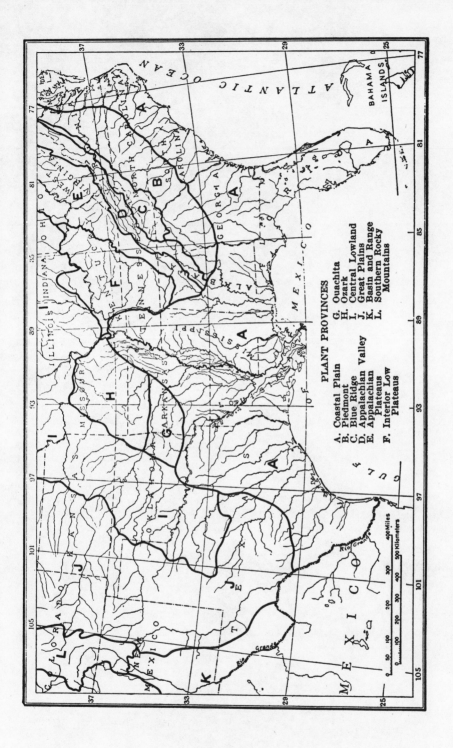

PLANT PROVINCES

A. Coastal Plain   G. Ouachita
B. Piedmont   H. Ozark
C. Blue Ridge   I. Central Lowland
D. Appalachian Valley   J. Great Plains
E. Appalachian   K. Basin and Range
    Plateaus   L. Southern Rocky
F. Interior Low   Mountains
    Plateaus

KEY TO THE ORDERS, FAMILIES, AND GENERA ILLUSTRATED FOR STUDENTS

KEY TO THE ORDERS

A. Foliage leaves with broad or narrow, entire, toothed, pinnate, or variously dissected blades—Fern-like plants.

   B. Spores of one kind, minute.

      C. Sporangium (spore-case) membranous, opening irregularly by an elastic ring: plants not succulent: vernation (arrangement of the leaf in the bud) spirally coiled (rarely bent).   Order 1. FILICALES.

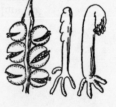

      C. Sporangium (spore-case) coriaceous, opening by a transverse slit: plants succulent: vernation (arrangement of the leaf in the bud) erect or inclined.   Order 2. OPHIOGLOSSALES.

   B. Spores of two kinds, numerous, minute microspores and fewer larger megaspores borne in sporocarps (spore-capsules).   Order 3. SALVINIALES.

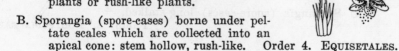

A. Foliage leaves scale-like or subulate, sometimes elongate, sometimes united into sheaths at the stem-nodes—Moss-like plants or rush-like plants.

   B. Sporangia (spore-cases) borne under peltate scales which are collected into an apical cone: stem hollow, rush-like.   Order 4. EQUISETALES.

17

B. Sporangia (spore-cases) borne in the axils of scale-like or relatively small leaf-like or long-subulate bracts: stem solid.

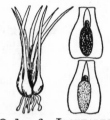

C. Leaves scale-like, flat, borne on erect or creeping stems and branches: terrestrial or rarely epiphytic plants. Order 5. LYCOPODIALES.

C. Leaves long-subulate, borne on and around a short corm-like caudex, the bases closely overlapping: aquatic or amphibious plants.

Order 6. ISOETALES.

ORDER 1. FILICALES

KEY TO THE FAMILIES

A. Leaves with filmy translucent blades: sporangia (spore-cases) sessile on a filiform receptacle borne within an urceolate, cupulate, funnel-form, or tubular indusium.

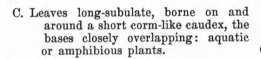

Family 1. HYMENOPHYLLACEAE.

A. Leaves with herbaceous or coriaceous opaque blades: sporangia (spore-cases) borne on the back or on the margins of partly or of wholly modified foliage leaves (sporophyls), sometimes forming spikes or panicles.

B. Sporangia (spore-cases) borne on the back or on the margin of a leaf-blade or (sporophyl) a division of one.

C. Sporangia (spore-cases) long-stalked.

Family 2. POLYPODIACEAE.

C. Sporangia (spore-cases) sessile or nearly so.

    D. Sporangia (spore-cases) not associated in definite sori: plants aquatic.   Family 3. CERATOPTERIDACEAE.

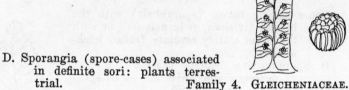

    D. Sporangia (spore-cases) associated in definite sori: plants terrestrial.   Family 4. GLEICHENIACEAE.

B. Sporangia (spore-cases) in panicles or spikes developed from the modified leaves (sporophyls) or parts of leaves.

    C. Sporangia (spore-cases) ovoid or pyriform, the ring or annulus apical, complete.   Family 5. SCHIZAEACEAE.

C. Sporangia (spore-cases) globose or subglobose, the ring or annulus rudimentary or incomplete.   Family 6. OSMUNDACEAE.

FAMILY 1. **Hymenophyllaceae**

Diminutive plants with creeping or horizontal
  rootstock, often growing in mats: leaf-blades
  flabellate, pinnatifid, or pinnate: indusia truncate or lobed at the mouth.

One genus in our range.   1. TRICHOMANES.

FAMILY 2. **Polypodiaceae**

KEY TO THE FERN GROUPS

A. Spore-bearing leaves (sporophyls) with the
  blades, divisions, or leaflets flat, or with
  the edges merely revolute (rolled backward).
  B. Spore-bearing leaflets (s p o r o p h y l s)
    densely clothed with masses of spor-
    angia (spore-cases).

  C. Leaves of two kinds (dimorphic), the
    sporophyl (spore-bearing) ones quite
    different from the other (foliage)
    leaves; veins free.   I. STENOCHLAENEAE.

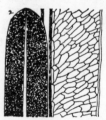

  C. Leaves of one kind, not dimorphic, the
    sporophyl (spore-bearing) ones not
    different from the foliage leaves:
    veins united to form a network
    (anastomosing).   II. ACROSTICHEAE.

  B. Spore-bearing leaflets (sporophyls) or
    leaf-segments with s p o r a n g i a
    (spore-cases) borne in separated
    sori (''fruit-dots'').
  C. Indusium (covering of a sorus) want-
    ing, the sori (''fruit-dots'')
    naked.
    D. Sori (''fruit-dots'') not borne in
      marginal lines along the leaf-
      edges.

E. Sori ("fruit-dots") circular or nearly so, borne on the veins on the back of the leaf-blade, leaflets, or leaf-lobes: leaflets entire or bluntly toothed or lobed: leaf-blades green beneath.

F. Leaf-blades entire, lobed or 1-pinnatifid or 1-pinnate: petioles jointed to the rootstock.

III. POLYPODIEAE.

F. Leaf-blades 2-pinnatifid or 2-pinnate: petioles not jointed to the rootstock. Genera *Meniscium, Goniopteris,* and *Phegopteris* in

X. DRYOPTERIDEAE.

E. Sori ("fruit-dots") irregular, borne along the veins of the leaflets or leaf-segments: leaflets sharply toothed, incised, or lobed: leaf-blades coated with white, ochroleucous, or yellow powder beneath.

IV. PITYROGRAMMEAE.

D. Sori ("fruit-dots") marginal, borne in a linear continuous or interrupted line along the leaf-edges.

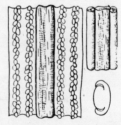

V. VITTARIEAE.

C. Indusium (covering of a sorus) present, of various shapes and completeness, sometimes evanescent.

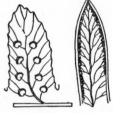

D. Sori ("fruit-dots") marginal or dorsal, but not borne in cup-like or pocket-like indusia which open towards the apex of the leaf.

E. Sori ("fruit-dots") marginal or essentially so: indusium (covering of a sorus) formed, in part, by the more or less modified leaf-margins.

F. S p o r a n g i a (spore-cases) borne on a continuous vein-like receptacle connecting the apices of the veins.

VI.　PTERIDEAE.

F. Sporangia (spore-cases) borne at or near the apices of unconnected veins, and interrupted along t h e margin.

VII.　ADIANTEAE.

E. Sori ("fruit-dots") dorsal: indusium not formed by
   part of the leaf-margin.

F. Sori ("fruit-dots") narrow,
   linear to elliptic: indusium (covering of
   the sorus) mostly more
   than thrice as long as
   broad.

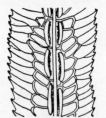

G. Sori ("fruit - dots")
   borne parallel to and
   contiguous to the mid-
   rib of the leaf-seg-
   ments, on specialized
   veins.

VIII. BLECHNEAE.

G. Sori ("fruit - dots")
   borne oblique to and
   away from the midrib
   of the leaf-blade or the
   leaf-segment on the
   ordinary veins.

IX. ASPLENIEAE.

F. Sori ("fruit-dots") broad,
   roundish or reniform:
   indusium (covering of
   the sorus) less than
   twice as long as wide.

G. Indusium (covering of a sorus) if present superior (opening below the sorus), orbicular or reniform.

H. Sori ("fruit-dots") mostly on the backs of the veins: indusia (covering of the sori) attached at or near the middle, opening all around: leaf-blades simple or compound, the leaflets not articulate, persistent.   X.   DRYOPTERIDEAE.

H. Sori ("fruit-dots") terminal on the veins: indusia (covering of the sori) attached at the side, opening laterally, mostly towards the margin of the leaflets: leaf-blades 1-pinnate, the leaflets articulate and deciduous.   XI.   NEPHROLEPIDEAE.

G. Indusium (covering of a sorus) wholly or partly inferior (opening above the sorus), hood-like or stellate: sorus seated in the indusium which it more or less covers.   XII.   WOODSIEAE.

D. Sori ("fruit-dots") borne in cup-like or pocket-like indusia which open towards the apex of the leaf-segment.

XIII. DAVALLIEAE.

A. Spore-bearing leaves (sporophyls) with the divisions closely rolled together, thus necklace-like or berry-like.

XIV. ONOCLEAE.

KEY TO THE GENERA

I. STENOCHLAENEAE

Creeping or climbing plants with spiny-toothed leaflets.

1. STENOCHLAENA.

II. ACROSTICHEAE

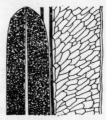

Erect plants with entire coriaceous leaflets.

2. ACROSTICHUM.

III. Polypodieae

A. Veins free: leaf-segments several or usually
    numerous and narrow.
  B. Sori ("fruit-dots") superficial: leaves
    not scaly.

3. POLYPODIUM.

  B. Sori ("fruit-dots") sunken in pits: leaves
    scaly.

4. MARGINARIA.

A. Veins anastomosing (forming a network):
    leaf-segments few or leaf-blades entire
    and broad.
  B. Leaf-blades broad, pinnatifid.

    C. Leaf-segments with nearly or quite
      uniform areolae (meshes between
      the veins and veinlets), each areola
      with a single free veinlet: sori
      ("fruit-dots") terminal on the in-
      cluded veinlet.

5. GONIOPHLEBIUM.

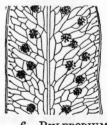

    C. Leaf-segments with irregular areolae
      (meshes between the veins and vein-
      lets), each areola along the midrib
      without a veinlet: sori ("fruit-
      dots") terminal on a pair of vein-
      lets.

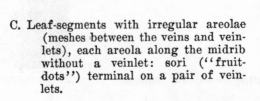

6. PHLEBODIUM.

B. Leaf-blades narrow, elongate, not pinnatifid, essentially entire.

C. Rootstocks short, not climbing: leaves
   in a crown: areolae (meshes between
   the veins and veinlets) in regular
   rows, or chiefly in one row in *C.
   angustifolium*.

7. CAMPYLONEURUM.

C. Rootstocks elongate, extensively climbing: leaves spaced on the rootstock:
   areolae (meshes between the veins
   and veinlets) irregular.

8. PHYMATODES.

IV. PITYROGRAMMEAE

Showy plants with leaves coated beneath with
white, ochroleucous, or yellow powder.

9. PITYROGRAMMA.

V. VITTARIEAE

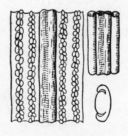

A. Veins obscure, forming a single row of areolae
   (meshes between the veins and veinlets)
   without included veinlets.

10. VITTARIA.

A. Veins freely anastomosing, the areolae with included veinlets.

11. PALTONIUM.

VI. PTERIDEAE

A. Indusium (covering of the sorus) single, formed by the modified leaf-margin: leaf-blades 1-pinnate or rarely 2-pinnate.

12. PYCNODORIA.

A. Indusium (covering of the sorus) double, an inner membranous portion arising from the receptacle: leaf-blades more than 2-pinnate.
  B. Veins forking, but free: middle division of leaf-blade 2-pinnate (in our species).

13. PTERIS.

  B. Veins anastomosing not free: middle division of leaf-blade 1-pinnate (in our species).

14. LITOBROCHIA.

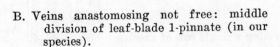

VII. Adianteae

A. Leaves with only the teeth or lobes of the divisions or leaflets recurved on the sori ("fruit-dots") as indusia.
B. Petioles (leaf-stalks) black or very dark, slender and wiry: leaflets flabellately veined, *i.e.*, disposed fan fashion.   15. Adiantum.

B. Petioles (leaf-stalks) yellowish to brown, stout, not wiry: leaflets pinnately veined.   16. Hypolepis.

A. Leaves with the margins of the segments wholly recurved over the sori ("fruit-dots").
B. Leaflets with pubescent blades: sporangia (spore-cases) in interrupted submarginal bands: veinlets with much thickened tips.   17. Cheilanthes.

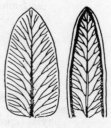

B. Leaflets glabrous except the midrib: sporangia (spore-cases) forming continuous submarginal bands: veinlets not thickened at the tip.   18. Pellaea.

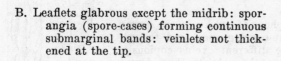

VIII. Blechneae

A. Blades of the leaflets or leaf-segments entire or toothed: veins free, or in spore-bearing leaflets connected near their bases by a transverse continuous receptacle: sori (''fruit-dots'') continuous or nearly so.

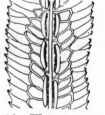

19. Blechnum.

A. Blades of the leaflets or leaf-segments pin-natifid or undulate: veins anastomosing (forming a network) near the midrib: sori (''fruit-dots'') interrupted, chain-like.
B. Leaves uniform, of one kind, the sporo-phyls (spore-bearing ones) and foliage leaves similar: veins free or sparingly anastomosing (united) in a row along the midrib or sori.
C. Veins forming a series of areolae (meshes) between the sori and the leaf-margin.

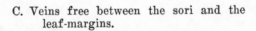

20. Woodwardia.

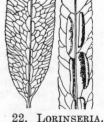

C. Veins free between the sori and the leaf-margins.

21. Anchistea.

B. Leaves dimorphous of two kinds, the sporo-phyls (spore-bearing ones) and foliage leaves quite different: veins copiously anastomosing throughout, thus form-ing fine areolae (meshes).

22. Lorinseria.

IX. ASPLENIEAE

A. Veins free: sori ("fruit-dots") all oblique, rather evenly disposed.
B. Sori ("fruit-dots") linear, confluent, the indusia contiguous in pairs, one on the upper side of a vein and one on the lower side of the adjacent vein, but appearing double: opening along the middle: leaf-blades simple.

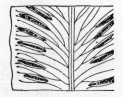

23. PHYLLITIS.

B. Sori ("fruit-dots") single on the outer side of the veinlet or crossing it: indusium opening on the outer side: leaf-blades 1-, 2-, or 3-pinnate.
C. Leaves evergreen; blades, or leaflets thin-or thick-coriaceous; petioles or rachis firm, slender and wiry.

24. ASPLENIUM.

C. Leaves not evergreen; blades, or leaflets herbaceous; petioles soft and relatively stout, not wiry, often stramineous.
D. Blades of the leaflets pinnatifid or pinnate: veins or veinlets running into the teeth of the margins.
E. Leaf-segments coarsely toothed; sori ("fruit-dots") very short, at least some of the indusia vaulted across the vein, opening all around the edge.

25. ATHYRIUM.

E. Leaf-segments entire or bluntly toothed: sori ("fruit-dots") rather long, at least some of the indusia double, placed back to back and opening in opposite directions.

26. DIPLAZIUM.

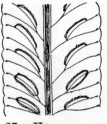

D. Blades of the leaflets shallowly
   toothed: veins or veinlets running into the sinuses of the
   margins.   27. HOMALOSORUS.

A. Veins copiously anastomosing: sori (''fruit-
   dots'') oblique, but variously disposed.   28. CAMPTOSORUS.

X. DRYOPTERIDEAE

A. Veins anastomosing (forming meshes).
   B. Indusium (covering of the sorus) present:
      veins copiously and irregularly
      anastomosing, the areolae (meshes)
      irregular: sori (''fruit-dots'') sepa-
      rated.
   C. Leaf-blades pinnatifid or pinnately 3-
      foliolate, the terminal leaflet larger
      than the others: petioles (leaf-
      stalks) with few fine scales.   29. TECTARIA.

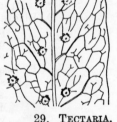

C. Leaf-blades pinnate, the leaflets several
   to many: petioles (leaf-stalks) with
   numerous coarse scales.   30. CYRTOMIUM.

B. Indusium (covering of the sorus) wanting: veins regularly and copiously anastomosing by pairs, the areolae (meshes) regular and many or irregular and few: sori ("fruit-dots") covering the back of the leaflets or spaced.

C. Veinlets joined regularly between the veins forming series of parallel areolae (meshes) between the midrib and the margin: sori ("fruit-dots") confluent.

31. MENISCIUM.

C. Veinlets joined irregularly to form few irregular areolae (meshes): sori ("fruit-dots") separated.

32. GONIOPTERIS.

A. Veins free or those of the lower one or two pairs joined and running merely to the sinus.

B. Indusium (covering of the sorus) present (or vestigial in *Thelypteris subtetragona* and *T. submarginalis*).

C. Indusium (covering of the sorus) reniform or suborbicular and with a narrow shallow sinus.

D. Leaf-segments entire or merely repand: veins simple or merely forked, the lower ones of adjacent segments converging to or meeting in the sinus, or one or two pairs of veins uniting in the tissues below the sinus and running into it: leaves not evergreen northward.

33. THELYPTERIS.

D. Leaf-segments toothed, lobed, or
   pinnatifid, the teeth blunt or
   spinescent: veins forked, the
   branches running to the margin
   remote from the sinus: leaves
   evergreen.   34. DRYOPTERIS.

C. Indusium (covering of the sorus)
   orbicular-peltate, without a sinus,
   opening all around.   35. POLYSTICHUM.

B. Indusium (covering of the sorus) want-
   ing: sori ("fruit-dots") naked.   36. PHEGOPTERIS.

XI. NEPHROLEPIDEAE

Epiphytic or terrestrial plants: leaves long and
narrow, often greatly elongate; leaflets numerous; blades toothed: indusia (covering of the
sori) reniform or orbicular-reniform.   37. NEPHROLEPIS.

XII. Woodsieae

A. Indusia attached by one side of the base, at one side of the sori, hood-like, truncate or prolonged into a tip.

38. Cystopteris.

A. Indusia attached by the middle of the base, beneath the sorus, thus wholly inferior, roundish or cleft into irregular broad or narrow lobes or stellate.

39. Woodsia.

XIII. Davallieae

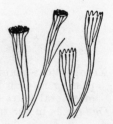

A. Indusium (covering of the sorus) flattish, attached at the base and the sides, the soral-pouch pocket-like: leaf-segments linear-cuneate, truncate and minutely toothed at the apex.

40. Sphenomeris.

A. Indusium (covering of the sorus) convex, adnate laterally to the concave opposed lobule, the soral-pouch cup-like: leaf-segments cuneate to ovate, rounded and toothed at the apex.

41. Dennstaedtia.

XIV. Onocleae

Terrestrial plants with extensively spreading rootstocks and erect leaves, the foliage leaves and the sporophyls (spore-bearing leaves) separate and quite different.

42. Onoclea.

Family 3. Ceratopteridaceae

Plants aquatic or amphibious, normally floating but sometimes anchored in mud, with succulent broadly divided foliage leaves and staghorn-like sporophyls.

One genus.

1. Ceratopteris.

Family 4. Gleicheniaceae

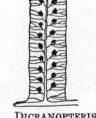

Xerophyllous plants, with wiry petioles usually passing into an indeterminate rachis with one or several pairs of opposite branches.

One genus in our range.

1. Dicranopteris.

Family 5. Schizaeaceae
Key to the Genera

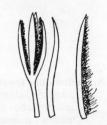

A. Plant erect: leaves not twining.
   B. Sporophyls (spore-bearing leaflets) borne on specialized leaves: leaves with narrow simple, terete, or flattish blades.

1. Actinostachys.

B. Sporophyls (spore-bearing leaflets) borne
   on the elongate branches of ordinary
   leaves: leaves with pinnately compound
   blades.

2. ANEMIA.

A. Plant climbing: leaves vine-like, twining.   3. LYGODIUM.

FAMILY 6. Osmundaceae

Erect plants with tufted leaves, the sporophyls
   separate and distinct from foliage leaves, or
   with the terminal or median portion of a foliage leaf spore-bearing: the fertile parts red
   or brown.
One genus in our range.

1. OSMUNDA.

ORDER 2. OPHIOGLOSSALES

FAMILY 1. Ophioglossaceae
KEY TO THE GROUPS

A. Foliage leaf with an entire or palmately
   lobed blade, the veins anastomosing (forming a mesh) and with some free included
   veinlets: sporangia (spore-cases) cohering
   or coalescent in more or less elongate
   spikes.   I. OPHIOGLOSSEAE.

A. Foliage leaf with 1–4-times pinnately or
   ternately divided blade, the veins simple or
   forking: sporangia (spore-cases) distinct
   from each other, borne in simple or compound, sometimes congested spikes or
   panicles.   II. BOTRYCHIEAE.

KEY TO THE GENERA

I. OPHIOGLOSSEAE

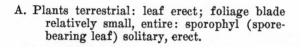

A. Plants terrestrial: leaf erect; foliage blade relatively small, entire: sporophyl (spore-bearing leaf) solitary, erect.

1. OPHIOGLOSSUM.

A. Plants epiphytic: leaf pendent; foliage blade typically palmately lobed: sporophyls (spore-bearing leaves) usually few or several, pendent from the side of the leaf-stalk below the blade or from the base of the blade.

2. CHEIROGLOSSA.

II. BOTRYCHIEAE

A. Leaf-segments succulent, crenulate, fimbriate, or serrulate, the epidermal cells straight: veins several-times forked: bud for the following year enclosed in the base of the common stalk.

3. BOTRYCHIUM.

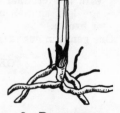

A. Leaf-segments membranous, pinnatifid, the epidermal cells curved: veins mostly once-forked: bud for the following year exposed along one side of the stalk.

4. OSMUNDOPTERIS.

ORDER 3. SALVINIALES

KEY TO THE FAMILIES

A. Plants rooting in muddy bottoms: stems
   (rootstocks) creeping or horizontal: sporocarps (spore-capsules) uniform, containing
   both megaspores and microspores: leaves
   filiform or with 2- or 4-foliate blades, the
   leaflets dilated.   Family 1. MARSILEACEAE.

A. Plants floating: stems pinnately branched:
   sporocarps (spore-capsules) of two kinds,
   small ones containing a megaspore, and
   larger ones containing pedicelled microsporangia: leaves with entire or 2-lobed
   blades.   Family 2. SALVINIACEAE.

FAMILY 1. Marsileaceae

KEY TO THE GENERA

A. Sporocarps (spore-capsules) ovoid or ellip-
   soid: leaves with 2- or 4-foliolate blades.   1. MARSILEA.

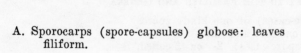

A. Sporocarps (spore-capsules) globose: leaves
   filiform.   2. PILULARIA.

FAMILY 2. **Salviniaceae**

KEY TO THE GENERA

A. Leaves minute, imbricate on pinnately branching stems.   1. AZOLLA.

A. Leaves large (1–1.5 cm. long), 2-ranked and
spreading on mostly simple stems.   2. SALVINIA.

ORDER 4. EQUISETALES

FAMILY 1. **Equisetaceae**

Terrestrial, rush-like plants, with extensively
creeping rootstocks, fluted stems and leaves
united into sheaths, the sporophyls collected
into a terminal cone.

One genus.   1. EQUISETUM.

ORDER 5. LYCOPODIALES

KEY TO THE FAMILIES AND GENERA

A. Sporangia (spore-cases) of one kind: spores
        minute, of one sort and size.
    B. Sporangia (spore-cases) 2- or 3-celled,
        opening by 2 or 3 apical valves,
        subtended by scale-like sporophyls
        (bracts): plants scaly.   Family 1. PSILOTACEAE.

One genus in our range.   1. PSILOTUM.

B. Sporangia (spore-cases) 1-celled, transversely 2-valved: hidden in leaf-like sporophyls (bracts): plants leafy.

Family 2. LYCOPODIACEAE.

One genus in our range.   1. LYCOPODIUM.

A. Sporangia (spore-cases) of two kinds, some with many minute spores (microspores), others with few large spores (megaspores).

Family 3. SELAGINELLACEAE.

KEY TO THE GENERA

A. Leaves soft, of two kinds, borne in two planes, the lateral one the larger and two-ranked; blades not bristle-tipped: diffuse or prostrate plants with creeping stems and branches.

1. DIPLOSTACHYUM.

A. Leaves stiff, all alike, several ranked and
   uniformly disposed; blades bristle-tipped:
   tufted plants with erect or ascending stems
   and branches.

2. SELAGINELLA.

ORDER 6. ISOETALES

FAMILY 1. Isoetaceae

Aquatic or amphibious plants, the quill-like
leaves with enlarged bases imbricate on a
corm-like caudex.

One genus.

1. ISOETES.

SUBKINGDOM PTERIDOPHYTA

FERNS AND FERN ALLIES

Plants containing woody and vascular tissues. They produce spores asexually, each of which, on germination, develops into a prothallium, a small thalloid body (gametophyte). The prothallia bear the reproductive organs; the female organ is known as an archegone, the male as an antherid. As a result of the fertilization of an egg in the archegone by a motile spermatozoid produced in the antherid, the asexual state of the plant (sporophyte) is developed; this phase is popularly known as a fern, a lycopod, or a quillwort. This phase sometimes propagates by buds or bulblets which are borne on the leaves.—About 6,000 species of living ferns and fern-allies are known. Perhaps an equal number of fossil species have been discovered. A great majority of the living forms grow only in tropical regions.

KEY TO THE ORDERS

Foliage leaves with broad or narrow, entire, toothed, pinnate, or variously dissected blades—Fern-like plants.
   Spores of one kind, minute.
      Sporangia membranous, opening irregularly by an elastic ring : plants not succulent : vernation spirally coiled (rarely bent). Order 1. FILICALES.
      Sporangia coriaceous, opening by a transverse slit : plants succulent : vernation erect or inclined. Order 2. OPHIOGLOSSALES.
   Spores of two kinds, minute microspores and larger megaspores, borne in sporocarps. Order 3. SALVINIALES.
Foliage leaves scale-like or subulate, sometimes united into sheaths—Moss-like plants or rush-like plants.
   Sporangia borne under peltate scales which are collected into an apical cone : stem hollow, rush-like. Order 4. EQUISETALES.
   Sporangia borne in the axils of scale-like or relatively small leaf-like or long-subulate bracts : stem solid.
      Leaves scale-like, flat, borne on erect or creeping stems and branches : terrestrial or rarely epiphytic plants. Order 5. LYCOPODIALES.
      Leaves long-subulate, borne on a short corm-like caudex : aquatic plants. Order 6. ISOETALES.

43

Order 1. **FILICALES**

Terrestrial or epiphytic, or in one family aquatic, plants, various in habit. Sporangia developed normally from single epidermal cells, variously disposed, mainly upon the under surface of the leaf, commonly in clusters (sori) upon the veins, or within special marginal indusia, or, less commonly, irregularly or in rows upon slender more or less non-foliose pinnae or segments. Spores of one sort. Indusia covering the sori in many cases, or sometimes wanting. Prothallia flattish or filamentous, green, terrestrial or epiphytic.—Includes several families, six of which occur in our range.

Key to the Families

Leaves with filmy translucent blades: sporangia sessile on a filiform receptacle borne within an urceolate, cupulate, funnel-form, or tubular indusium. **Fam. 1.** Hymenophyllaceae.
Leaves with herbaceous or coriaceous opaque blades:
    sporangia borne on the back or on the margins of partly or of wholly modified foliage leaves, sometimes forming spikes or panicles.
  Sporangia borne on the back or on the margin of a leaf-blade or a division of one.
    Sporangia long-stalked. **Fam. 2.** Polypodiaceae.
    Sporangia sessile or nearly so.
      Sporangia not associated in definite sori: plants aquatic. **Fam. 3.** Ceratopteridaceae.
      Sporangia associated in definite sori: plants terrestrial. **Fam. 4.** Gleicheniaceae.
  Sporangia in panicles or spikes developed from the modified leaves or parts of leaves.
    Sporangia ovoid or pyriform, the ring or annulus apical, complete. **Fam. 5.** Schizaeaceae.
    Sporangia globose or subglobose, the ring or annulus rudimentary or incomplete. **Fam. 6.** Osmundaceae.

Family 1. **HYMENOPHYLLACEAE**

Filmy-fern Family

Delicate or dainty, mostly matted small plants with filiform or slender creeping or suberect rootstocks. Leaves often numerous and crowded: blades very thin, translucent, entire, erose, toothed, or usually much divided, the leaf-tissue pellucid, usually consisting of a single layer of cells. Sporangia sessile on a filiform, usually elongate receptacle within an urceolate, cup-like, funnelform, or tubular, either truncate or 2-lipped, marginal indusium which arises at the tip of a vein; ring complete, transverse, opening vertically.—There are two genera in the filmy-fern family, the following and *Hymenophyllum*. The latter genus, common throughout wet tropical regions, has not yet been found within our range.

1. **TRICHOMANES** L.

Plants extensively creeping, often densely matted, with intricately branched wiry rootstocks, terrestrial, epiphytic, or epipetric. Leaves remote or close together on the rootstock: blades entire, lobed, or pinnatifid, or several times pinnately divided or flabellate. Indusium tubular or funnelform, immersed in the leaf-blade or exserted, truncate or sometimes broadly 2-lipped, the sporangia mostly upon the lower portion of the slender, often exserted, receptacle.—FILMY-FERNS. FILMYS.—About 250 species of wide distribution in tropical and subtropical regions.—The genus is based on *Trichomanes crispum* L.—The name is ancient Greek for some fern.—The following species are sometimes considered under the generic name *Didymoglossum* Desv.—Three of the following species occur in a limestone region, while one is confined to sandstone. Two species occur on both limestone and sandstone.

Indusia more or less exserted beyond the leaf-margins : receptacle bristle-
like, slightly exserted from the indusium-mouth.   I. SETOSA.
Indusium immersed or included in the leaf-sinuses : receptacle capillary, long-exserted from the indusium-
mouth.   II. CAPILLARES.

I. SETOSA

Leaf-blades flabellate, crenate, lobed or incised : plants
mostly terrestrial, often epipetric.
Indusia funnelform, the mouth flaring : leaf-blades
thinly few-veined, the veins not running to
the margins.   1. *T. Petersii.*
Indusia subcylindric, two-lipped at the mouth : leaf-
blades many-veined.
Veins even, slightly tapering or slightly enlarging, the tips narrower, blunt, or fading
out.
Veins numerous, spaced, mostly separated by
several rows of cells : plant of the Ever-
glade Key region, Fla.   2. *T. punctatum.*
Veins very numerous, rather close together,
mostly separated by 1, 2, or 3 rows of
cells : plant of the Oligocene Island
region, Fla.   3. *T. sphenoides.*
Veins conspicuously enlarging toward the mar-
gin of the blade, ending in truncate tips at
the margin.   4. *T. lineolatum.*
Leaf-blades pinnatifid, the segments pinnatifid : plants
epiphytic or epipetric.   5. *T. Krausii.*

II. Capillares

Indusium not exserted beyond the leaf-segments, slightly 2-lipped.   6. *T. Boschianum*.

1. T. Petersii A. Gray. Plants terrestrial: rootstocks widely creeping, matted, sometimes forming long string-like series of leaves: leaves with a few black hairs along the margins when young; blades ovate, linear-oblong, obovate, or spatulate, entire or crenate, 6–24 mm. long, on slender petioles: indusium solitary, terminal, mainly immersed, funnelform, expanded at the mouth.—(FILMY-FERN.)—Under moist rocks, Coastal Plain, Fla. to La., and more northern provinces, Ga. to Ala., Ill., and S. C.—Spores mature in summer.—Fig. enlarged, insert natural size.

The two kinds of filmy-ferns, *Trichomanes Boschianum* and *T. Petersii*, discovered in Alabama and described in 1853, remained the only two representatives of this large tropical genus known in the United States for half a century. The original specimens of the latter were collected near the Sipsey River, Hancock, now Winston County, Alabama. At the beginning of the present century three species were discovered in southern peninsular Florida. Whereas one of the two species discovered in Alabama is confined to Ohio and the southeastern United States and the other is known only on the other side of the Gulf Stream and in South America, the three species discovered in southern Florida are well-known tropical American plants. Furthermore, *Trichomanes Boschianum* stands alone among the filmy-ferns of our region, while *T. Petersii* resembles, in habit, the species of southern Florida. The plants grow in dense moss-like tufts on the face of sandstone rocks. They are kept moist the greater part of the year by percolating water or by the spray from adjacent waterfalls. More recent activities in collecting in the southeastern states have discovered this filmy in Georgia, South Carolina, Tennessee, and Mississippi as well as in additional stations in Alabama. Even more recently the geographic range has been extended to Louisiana and Illinois. This fern is found up to 1200 feet altitude in Alabama and up to 1500 feet in Tennessee. Its occurrence in this temperate latitude is rather a mystery. Its ancestors may have come from the West Indies and been part of the vegetation of the ancient Oligocene Island whence the descendants travelled northwestward and adjusted themselves through the ages to cooler and more changeable temperatures after the final elevation of that part of the continent took place. With this possibility in mind careful search in the territory formerly included within the limits of the ancient Oligocene Island resulted in the discovery[1] of a small

[1] First collected in Florida by Edward P. St. John, March 8, 1936.

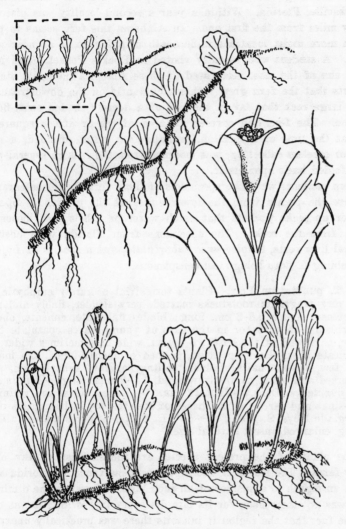

TRICHOMANES PETERSII

colony of this fern growing on detached rocks at a distance from flowing or standing water in a rocky, hilly, moderately dry hammock near Brooksville, Florida. Within a year a second locality was discovered many miles from the first one. In Alabama this fern seems to prefer much more moist locations underneath dripping rocks or near waterfalls. A student who recently visited at Buck's Pocket, Sand Mountain, one of the most celebrated of these Alabama botanical stations, reports that the fern grew rather abundantly on the downstream side of a large rock that lay in the bed of a densely shaded swift-flowing stream. The fern had covered an area of ten or fifteen square feet but at the time of inspection, perhaps as a result of flood, a recent fire, or careless collecting, was loosened from the rock in several places and folded back upon itself.

Fern students who take specimens of filmy fern should be careful to remove the plants from the lower edges of the growth as openings higher up make pockets that catch water or debris that loosens the mats from the rocks. The specimens from Florida were hosts for several liverworts, *Cololejeunea tuberculata*, and a species of *Lejeunea* resembling *L. flava* being most conspicuous.

2. **T. punctatum** Poir. Plants terrestrial or rarely epiphytic, usually very fragrant: rootstocks matted, very slender, finely and softly radiculose: leaves 0.8–2 cm. long; blades flabellate, cuneate, obovate, or orbicular-obovate (or in the case of young leaves spatulate to obovate, narrowed at the base), 3–8 mm. wide or sometimes wider, with a cuneate base, slender-petioled, incised or incised-lobed, the margins with few, stellate hairs: indusia solitary or few, subcylindric, partly immersed and often narrowly winged, 1.5–2 mm. long.—[*Didymoglossum punctatum* Desv.]—(FILMY-FERN.)—Edges, sides, and vicinity of lime-sinks and rarely on the bases of tree-trunks, in hammocks on the Everglade Keys, S. pen. Fla.—(*W. I., S. A.*)—Spores mature all year. —Fig. enlarged, insert natural size.

The plants of the present species are the smallest of any of our filmy-ferns. The leaves of the first specimens found in Florida varied from an eighth to a quarter of an inch high. However, the diminutive size was not the reason for its late discovery in Florida; it was owing to the fact that the region it inhabits there was practically unexplored country up to the beginning of the present century.

The geographic range of this filmy indicates that it long ago came out of the West Indies, and then secured a foothold in tropical Florida. If it came in the second invasion it did not progress north. It is almost always terrestrial, but occasionally occurs on the bases of

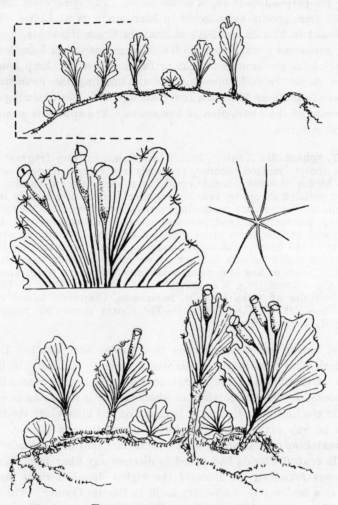

TRICHOMANES PUNCTATUM

tree-trunks about lime-sinks where the ferns grow in abundance. It occurs either in small patches or in dense carpets, sometimes entirely lining the perpendicular edges of the sinks. The species was described in 1808 from specimens collected in Martinique, West Indies. It was first found in Florida in 1901[1] in Snapper Creek Hammock, and then listed, erroneously, as *T. sphenoides*. Since then it has been found in several of the pineland hammocks as far southwest as Camp Longview and in Royal Palm Hammock. Notwithstanding the abundance of this fern in southern Florida a few years ago, it is now becoming scarce on account of the destruction of hammocks. The species is common in tropical America.

3. T. sphenoides Kunze. Plants terrestrial, not very fragrant: rootstocks densely matted, slender, copiously radiculose: leaves 6–20 mm. long; blades obovate, cuneate, oval, or suborbicular, 4–11 mm. wide, slender-petioled except on running rootstocks, undulate, bluntly toothed or laciniate (sometimes producing narrow proliferous blades from the margin), the margins (and petioles) more or less copiously or densely ciliate with stellate hairs often with 5–9 branches, broadly or narrowly cuneate at the base: veins very numerous, mostly separated by 1, 2, or 3 rows of cells: indusia solitary or as many as four together, subcylindric, more or less immersed, sometimes with mere wings along the sides, about 2 mm. long. [*Didymoglossum sphenoides* Presl.]—(FILMY-FERN.)—Sides of rocks on hills, hammocks, Oligocene Island region, cent. Fla.—(*W. I., C. A., S. A.*)—The spores mature all year.—Fig. enlarged, insert natural size.

This, among recent discoveries in Florida, adds another tropical American filmy-fern to our southeastern region.[2] Centrary to the behavior of the filmys of the Everglade Keys which grow where breezes are checked by dense vegetation or where the air is stagnated in erosion holes in the lime-rock, this plant is found on the hills where the breezes are in no way conducive to the storing of moisture in the air. After long search among dripping mossy rocks in damp deeply-shaded locations in central Florida had failed to disclose any filmy fern, *T. sphenoides* was found on the sides of the higher detached rocks near the crest of a moderately shaded dry knoll in Sumter County. The collections of mosses and liverworts made on the Everglade Keys two or three decades ago contained many rare and some new species. Some of these were closely associated with the filmy-ferns and even epiphytic on their leaves. The latter condition was possible through either the

---

[1] First collected in Florida by J. K. Small, October 27, 1901.
[2] First collected in Florida seven miles east of Floral City, February 7th, 1936, by Robert P. St. John.

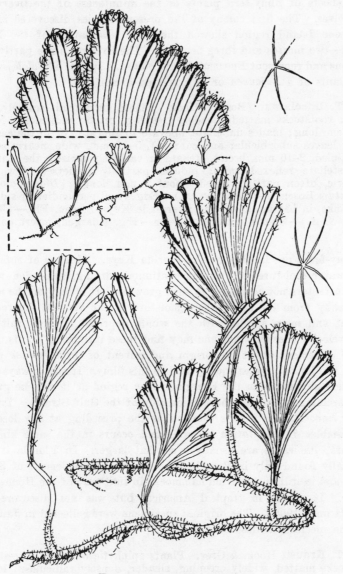

TRICHOMANES SPHENOIDES

large sheets of filmy-fern plants or the minuteness of the liverworts themselves. The first colony of the present species discovered in the Oligocene Island region showed the same association of the lower plants—two mosses and three hepatics. The liverworts are partly epiphyllous and represent *Euosmolejeunea clausa*, a species of *Cololejeunea*, and plants of a *Lejeunea* or of a related genus.

4. **T. lineolatum** (Bosch) Hook. Plants terrestrial, scarcely fragrant: rootstocks matted, slender, creeping, bristly radiculose: leaves 1.5–3 cm. long; blades flabellate, obovate to cuneate (or in the case of young leaves suborbicular and cordate), 5–12 mm. wide, nearly sessile or petioled, 2–10 mm. broad, crenate or variously incised, the margins with stellate reflexed hairs: indusia partially immersed, few, subcylindric, often partly winged, about 2 mm. long. [*Didymoglossum lineolatum* Bosch.]—(FILMY-FERN.)—Edges and perpendicular sides of lime-sinks, in hammocks on the Everglade Keys, S. pen. Fla.—(*W. I., C. A., S. A.*)—Spores mature all year.—Fig. enlarged, insert natural size.

Filmy-ferns are lacking on the Florida Keys. Absence of sufficient fresh-water moisture and almost continuous drying, salt-laden winds are two factors not conducive to such growths. It is only on the mainland away from the coast where moisture in the air and the rock is present and more stable, with the winds deprived of their salt and their velocity checked, that one may find these intriguing plants.

The statement about the origin and advent of *Trichomanes punctatum* in Florida applies equally well to this filmy. It may always have been less ubiquitous in the Everglade Key region or it may be gradually becoming extinct on the Florida side of the Gulf Stream. *Trichomanes lineolatum* is not as common as the preceding at any locality. It resembles *T. punctatum* in habit and occurs in the same kind of habitats; its leaves are usually somewhat larger. In Florida it was originally found only in Ross Hammock near the settlement of Silver Palm, and is still known from hammocks in that part of the Homestead region. It occurs in tropical America, but was not discovered in Florida until 1906.[1] The original specimens were collected in Jamaica and the species was described in 1864.

5. **T. Krausii** Hook. & Grev. Plants epiphytic or rarely terrestrial: rootstocks matted, widely creeping, slender, densely radiculose: leaves 2–6 cm. long; petioles short, bristly, sometimes winged above; blades variable, elliptic to broadly elliptic or ovate, 5–15 mm. wide, deeply pinnatifid, the rachis thus narrowly winged, the segments linear to

[1] First collected in Florida by J. K. Small and J. J. Carter, November 12, 1906.

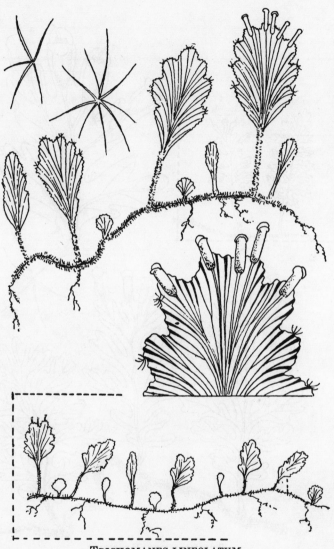

TRICHOMANES LINEOLATUM

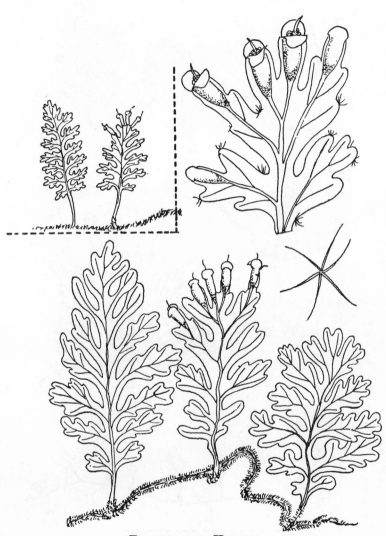

TRICHOMANES KRAUSII

elliptic, pinnatifid, the lower ones deeply lobed, each sinus bearing a
small black stellate hair, the upper edge not parallel to the rachis:
indusia few or several, exserted from the leaf-segments, but narrowly
winged, about 2 mm. long. [*Didymoglossum Krausii* Presl.]—
(FILMY-FERN.)—Bases of tree-trunks, roots, logs, stems of shrubs and
rarely on rocks, in hammocks, on the Everglade Keys, S. pen. Fla.—
(*W. I., C. A., S. A.*).—Spores mature all year.—Fig. enlarged, insert
natural size.

A pinnatifid leaf-blade at once distinguishes this filmy from our four
dwarf species. Evidently of tropical origin and dissemination, it must
once have crossed the Florida Straits and lodged in the southern part
of the Florida peninsula. There is no evidence that it ever grew
further north than its present geographic limits, although it may once
have been more abundant within its present range when more extensive
favorable habitats existed there. It has been found in a half dozen
hammocks from the Silver Palm region to near Camp Longview. It
occurs in dense hammocks and grows not only on trees and shrubs near
the ground, but quite high up, sometimes completely covering the
trunks and limbs with masses that can be stripped off as mats of
several square feet in extent. The original specimens were collected
in Dominica, W. I., and described in 1829. It was first found in
Florida in 1903,[1] but was previously known in both the neighboring
and distant parts of tropical America.

6. T. Boschianum Sturm. Plants terrestrial: rootstocks elongate,
wiry, tomentose: leaves ascending; petioles naked or nearly so; blades
lanceolate or ovate-lanceolate, 5–20 cm. long, 2- or 3-pinnatifid, the segments inequilaterally ovate, obtuse, toothed or cut into linear or narrowly ovate divisions, the upper edge of the cuneate base parallel to
the winged rachis or nearly so: indusia 1–4 to a segment, 1.5–2 mm.
long, immersed in the tissue of the leaf-segment. [*T. radicans* A.
Gray, not Sw.]—(BRISTLE-FERN.)—Damp or wet rocks or ledges,
Coastal Plain and adj. provinces, W. Fla. (?) to Ala., Ky., Ohio and
Ga.—Spores mature in summer.—Fig. natural size.

Habit and technical characters remove this filmy from our other
species. The coarse, black-bristly, widely creeping, foliose rootstock
and the wholly immersed indusia with capillary elongate receptacles are
all distinctive marks. Its ancestors evidently came from the great
tropical filmy-fern reservoir, perhaps as far back as when the ancient
Oligocene Island was the only part of present Florida above the sea.
As they migrated northward they became somewhat immune to cold,

[1] First collected in Florida by J. K. Small and J. J. Carter, November
9, 1903.

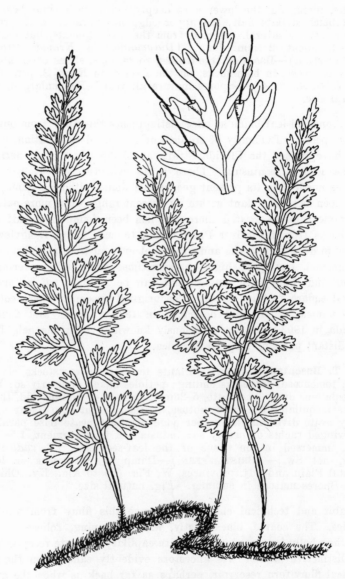

TRICHOMANES BOSCHIANUM

and at the same time gradually became extinct in their more southern continental range. Like *Trichomanes Petersii,* it changed from a calcareous habitat to an acid one. Now, however, all connection with the original or typical home of the filmy-ferns has been lost. The plant is most abundant and reaches its best development in Alabama, far, both in distance and climate, from the tropics and even the tropical part of Florida. It has been found also in northern Georgia and extends northward to Ohio. The bristle-fern is our largest filmy-fern. It often grows in strongly acid soils, thus differing from the calcareous species of tropical Florida. The original specimens were collected twenty-five miles south of Moulton, Alabama, in 1853. The fern grows most frequently on the face of sandstone cliffs which overhang small streams. The usual habitat is on the under side of overhanging rocks, sheltered from the sun and rain, receiving moisture from percolating water or the spray from nearby cascades. Its maximum altitude in Alabama is about 1000 feet. The Florida station for it appears to be lost to science. The species was originally referred to the very widely distributed *Trichomanes radicans* of the tropics.

FAMILY 2. **POLYPODIACEAE**

FERN FAMILY

Terrestrial or epiphytic, swamp, bog, marsh, wood, or rock plants. Rootstocks elongate, creeping or horizontal, or short and erect. Leaves sometimes dimorphic, coiled in vernation or sometimes bent, erect, spreading, or pendulous when expanded, sometimes tufted: petioles continuous with or jointed to the rootstock; blades simple, once pinnatifid or several times pinnatifid, or pinnate, or decompound. Veins simple or forked, free or united and forming areolae. Sporangia borne either promiscuously or in clusters (sori) on the lower side or on the margins of the leaf-blades, stalked, provided with an incomplete vertical ring of thickened cells, opening transversely, the sori either with or without a membranous covering (indusium). Prothallia green.—The largest of the families of ferns. It includes nearly one hundred and fifty genera and about five thousand species. It is represented in arctic, temperate, and tropical regions.

Key to the Fern Groups and Genera

Spore-bearing leaves (sporophyls) with the blades, divisions, or leaflets flat, or with the edges merely revolute.
  Spore-bearing leaflets densely clothed with masses of sporangia.
    Leaves dimorphic, the sporophyl quite different from the other leaves: veins free.   **I. Stenochlaeneae.**
    Leaves not dimorphic, the sporophyl not different from the other leaves: veins anastomosing.   **II. Acrosticheae.**
  Spore-bearing leaflets, or leaf-segments, with sporangia borne in separated sori.
    Indusia wanting, the sori naked.
      Sori not borne in marginal lines along the leaf-edges.
        Sori circular or nearly so, borne on the veins on the back of the leaf-blade, leaflets or leaf-lobes; leaflets entire or bluntly toothed or lobed: leaf-blades green beneath.
          Leaf-blades entire, lobed or 1-pinnatifid or 1-pinnate: petioles jointed to the root-stock.   **III. Polypodieae.**
          Leaf-blades 2-pinnatifid or 2-pinnate: petioles not jointed to the rootstock. Genera *Meniscium, Goniopteris,* and *Phegopteris* in   **X. Dryopterideae.**
        Sori irregular, borne along the veins of the leaflets or leaf-segments: leaflets sharply toothed, incised, or lobed: leaf-blades coated with white, ochroleucous, or yellow powder beneath.   **IV. Pityrogrammeae.**
      Sori marginal, borne in a linear continuous or interrupted line along the leaf-edges.   **V. Vittarieae.**
    Indusia present, of various shapes.
      Sori marginal or dorsal, but not borne in cup-like or pocket-like indusia which open towards the apex of the leaf.
        Sori marginal or essentially so: indusium formed, in part, by the more or less modified leaf-margins.
          Sporangia borne on a continuous vein-like receptacle connecting the apices of the veins.   **VI. Pterideae.**
          Sporangia borne at or near the apices of unconnected veins.   **VII. Adianteae.**
        Sori dorsal: indusium not formed by part of the leaf-margin.
          Sori narrow, linear to elliptic: indusium more than thrice as long as broad.
           Sori borne parallel to and contiguous to the mid-

rib of the leaf-segments, on specialized veins.

VIII. BLECHNEAE.

Sori borne oblique to and away from the midrib of the leaf-blade or the leaf-segment on the ordinary veins.

IX. ASPLENIEAE.

Sori broad, roundish or reniform: indusium less than twice as long as wide.

Indusium (if present) superior, orbicular or reniform.

Sori mostly on the backs of the veins: indusia attached at or near the middle, opening all around: leaf-blades simple or compound, the leaflets not articulate, persistent.

X. DRYOPTERIDEAE.

Sori terminal on the veins: indusia attached at the side, opening laterally, mostly towards the margin of the leaflets: leaf-blades 1-pinnate, the leaflets articulate and deciduous.

XI. NEPHROLEPIDEAE.

Indusium wholly or partly inferior, hood-like or stellate.

XII. WOODSIEAE.

Sori borne in cup-like or pocket-like indusia which open towards the apex of the leaf-segment.

XIII. DAVALLIEAE.

Spore-bearing leaves (sporophyls) with the divisions closely rolled together, thus necklace-like or berry-like.

XIV. ONOCLEAE.

I. STENOCHLAENEAE

Creeping or climbing plants with spiny-toothed leaflets.

1. STENOCHLAENA.

II. ACROSTICHEAE

Erect plants with entire leaflets.

2. ACROSTICHUM.

III. POLYPODIEAE

Veins free: leaf-segments several or usually numerous and narrow.

Sori superficial: leaves not scaly.

3. POLYPODIUM.

Sori sunken in pits: leaves scaly.

4. MARGINARIA.

Veins anastomosing: leaf-segments few or leaf-blades entire and broad.

Leaf-blades broad, pinnatifid.

Leaf-segments with nearly or quite uniform areolae, each areola with a single free veinlet: sori terminal on the included veinlet.

5. GONIOPHLEBIUM.

Leaf-segments with irregular areolae, each areola along the midrib without a veinlet: sori terminal on a pair of veinlets.

6. PHLEBODIUM.

Leaf-blades narrow, elongate, not pinnatifid, essentially entire.

Rootstocks short, not climbing: leaves in a crown: areolae in regular rows, or chiefly in one row in *C. angustifolium*.   7. CAMPYLONEURUM.

Rootstocks elongate, extensively climbing: leaves spaced on the rootstock: areolae irregular.   8. PHYMATODES.

IV. PITYROGRAMMEAE

Showy plants with the leaves coated beneath with white, ochroleucous, or yellow powder.   9. PITYROGRAMMA.

V. VITTARIEAE

Veins obscure, forming a single row of areolae without included veinlets.   10. VITTARIA.

Veins freely anastomosing, the areolae with included veinlets.   11. PALTONIUM.

VI. PTERIDEAE

Indusium single, formed by the modified leaf-margin: leaf-blades 1-pinnate or rarely 2-pinnate.   12. PYCNODORIA.

Indusium double, an inner membranous portion arising from the receptacle: leaf-blades more than 2-pinnate.

Veins forking, but free: middle division of leaf-blade 2-pinnate (in our species).   13. PTERIS.

Veins anastomosing: middle division of leaf-blade 1-pinnate (in our species).   14. LITOBROCHIA.

VII. ADIANTEAE

Leaves with only the teeth or lobes of the divisions or leaflets recurved on the sori as indusia.

Petioles black or very dark, slender and wiry: leaflets flabellately veined.   15. ADIANTUM.

Petioles yellowish to brown, stout, not wiry: leaflets pinnately veined.   16. HYPOLEPIS.

Leaves with the margins of the segments wholly recurved over the sori.

Leaflets with pubescent blades: sporangia in interrupted submarginal bands: veinlets with much thickened tips.   17. CHEILANTHES.

Leaflets glabrous except the midrib: sporangia forming continuous submarginal bands: veinlets not thickened at the tip.   18. PELLAEA.

VIII. BLECHNEAE

Blades of the leaflets or leaf-segments entire or toothed: veins free, or in spore-bearing leaflets connected near their bases by a transverse continuous receptacle: sori continuous or nearly so.   19. BLECHNUM.

Blades of the leaflets or leaf-segments pinnatifid or undulate: veins anastomosing near the midrib: sori interrupted, chain-like.

Leaves uniform, the sporophyls and foliage leaves similar: veins sparingly anastomosing.

Veins forming a series of areolae between the sori and the leaf-margin.   20. WOODWARDIA.

Veins free between the sori and the leaf-margin.   21. ANCHISTEA.

Leaves dimorphous, the sporophyls and foliage leaves quite different : veins copiously anastomosing, thus forming fine areolae.   22. LORINSERIA.

IX. ASPLENIEAE

Veins free : sori all oblique.
 Sori confluent in pairs : indusia single, contiguous, but appearing double.   23. PHYLLITIS.
 Sori single on the outer side of the veinlet or crossing it.
  Leaves evergreen ; blades, or leaflets thin- or thick-coriaceous ; petioles or rachis firm, slender and wiry.   24. ASPLENIUM.
  Leaves not evergreen ; blades, or leaflets herbaceous ; petioles soft and relatively stout, not wiry, often stramineous.
   Blades of the leaflets pinnatifid or pinnate : veins or veinlets running into the teeth of the margins.
    Leaf-segments coarsely toothed : sori very short, at least some of the indusia, vaulted across the vein, opening all around.   25. ATHYRIUM.
    Leaf-segments entire or bluntly toothed : sori rather long, at least some of the indusia double, placed back to back and opening in opposite directions.   26. DIPLAZIUM.
   Blades of the leaflets shallowly toothed : veins or veinlets running into the sinuses of the margins.   27. HOMALOSORUS.
Veins copiously anastomosing : sori variously disposed.   28. CAMPTOSORUS.

X. DRYOPTERIDEAE

Veins anastomosing.
 Indusia present : veins copiously and irregularly anastomosing, the areolae irregular : sori separated.
  Leaf-blades pinnatifid or pinnately 3-foliolate, the terminal leaflet larger than the others : petioles with few fine scales.   29. TECTARIA.
  Leaf-blades pinnate, the leaflets several to many : petioles with numerous coarse scales.   30. CYRTOMIUM.
 Indusia wanting : veins regularly and copiously anastomosing by pairs, the areolae regular and many or irregular and few : sori covering the back of the leaflet or spaced.
  Veinlets joined regularly between the veins forming series of parallel areolae between the midrib and the margin : sori confluent.   31. MENISCIUM.
  Veinlets joined irregularly to form few irregular areolae : sori separated.   32. GONIOPTERIS
Veins free or those of the lower one or two pairs joined and running merely to the sinus.
 Indusia present (or vestigial in *Thelypteris tetragona* and *T. submarginalis*).
  Indusia reniform or suborbicular and with a narrow sinus.
   Leaf-segments entire or merely repand : veins simple or merely forked, the lower ones of adjacent segments con-

verging to or meeting in the sinus, or one or two pairs of veins uniting in the tissues below the sinus and running into it : leaves not evergreen northward.　　　　　　33. THELYPTERIS.

Leaf-segments toothed, lobed, or pinnatifid, the teeth blunt or spinescent : veins forked, the branches running to the margin remote from the sinus : leaves evergreen.　　　　　　34. DRYOPTERIS.

Indusia orbicular-peltate, without a sinus.　35. POLYSTICHUM.
Indusia wanting.　　　　　　36. PHEGOPTERIS.

XI. NEPHROLEPIDEAE

Epiphytic or terrestrial plants : leaves long and narrow, often greatly elongate : leaflets numerous ; blades toothed : indusia reniform or orbicular-reniform.　　　　　　37. NEPHROLEPIS.

XII. WOODSIEAE

Indusia attached by one side of the base, at one side of the sori, hood-like, truncate or prolonged into a tip.　　　　　　38. CYSTOPTERIS.

Indusia attached by the middle of the base, wholly inferior, roundish or cleft into irregular lobes or stellate.　　　　　　39. WOODSIA.

XIII. DAVALLIEAE

Indusia flattish, attached at the base and the sides, the soral-pouch pocket-like : leaf-segments linear-cuneate, truncate and minutely toothed at the apex.　　　　　　40. SPHENOMERIS.

Indusia convex, adnate laterally to the concave opposed lobule, the soral-pouch cup-like : leaf-segments cuneate to ovate, rounded and toothed at the apex.　　　　　　41. DENNSTAEDTIA.

XIV. ONOCLEAE

Terrestrial plants with extensively spreading rootstocks and erect leaves, the foliage leaves and the sporophyls separate and quite different.　42. ONOCLEA.

1. STENOCHLAENA J. Smith.

Rigid terrestrial or epiphytic wood-plants or rock-plants, with creeping or climbing woody often scaly sometimes armed rootstocks. Leaves borne singly or clustered on the rootstock, mostly dimorphous : petioles scaly at the base, otherwise often glabrous : blades 1-pinnate, relatively narrow, often elongate : leaflets thick, often coriaceous, usually numerous, usually toothed, sometimes spiny-toothed, those of the sporophyls narrower than the others. Veins free, extending from the midrib to the margin, simple or forked. Sporangia numerous, confluent and clothing the lower surface of the leaflets. Indusia wanting. —About forty species, natives of the tropics.—The genus was based on *Lomaria scandens* Willd., a synonym of *Stenochlaena palustris* (L.) Bedd. The name is Greek, referring to the narrow indusiform margins of the leaflets. There is often a great difference in juvenile and mature leaves.—Spores mature all year.

Leaf-rachis winged : leaflets without a gland at the base of the blade : sporophyl 1-pinnate.   1. *S. Kunzeana.*
Leaf-rachis not winged : leaflets with a gland at the base of the blade : sporophyl 2-pinnate.   2. *S. tenuifolia.*

1. **S. Kunzeana** (Presl) Underw. Rootstock elongate, creeping over rocks or on the bases of tree-trunks, flattened, with ovate-lanceolate scales: leaves dark-green, 1–6 dm. long; petioles margined, green or purple-tinged; blades oblanceolate to spatulate in outline, much longer than the petioles, the leaflets few to many, the blades various, ovate to reniform and very small at the base of the rachis to lanceolate or linear-lanceolate and larger (4–12 cm.) above, the larger ones acuminate, all pale-green beneath, dark-green above, irregularly dentate or serrate-dentate, cuneate at the base, short-stalked: veins simple or once-forked, extending into the teeth: sporophyls smaller than the other leaves, the leaflets with much narrower blades, which are thickly covered with sporangia beneath.—(HOLLY-FERN.)—Hammocks, Everglade Keys, S. pen. Fla.—(*W. I.*)—Fig. reduced.

Climbing or vine-like ferns are not plentiful in our range. However, there are two types: the one (*Lygodium*) climbs by its elongate leaves, the other by the stems or rootstocks. The holly-ferns belong to the latter class. The rootstocks climb over rocks and tree-trunks. As is the case with several of our ferns of tropical origin, this one apparently never migrated far from its point of debarkation from the West Indies. However, it may have reached the ancient Oligocene Island with the first invasion and later migrated down to the Everglade Keys where it now maintains a precarious existence in a very limited area. Perhaps it was more abundant when the hammocks of the Everglade Keys were more extensive. Now it seems in a fair way to be eliminated from our range. The holly-fern is quite distinctive from all other native ferns in our region. On account of the arrangement of the sporangia, it was formerly considered to be closely related to *Acrostichum* and even included in that genus. However, it differs from it in the dimorphous leaves and in the venation. It is more vine-like than most of our other ferns. The elongate rigid rootstocks creep or clamber about the edges of the well-like lime-sinks and about the bases of shrubs and trees. It is now known from a half dozen hammocks, several in the Biscayne pineland and one in the Long Key pineland. It was discovered in Florida in 1903.[1] It occurs also on some of the larger West Indian

[1] First collected in Florida by J. K. Small, J. J. Carter, and A. A. Eaton, November 9, 1903.

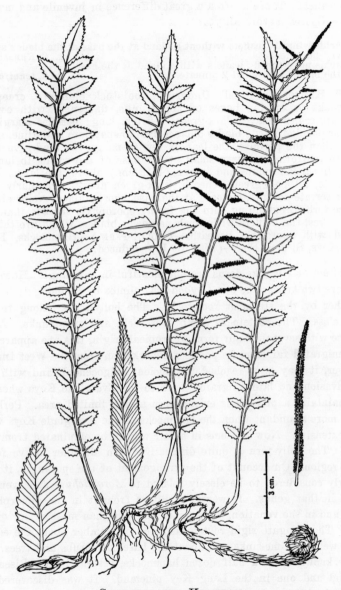

STENOCHLAENA KUNZEANA

islands. The original specimens were collected in Cuba, early in the nineteenth century.

2. S. tenuifolia (Desv.) Moore. Rootstock with narrow brown scales, greatly elongate, climbing on tree-trunks: leaves erect or drooping, curving away from the rootstock; petioles stramineous, glabrous above the base; blades glabrous, shining, pinnate, 1 m. long or less, the leaflets numerous, jointed to the rachis, the blades lanceolate to linear-lanceolate, acuminate, pungently serrate towards the apex, oblique at the base, and furnished with a marginal gland on the upper edge: sporophyls with narrower leaflets: veins simple or forked, generally free to the thickened margin, rarely the forks or two separate veins anastomosing in the middle of or towards the margin of the leaflets: sporangia covering the lower side of the leaflets of the sporophyls. [*Lomaria tenuifolia* Desv.]—Hammocks and waste grounds, pen. Fla.—Native of Asia, and cultivated.—Fig. reduced.

Vigorous garden plants of foreign origin often promptly ''escape'' and seek habitats to their liking. They may soon be found well established members of our naturalized flora. The present fern[1] is one of the later arrivals in our territory. This species was described from specimens collected in India, in 1768. Recent letters from a fern student in Florida contain the following information: ''Under separate cover I sent you a frond from a climbing fern that I have come across. It has made its appearance in three different localities. Two places it was climbing up trees, up so far as six feet from the ground, the other place it has nothing to cling to so ran along the ground. It likes dense shade. Some of the leaves measure three feet in length. The rootstock was not densely covered with hair as in some of our ferns, but would send up leaves from the sections where it would take root, but the running rootstocks were neither jointed or had nodes. I have been watching the plants but can find no difference between the development of the leaves, except the juvenile leaves have a softer texture, the leaflets of some, broader, with a pinkish tinge to the light-green color. One rootstock sent up two very small leaves, the leaflets taking a somewhat oblique position on the midrib, while unrolling; but I have not found any sporophyls so far. The fern seems to grow from the underground rootstocks, which are from 3 to 6 feet long. If they can get under the roots of a tree or anything they can ''hide'' under, they seem to like it, and it is very hard to dislodge them.''

Subsequent reports have been received from other parts of Florida

[1] First collected in Florida by Bessie W. Miles, September, 1932.

STENOCHLAENA TENUIFOLIA

indicating the existence of naturalized plants of this fern that escaped from vigorous specimens in cultivation.

2. ACROSTICHUM L.

Tall coarse usually very robust swamp plants, with very stout, short or somewhat elongate, scaly rootstocks. Leaves erect, in a heavy or massive crown, pliable or not, arching: petioles stout, very coriaceous, smooth or with several wart-like spurs: blades pinnate, greatly elongate: leaflets leathery, the blades thick-coriaceous, entire or obscurely toothed, flat, erect or spreading. Veins anastomosing, forming copious minute areolae without free veinlets. Sporangia very numerous, covering the entire lower surface of all the leaflets or of the upper leaflets only, with a red or brown felt-like coating.—About five species, widely distributed in the tropics.—LEATHER-FERNS.—The genus was based on *Acrostichum aureum*, the first species following. The name is Greek, alluding to the distal spore-bearing leaflets of the species concerned.—Twenty-five or thirty feet above sea-level is the maximum altitude of the species in Florida.—Spores mature all year.

Sporophyls with some of the upper leaflets spore-bearing: leaflets mostly widely separated: meshes of the areolation with their long axes obliquely placed, those bordering the midrib usually three or four times as long as broad.   1. *A. aureum.*

Sporophyls with nearly all the leaflets spore-bearing: leaflets mostly approximate or overlapping: meshes of the areolation with axes divergent or slightly oblique to the midrib, those bordering the midrib usually not more than twice as long as broad.   2. *A. danaeaefolium.*

1. A. aureum L. Leaves loosely tufted, more or less arching, 1–3 m. tall, pliable; blades much longer than the petioles, the leaflets 12 pairs or more, the blades coriaceous, but thinnish, broadly linear to linear-lanceolate, the larger ones mostly 1.5–2 dm. long, light-green, pliable, more or less separated, sometimes long-stalked; areolation coarser than that of the following species, very oblique to the midrib: sporangia confined to the upper quarter or half of the leaflets of the spore-bearing leaves.—(LEATHER-FERN.)—Mangrove swamps, salt-marshes, and low hammocks near salt-water, coastal regions of peninsular Florida and Florida Keys.—(*W. I., Mex., C. A., S. A.*)—Fig. reduced.

Among the nearly two hundred native and naturalized ferns in the southeastern states some are outstanding on account of the extremely delicate laciness of their leaves; others by their coarseness and clumsy bulk. The leather-ferns are quite suggestive of primeval vegetation. They lack the grace and refinement that some other ferns have developed

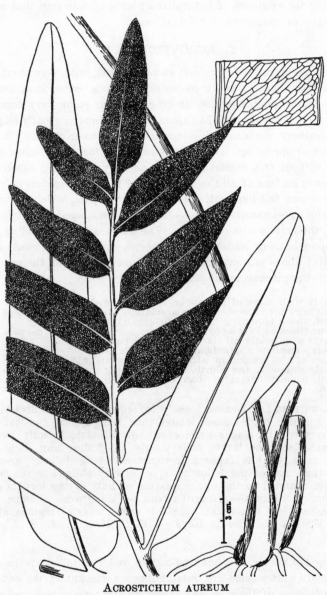

ACROSTICHUM AUREUM

through their experiences during the ages. They are strictly tropical types and have made very sure of distributing themselves by the production of an inordinate number of spores and perpetuating themselves by very strong rootstocks. The above and the following species may have been introduced into Florida with the first invasion of tropical vegetation on the Oligocene Island and also with a second invasion to the Everglade Keys, unless they migrated southward from the Oligocene Island. Up to the end of the eighteenth century, *A. aureum* had been considered the only representative of *Acrostichum* in the United States. Now it is known to be even less common than the following species of leather-fern, with which it was confused. It is most abundant in salt-marshes and mangrove swamps on the Everglade Keys and in low hammocks on the Florida Keys. Luxuriant growths are to be found in the large lime-sinks in the original forest on the northern end of Key Largo. It thrives best in shaded localities. This plant is common in the West Indies and in continental tropical America. It was discovered in Florida in the latter part of the eighteenth century.[1] The first collection in Florida made by Michaux during the latter part of the Bartram activities there, occurred on the Aisa Hatcha (River of the Ais). The Ais were a tribe of Florida aborigines that once lived along the Indian River. The original specimens were collected in Jamaica and Dominica early in the eighteenth century and named in 1753.

2. **A. danaeaefolium** Langsd. & Fisch. Leaves closely tufted, ascending or erect, stiff, 1.5–4 m. tall; blades much longer than the petiole, the leaflets usually numerous, the blades thick-coriaceous, lanceolate to linear-lanceolate, the larger ones mostly 2–3 dm. long, sometimes deep-green, stiff, approximate or overlapping, short-stalked; areolation fine, slightly divergent or oblique to the midrib: sporangia usually covering the lower surface of nearly all the leaflets of the spore-bearing leaves. [*A. lomarioides* Jenman. *A. excelsum* Maxon.] — (LEATHER-FERN. GIANT-FERN.) — Freshwater marshes, brackish swamps, low prairies, and wet hammocks, southern part of the lake region of peninsular Florida and southward.—(*W. I., Mex., C. A., S. A.*) —Fig. reduced.

When the coastal regions of southern peninsular Florida were the only well-known parts, it was taken for granted that the leather-fern was confined to the coast and adjacent lowlands. The plants of the preceding species were then considered to represent the maximum size of our ferns. When the interior parts of the state became known it was

[1] First collected in Florida by A. Michaux in 1789.

3 cm.

ACROSTICHUM DANAEAEFOLIUM

found that the present fern so far as mass is concerned had the largest leaves of any of our fern-plants. In favorable localities leaves often measure nearly four meters in length. Away from the influence of salt water it reaches its greatest development, both in size and quantity. In the prairie-like outlets of the Everglades and far north about Lake Okeechobee areas acres in extent are covered with a magnificent growth of this fern. The tangled masses of rootstocks and the close-set stout leaf-stalks make these thickets almost impenetrable. It thrives best in places fully exposed to the sun. This plant is common in insular and continental tropical America, and was first found in Florida in the earlier half of the past century.[1] It was discovered on the island of St. Catharine, Brazil, in the eighteenth century and described in 1810.

3. **POLYPODIUM** L.

Low epiphytic or terrestrial wood-plants, with creeping or horizontal rootstocks. Leaves borne singly or approximate, erect or spreading; petioles jointed to the rootstock: blades lobed or pinnatifid, the segments thin or coriaceous, entire or toothed. Veins free or only casually anastomosing. Sori orbicular, borne in one row or in several rows on the back of the leaf-blade on either side of the midrib or on the back of the leaf-segment on either side of the midrib. Indusium wanting.— Almost two hundred species are known in this genus. They are widely distributed in temperate and tropical regions.—POLYPODIES.—This genus, based on the common polypody of Europe, *Polypodium vulgare* L., was described in 1753. The name is Greek, alluding to the numerous scars on the rootstock.—Great extremes in altitude are represented by the following species.—For notes on varieties and forms see Am. Fern Jour. 27: 53–55. 1937.

Leaf-blades of herbaceous tissue, not tightly inrolled in drying: segments little if at all reduced in length at the base of the blade: sori large (about 2 mm. in diameter).   1. *P. virginianum.*
Leaf-blades of membranous tissue, tightly inrolled in drying: segments much reduced in length at the base of the blade: sori small (about 1 mm. in diameter).
    Leaf-rachis finely pubescent: reduced leaf-segments at the base of the blade few: veins 1-forked.   2. *P. Plumula.*
    Leaf-rachis hispidulous: reduced leaf-segments at the base of the blade forming a scalloped wing on the rachis: veins mostly 2-forked.   3. *P. pectinatum.*

1. P. virginianum L. Rather small, terrestrial or rarely epiphytic plants with widely creeping rootstocks which are densely covered with

[1] First collected in Florida by F. Rugel about 1843.

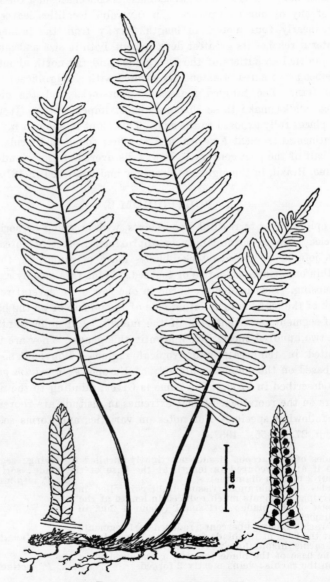

POLYPODIUM VIRGINIANUM

cinnamon-colored scales: leaves evergreen, mostly 1–4 dm. long, clustered or spaced on the rootstocks; petioles light-colored, glabrous;
blades ovate-oblong or narrowly oblong in outline, slightly coriaceous,
glabrous, deep-green above, paler beneath, deeply pinnatifid, the segments few or several, linear to linear-oblong, or rarely lanceolate, mostly
undulate or obscurely toothed and obtuse, or sometimes prominently
toothed and rarely acute or acuminate: veins rather obscure, once or
twice forked: sori rather large, medial, red or red-brown. [*P. vulgare*
Michx., not L.]—(GOLDEN-POLYPODY, COMMON-POLYPODY.)—Thin soil
on rocks or rocky banks, rarely on trees, various provinces, Ga. to Ala.,
Ark., Man., Keewatin, Lab., and Newf.—Occurs in several variations
from the typical form in the shape, the toothing, and the deeper cutting
of the leaf-segments.—Spores mature in summer and fall.—Fig. reduced.

On account of its wide range and usually great abundance in the
northeastern states and in the higher parts of the southeast, the common polypody is the first introduction for the beginning botanist to
the smaller native ferns. Regions with rocks and cliffs are to the
liking of this fern. Consequently it is rare in the Coastal Plain.
Where soil rich in humus has accumulated on rocks or in cavities and
crevices, this fern may be sought. The leaves are evergreen, hence are
frequently found in winter, when they are prominent. The foliage is
deep-green, the leaf-blades being particularly bright-green on the upper
side, or somewhat lustrous and with a golden or coppery tint. It was
discovered in North America early in the eighteenth century and was
named and described in 1753. Being such a wide-spread fern it has
received many common names. Some of these are: MY MANY-FEET,
GOLDEN-POLYPODY, GOLDEN-LOCKS, MOSS-FERN, SWEET-FERN, ROCK-
BRAKE. It occurs up to nearly 6000 feet altitude in North Carolina.
At both high and low altitudes plants often grow on moss-covered
limbs and trunks of trees. Variations referred to under the specific
description may be summarized as follows: *P. virginianum acuminatum*
has the leaf-segments toothed near the acuminate or attenuate tips;
P. virginianum deltoideum has the lower segments auricled at the base;
P. virginianum cambricoides has the segments toothed or pinnatifid;
P. virginianum cristatum has the segments once or several times forked
at the tip.

2. **P. Plumula** Humb. & Bonpl. Rootstock short, stout, often stubby,
brown-scaly: leaves clustered, 1–5 dm. long, deep-green, erect, arching,
spreading, or drooping: petioles black or dark-purple, very narrowly
margined, usually finely pubescent; blades nearly linear to linear-lanceolate, much longer than the petioles, sometimes greatly elongate, often
with a strong lateral curve, the segments very numerous, narrowly linear

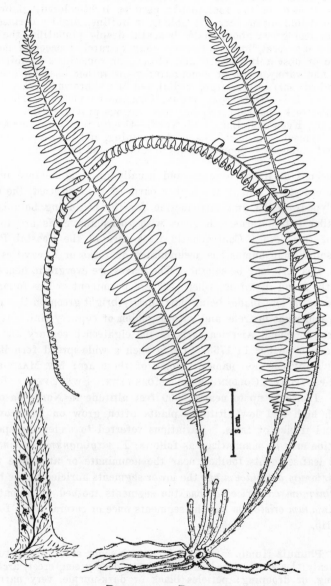

POLYPODIUM PLUMULA

or linear-lanceolate, the longest ones less than 3 cm. long, with the mid-rib arising in a curve much below the middle of the base, the much reduced ones at the base of the blade few: veins obscure, once forked: sori minute, brown, sometimes dark-brown, supramedial.—(POLYPODY.) —Hammocks, on rock, moist banks, tree-trunks, and logs, pen. Fla. and Florida Keys.—(*W. I., Mex., C. A., S. A.*)—Spores mature all year.—Fig. reduced.

The preceding species is a very hardy plant. Freezing weather and snow seem to increase its vigor. In our range, also, a quite different type exists, represented by two tropical species whose plants are very tender, as far as low temperatures are concerned, and freezing weather is often fatal to them. The present species and the one following came long ago from the West Indies in two migrations, the first to the Oligocene Island, the second to the Florida Keys and the Everglade Keys. Both species have maintained themselves in the northern and the southern tropical areas in peninsular Florida. *Polypodium Plumula,* thus, is known in our range only in two widely separated areas. It occurs in the upper part of the Florida peninsula more abundantly than it does in the hammocks of the Everglade Keys. On Pumpkin Key and Key Largo, where it seems to be most plentiful on the Keys, it grows on well-rotted logs and in humus on the floor of the dense ham-mock. In some places it occurs in colonies, in others it is found only as an isolated plant. Its local distribution and abundance seems to be governed, in part at least, by the abundance or lack of moisture. Where water is scant or irregular the plants seem to prefer rocks and shaded clay banks. The rocks may contain capillary water longer than the other habitats, so the plant may have a continuous supply of moisture, even if it be scant. Where the moisture supply is irregularly plentiful or always scant the plants seem to betake themselves to tree-stumps and logs. Where atmospheric moisture is regularly present the fern often grows high up on tree-trunks. The geographic range of this fern includes the mainland and islands of tropical America. This species and the following seldom reach an altitude of 200 feet in Florida. It was discovered in Florida in the earlier half of the last century.[1] The original specimens came from Venezuela in the eight-eenth century and were first named in 1810.

3. P. pectinatum L. Rootstock short, but often elongating in age, stout, densely brown-scaly: leaves clustered, 4–10 dm. long, deep-green, arching or spreading; petioles purple, often very dark, narrowly

[1] First collected in Florida by M. C. Leavenworth about 1839.

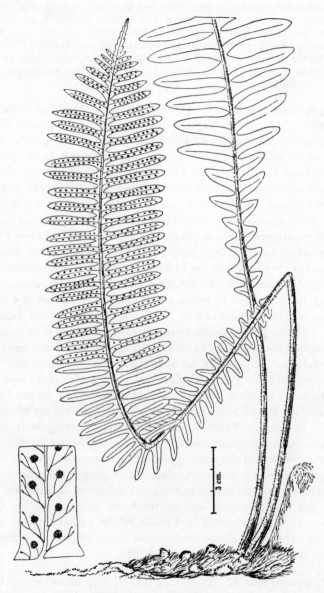

3 cm.

POLYPODIUM PECTINATUM

margined, like the rachis more or less hispidulous; blades almost linear
to narrowly elliptic or lanceolate, longer than the petioles, often much
longer, the segments numerous, but not conspicuously so, linear-tapering
to linear-lanceolate, the longest ones at the widest part of the blade
over 3 cm. long, with the midrib arising straight from the rachis at
about the middle of the base, the much reduced ones several to many,
forming a scalloped wing at the base of the blade: veins twice or thrice
forked: sori relatively large, red or red-brown, medial.—(POLYPODY.)
—Hammocks, clay banks, rocks, tree-trunks, logs, and lime-sinks, pen.
Fla.—(*W. I., Mex., C. A., S. A.*)—Spores mature all year.—Fig.
reduced.

The two tropical polypodys of our range have about the same geographical distribution in peninsular Florida. However, the present
one is, as yet, unknown on the Florida Keys. It apparently is more
abundant in the northern tropical area, or the ancient Oligocene Island
region. This fern is more selective of its habitats than are many of
our other ferns. It prefers dense hammocks where it grows either in
humus or on rotting logs and stumps, and sometimes also even more
abundantly on the rock walls of lime-sinks. Its local distribution
is somewhat similar to that of the next preceding species. Frequently
it is most abundant and luxuriant on the steep clay banks of deep
gullies. It is less likely to be found on tree trunks than is *Polypodium
Plumula*. In rocky hammocks, especially if wet, its favorite places
of growth are on the rocks themselves or on the bases of tree-trunks.
This polypody is common to both continental and insular tropical
America and was discovered in Florida in the latter half of the past
century.[1] The original specimens were collected in Jamaica early in
the eighteenth century and botanically named in 1753. Plants of this
species sometimes seem difficult to distinguish from *P. Plumula*, especially where the two grow together. It may be that there are cases of
hybridization in some localities. In addition to their extreme sensitiveness to cold, the leaves of this and the next preceding polypody are
very sensitive to drought. However, being resurrection-ferns as it
were, the leaves, curled and coiled for want of moisture during dry
spells, unfold and assume their proper functions as soon as sufficient
rains fall.

4. MARGINARIA Bory.

Epiphytic or terrestrial plants, with creeping or horizontal appressed-
scaly rootstocks, the foliage clothed with brown and pale-margined

[1] First collected in Florida by C. E. Faxon, April 2, 1873.

scales.   Leaves separated on the rootstock, erect; petioles closely pel-
tate-scaly: blades rather narrow, pinnatifid, sparingly scaly above, copiously scaly beneath.   Venation concealed, with the veins merely forking
in our species and anastomosing with a veinlet in an areola in some
species.   Sori immersed, terminal on the free vein.   Indusium wanting.
—RESURRECTION-FERNS.—About ten species, widely distributed in the
tropics.—The genus was founded on *polypodium ceteraccinum* Michx., a
synonym of the following species, in 1826.   The name is Latin, alluding
to the submarginal position of the sori.

  1. **M. polypodioides** (L.) Tidestrom.   Rootstock elongate, widely
creeping, slender: leaves scattered along the rootstock, bright-green,
or grayish when dry, 0.5–2.5 dm. long; petioles copiously scaly, slender;
blades lanceolate to oblong. or sometimes elliptic-ovate, as long as the
petioles or longer, the segments linear to elliptic, entire or undulate,
usually without scales above, densely scaly beneath, the scales dark-
centered: veins very obscure, forking: sori near the margin, mostly
oval, 1.5–2 mm. long, protruding from the pockets in which they are
borne.   [*Acrostichum polypodioides* L.   *Polypodium incanum* Sw.
Polypodium   polypodioides   Watt.]—(RESURRECTION-FERN.)—Hammocks, various provinces, nearly through the Fla. mainland and on
the Florida Keys to Tex., Mo., and Del.—(*W. I., Mex., C. A., S. A.,
Africa.*)—Spores mature all year southward.—Fig. reduced.

  There is a varying resistance to adverse climatic conditions, cold,
heat, and drought, among both tropical and temperate ferns.   In the
case of the present tropical type one would not be surprised that after
coming out of the West Indies and sojourning in Florida for a period,
it was able to adjust itself to the cold of the southeastern Coastal
Plain; but that it was able to proceed with impunity into the land
of ice and snow and zero weather where it not only maintains an existence, but flourishes, is surprising.   All this indicates that the resurrection-fern is an old resident of Florida.   It doubtless grew on the
ancient Oligocene Island whence it migrated northward, and perhaps
also southward.   The resurrection-fern has the distinction of being the
most abundant and common of all the small ferns of the hammocks in
our range.   In dry weather the leaves shrink, shrivel, and curl up, but
after a rain-storm or a rainy period they are restored to a perfectly
fresh state, whence the most popular common name, cited above.   It
grows in probably nearly all the hammocks of northern Florida and
the peninsula, and in many places on the Florida Keys.   It occurs in
abundance on the trunks and the limbs of the live-oak and on other
rough-barked trees and also on dead stumps and prostrate rotting logs.

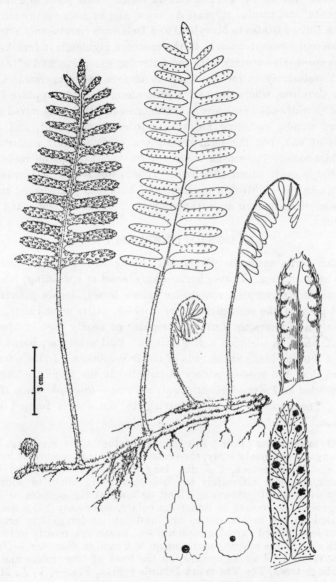

3 cm.

MARGINARIA POLYPODIOIDES

It is more rare on the ground and on rocks. This plant is common in continental and insular tropical America, and extends northward in the eastern United States to Maryland and Delaware (mistakenly attributed to Iowa and Pennsylvania.) In the southern highlands it forsakes trees and its epiphytic habitats, with the following exception, and often grows almost exclusively on rocks. There is an area in Transylvania County, North Carolina, where for half a mile along the old Sapphire Road it occurs on white-oaks exclusively. This area has the usual mixed growth of hard woods, including hickory, an occasional walnut, and several species of oak, but the resurrection-fern confines itself exclusively to the white-oaks. The reason is not apparent. It occurs on rocks in the Blue Ridge up to about 4500 feet. It was discovered in Virginia and Jamaica in the eighteenth century, and botanically described in 1753. It is sometimes known as SCALY-POLYPODY, TREE-POLYPODY, and GRAY-POLYPODY.

5. GONIOPHLEBIUM Presl.

Rather large epiphytic plants, with elongate rootstocks which cling to the bark of trees. Leaves borne singly, erect or spreading, jointed on the stout scaly creeping rootstock: blades broad, deeply pinnatifid or almost pinnate, the segments firm or thickish, entire or undulate. Veins regularly anastomosing, forming irregular or nearly regular areolae in each of which is included a free veinlet. Sori orbicular, borne on the back of the leaf-blade at the ends of the free veinlets. Indusia wanting. —More than 100 species, widely distributed in the tropics.—The genus was founded on *Polypodium attenuatum* Presl.—*Goniophlebium Haenkei* Presl. The name is Greek, referring to the angles formed by the venation.

1. G. brasiliense (Poir.) Farwell. Rootstock stout, creeping, becoming elongate, copiously scaly, the scales brown: leaves more or less scattered on the rootstock, 2–5 dm. long, bright-green; petioles brown, glabrous, at least ultimately so; blades varying much in width, but usually ovate to elliptic-ovate, about as long as the petioles or longer, the segments lanceolate to linear-lanceolate, commonly 1–1.5 dm. long, separated on the rachis, entire and undulate or irregularly erose and more or less crisped: areolae copious: sori numerous, mostly in two rows on each side of the midrib, nearly or quite 2 mm. in diameter.—(BRAZIL-IAN-POLYPODY.)—Low hammocks, on the bark of tree-trunks and stems of cabbage-trees, Ten Thousand Islands region, Fla.—(*W. I., Mex., C. A., S. A.*)—Spores mature all year.—Fig. reduced.

There are now more of the tropical ferns in Florida growing on the lower eastern coast and the ancient Oligocene region in the northern part

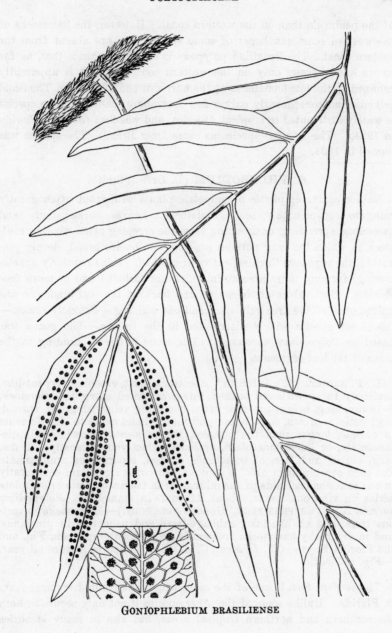

GONIOPHLEBIUM BRASILIENSE

of the peninsula than on the western coast. However, the hammocks of the western coast can boast of some species that are absent from the eastern coast. The Brazilian polypody is one of the kinds that, as far as we know, grows only on the western coast where it is apparently confined to the low hammocks at the northern end of the Ten Thousand Islands, and consequently only a few feet above sea-level. The species is widely distributed in tropical America, and was first found in Florida in 1924.[1] The original specimens came from Brazil. The species was named in 1804.

6. **PHLEBODIUM** (R. Br.) J. Smith.

Rather coarse epiphytic or epipetric plants with stout often greatly elongate conspicuously scaly rootstocks. Leaves borne singly and ascending, spreading, or drooping from the creeping often winding rootstock to which the long petioles are jointed: blades broad, deeply pinnatifid, the segments thickish, entire or toothed. Veins regularly anastomosing, forming large areolae in which are included two or more free veinlets. Sori orbicular, borne on the back of the leaf-blade, on the united ends of the free veinlets. Indusia wanting.—SERPENT-FERNS.— About six species widely distributed in the tropics.—The genus was based on *Polypodium aureum* L. The name is Greek, alluding to the veins of the leaf-segments.

1. **P. aureum** (L.) J. Smith. Rootstock stout, creeping serpent-like, copiously fuzzy with red scales: leaves scattered along the rootstock, 3–13 dm. long, bright-green or often becoming yellowish-green, spreading; petioles brown, smooth and glabrous; blades ovate to elliptic-ovate in outline, longer than the petioles, the segments lanceolate, elliptic-lanceolate, or linear-lanceolate, or linear when young, mostly 1–2 dm. long, entire, undulate, or sometimes crisped, separate or approximate and even overlapping: areolae copious, somewhat irregular: sori mostly in one series on each side of the midrib, or in two incomplete or complete series on vigorous leaves, about 2.5 mm. in diameter. [*Polypodium aureum* L.]—(SERPENT-FERN. GOLDEN-POLYPODY.)—Hammocks on various trees, and on live-oaks, cabbage-trees and palmettos in pinelands, and in dry rocky hammocks frequently on rock outcrops, pen. Fla. and the Florida Keys.—(*W. I., Mex., C. A., S. A.*)—Spores mature all year. —Fig. reduced.

The serpent-fern is one of the more widely distributed tropical ferns in Florida. Unlike some of the other species it not only occurs in both the southern and northern tropical areas, but also in many localities

[1] First collected in Florida by J. K. Small and C. A. Mosier, April 5, 1924.

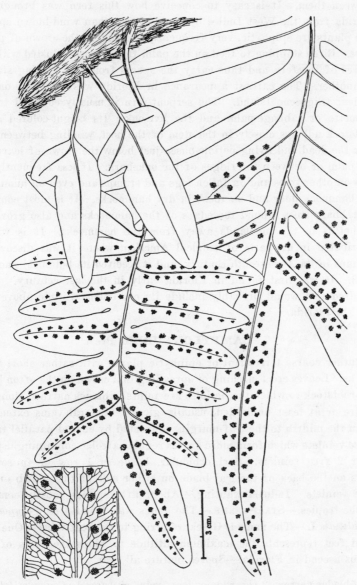

PHLEBODIUM AUREUM

between them. It is easy to conceive how this fern was brought to Florida from the West Indies by agents other than wind-blown spores. The plants are epiphytic, very frequently growing in the crown of palm-trees. Birds stopping to feed on the palm fruits become dusted with the spores of the fern and thus carry the spores from one feeding station to another. The earliest appearance in Florida was evidently on the ancient Oligocene Island. The serpent-fern is usually confined to the palmetto or cabbage-palm and the live-oak. Its bright-colored scaly rootstock adheres closely to the stem of the host, winding between and over the dead and living petiole-bases just below the crown of leaves of the palm or between the ridges of the oak bark. It less frequently occurs on other trees and on fallen logs and stumps and even on humus on the hammock floor and on rocks in dry hammocks. It is most common on cabbage-trees around the edges of the hammocks and also grows on palmettos in the pinelands away from the hammocks. It is widely distributed in all parts of tropical America, where it was discovered, perhaps in the seventeenth century, and it received its botanical name in 1753. It was first found in Florida early in the last century.[1] One hundred feet would probably include its maximum altitude above sea-level in Florida.

7. **CAMPYLONEURUM** Presl.

Rather coarse terrestrial or epiphytic plants with rather short root-stocks. Leaves erect, arching or spreading in a crown on the often knotted rootstock to which the petioles are jointed: blades narrow, elongate, entire or at least undivided, usually glossy. Lateral veins extending from the midrib to the leaf-margin, connected by curved parallel transverse veinlets which form more or less regular areolae containing usually 1 or 2 free veinlets. Sori orbicular, borne in 1 row or in several rows on the back of the leaf-blade on either side of the midrib on the free veinlets. Indusia wanting.—About fifty species, mostly confined to the tropics.—STRAP-FERNS.—The genus was founded on *Polypodium Phyllitidis* L.—The name is Greek, referring to the bent veins.—One hundred feet represents the maximum altitude to which the ferns of this genus ascend in Florida.—Spores mature all year.

Leaf-blades narrow, 2 cm. wide or less: veins obscure. 1. *C. angustifolium.*
Leaf-blades relatively broad, 3–8 cm. wide or more:
    veins prominent.

[1] First collected in Florida by J. L. Blodgett about 1838.

Leaf-blades long-acuminate, acute, or obtuse,
    rather translucent : veins conspicuous or
    evident.
Petioles very short : areolae relatively few and
    large.   2. *C. Phyllitidis.*
Petioles elongate : areolae many and small.   3. *C. latum.*
Leaf-blades abruptly caudate-acuminate, nearly
    opaque : veins obscure.   4. *C. costatum.*

1. C. angustifolium (Sw.) Fée. Rootstock rather slender: leaves
usually many together, arching, 2–5 dm. long; blades elongate-linear,
more or less falcate, tapering to each end, shining, somewhat paler
beneath than above, often slightly revolute, short-petioled : veins obscure,
sparingly anastomosing: sori in an irregular row on each side of the
midrib.—(STRAP-FERN.)—Hammocks, Everglade Keys and Fahkahatchie Cypress, Fla.—(*W. I., Mex., C. A., S. A.*)—Fig. reduced.

Three of our four kinds of strap-ferns are of limited distribution in
the geographic limits of this work. Collected only a few times in
Florida, this narrow-leaved strap-fern is one of our rarer species.
It occurs only in a few hammocks on the Everglade Keys and in the
Fahkahatchie Cypress stand in the Big Cypress Swamp, where it grows
mostly on live-oak trees. It was discovered in Florida in 1903,[1] but was
long known as a widely distributed fern in the West Indies and in
continental tropical America. The original specimens were collected in
Jamaica, West Indies, early in the eighteenth century and named in
1788.

2. C. Phyllitidis (L.) Presl. Rootstock stout: leaves several together, erect or arching, 2.5–14 dm. long; blades elongate, linear and
tapering to each end, shining, somewhat leathery, slightly paler beneath
than above, entire or undulate, short-petioled: veins rather prominent,
copiously anastomosing, the areolae large: sori in several irregular lines
on each side of the midrib. [*Polypodium Phyllitidis* L.]—(STRAP-
FERN.)—Hammocks, lower two thirds of the Florida peninsula and
Florida Keys.—(*W. I., Mex., C. A., S. A.*)—Fig. reduced.

The hammocks of Florida possess many kinds of ferns that would not
be recognized as such from their leaves, by one brought up among the
ferns of northern regions. This strap-fern is one of the more common
ones of this type. Contrary to the very circumscribed geography of its
three generic associates, the range of this fern, since its landing in
Florida from the West Indies, has spread well up towards the northern
end of the peninsula, where its limit is reached at the northern tropical
area. It occurs in all the large and dense hammocks of the lower part
of the peninsula. In the high pineland hammocks of the Everglade

[1] First collected by J. J. Soar and A. A. Eaton, December, 1903.

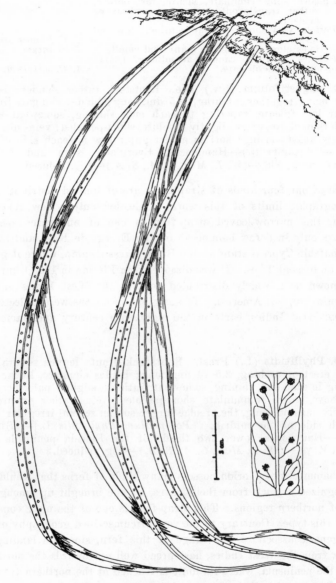

CAMPYLONEURUM ANGUSTIFOLIUM

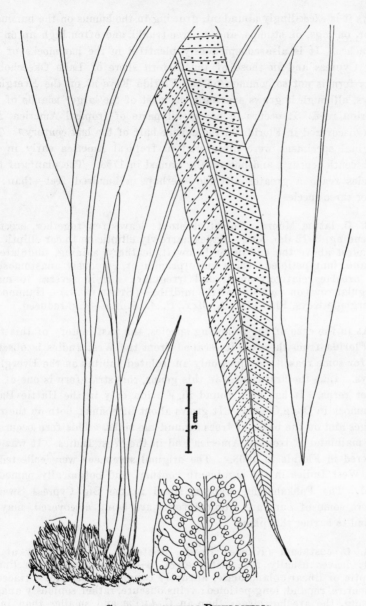

CAMPYLONEURUM PHYLLITIDIS

Keys it is exceedingly abundant, growing in the humus on the hammock floor, on logs, on stumps, and on tree-trunks and often high up on the branches. It is also conspicuously plentiful in the hammocks of the Big Cypress and in those of the eastern shore of Lake Okeechobee. This fern is not so common on the Florida Keys as on the Everglade Keys, although it grows sparingly on most of the larger islands of the Florida reef. It occurs in nearly all parts of tropical America, and was discovered in Florida in the earlier half of the last century.[1] The original specimens were discovered in tropical America early in the eighteenth century, and botanically named in 1753. The plants of this species reach a greater altitude—perhaps a hundred feet—than the other three species.

3. **C. latum** Moore. Rootstock stout: leaves few together, erect or ascending, 3–12 dm. long; blades narrowly elliptic to linear-elliptic, or broadest above the middle or below it, leathery, shining, undulate or repand, long-petioled: veins quite prominent, copiously anastomosing, the areolae relatively small and irregular: sori in several to many irregular rows on each side of the midrib.—(STRAP-FERN.)—Hammocks, Everglade Keys, Fla.—(*W. I., Mex., C. A., S. A.*)—Fig. reduced.

As in the case of the following species, the past history of this fern in Florida from the time it escaped from the West Indies is obscure. It, for some reason, occupies only an isolated habitat on the Everglade Keys. Like the first species in this genus, this strap-fern is one of our rarer ferns. It has been found in Florida only in the Hattie Bauer hammock in Dade County. It grows about lime sinks, both on the rock ledges and on the bases of trees around the sinks. This fern occurs on the mainland of tropical America and in the West Indies. It was discovered in Florida in 1903.[2] The original specimens were collected in the West Indies in the eighteenth century, and botanically named in 1861. The Fahkahatchie Cypress stand in the Big Cypress Swamp, where some of our rare tropical ferns are being discovered, may be found to harbor this plant.

4. **C. costatum** (Kunze) Presl. Rootstock stoutish, scaly at the end: leaves usually few, stiffly erect, 3–4 dm. long; blades linear-elliptic or linear-oblanceolate, abruptly caudate-acuminate, coriaceous, subentire, repand, long-petioled: veins obscure, rather copiously anastomosing, the areolae larger than in *C. latum* and smaller than in *C.*

[1] First collected in Florida by J. L. Blodgett about 1838.
[2] First collected in Florida by J. J. Soar and A. A. Eaton, December, 1903.

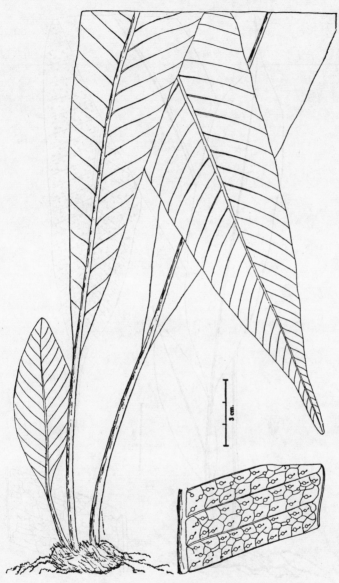

CAMPYLONEURUM LATUM

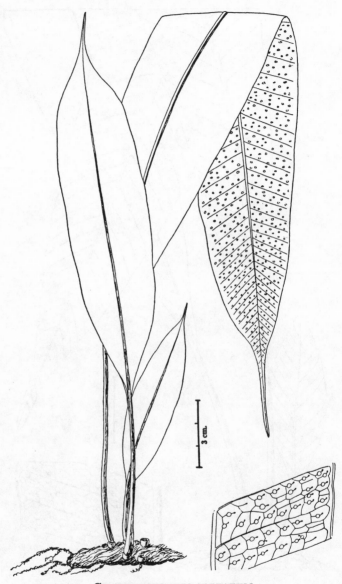

3 cm.

CAMPYLONEURUM COSTATUM

Phyllitidis: sori in few lines on each side of the midrib.—(STRAP-FERN.)—Hammocks, Fahkahatchie Cypress, Big Cypress Swamp.—(*W. I.*)—Fig. reduced.

The geographic ranges of the strap-ferns in Florida are erratic. Aside from *Campyloneurum Phyllitidis* the present ranges indicate imperfect or restricted development on mere remnants of former wider areas occupied by the ferns. This strap-fern is very rare in our range, and, like *C. latum,* it has been found in only one locality. It is strongly characterized by the long slender tip of the leaf-blade and the obscure veins. The low hammock is the home of this fern. It is epiphytic and grows on trees, on logs, and on cypress knees. It was discovered in Florida in 1904.[1] Outside of the United States it is known in the West Indies.

It is not evident just how this fern escaped from the West Indies. The spores may have been carried by the wind or on the plumage of migratory birds. Where it began its career in Florida is another mystery. It may have been carried directly to its present isolated habitat in the Big Cypress Swamp or it may have started on the Florida Keys or in the Cape Sable region, and as it worked its way northward, died out in the rear of its course. The original specimens were collected in Cuba and named in 1834.

8. PHYMATODES Presl.

Delicate epiphytic climbing plants with vine-like rootstocks. Leaves borne at intervals along the extensively creeping rootstock to which the petioles are jointed: blades various in shape, entire, toothed, or slightly lobed, but undivided, the spore-bearing ones usually the narrower. Veins copiously anastomosing and forming irregular areolae, the free veinlets spreading in various directions. Sori orbicular, variously placed on the back of the leaf-blades. Indusia wanting.—About sixty species, distributed throughout the tropics.—The genus was founded on *Polypodium Phymatodes* L. The name is Greek, referring to the swollen tips of the veins.

1. **P. heterophyllum** (L.) Small. Rootstocks slender, greatly elongate, creeping closely along the stems of shrubs or trees, with lax reddish scales: leaves irregularly spaced, appressed or spreading; petioles slender, green, less than 1.5 cm. long; blades short and broad when young, the mature ones linear, elliptic or lanceolate, 4–15 cm. long,

[1] First collected in Florida by A. A. Eaton, January 11, 1904.

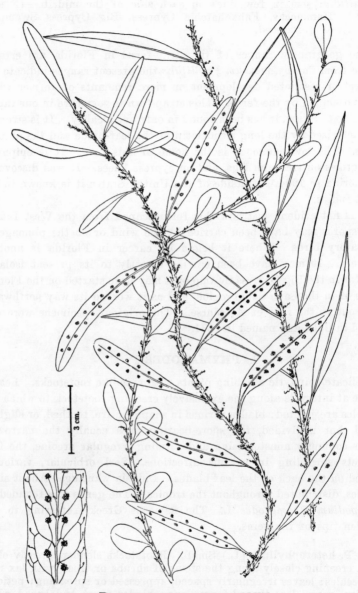

3 cm.

PHYMATODES HETEROPHYLLUM

entire, sometimes undulate, narrowed to both ends, and usually acuminate, but sometimes obtuse at the apex, slightly paler beneath than above: areolae large, few, rather irregular: sori in a line on each side of the midrib, about 1.5 mm. in diameter. [*Polypodium serpens* Sw. *Polypodium exiguum* Heward. *P. exiguum* Underw.]—(VINE-FERN.)— Hammocks, southern pen. Florida and Florida Keys.—(*W. I., S. A.*)— Spores mature all year.—Fig. reduced.

Among the climbing ferns the plants of this species are clinging vines, *par excellence*. The slender usually greatly elongate stems (rootstocks) are flattened against the trunk of the host and held secure by myriad clinging rootlets, as if glued to the bark. Considering the ages that have passed since this fern reached Florida from tropical America, it seems strange that its distribution there is so limited. The lack of abundance is, probably, due to the fact that the leaves produce relatively few spores by which it might be disseminated to distant points. In a given locality a plant is well able to reproduce and multiply vegetatively, for the tips of the stem and branches have the power of endless growth, and a detached piece may form a new plant. On the northern part of Key Largo in Florida in 1882[1] this climbing-fern was discovered. In 1903 it was first collected on the mainland in Hattie Bauer hammock on the Everglade Keys. Where it grows it is usually very plentiful. The stems and branches are closely appressed and adhere tightly to the stems of shrubs and trees, especially those of smooth-barked kinds which it often favors. Occasionally it climbs up trees to a height of twenty-five feet. It grows on the southern part of Key Largo as well as on the northern, and also on Adams Key. Subsequently it was collected on the western side of Florida as far north as Chokoloskee Bay. An additional locality where this fern is very abundant is the so-called Pine Crest region where the southern part of the Big Cypress Swamp and the Everglades meet. Curiously enough, in spite of severe forest fires which nearly wipe out the hammocks, this very delicate fern seems to be on the increase. The plant was discovered in tropical America in the early eighteenth century and named in 1753. It reaches but a few feet altitude in Florida.

9. **PITYROGRAMMA** Link.

Graceful, small or medium-sized plants of dry or rocky woods or banks, with erect or short-branched often clustered scaly rootstocks. Leaves usually clustered, uniform, not jointed to the rootstock, erect or

[1] First collected in Florida by A. H. Curtiss, February 11, 1882.

ascending: petioles stiff, mostly dark and shining: blades 1–3-pinnate, narrow, sometimes linear to deltoid-pentagonal, covered with white, ochroleucous, sometimes bright-yellow powder beneath, sometimes glandular above, usually devoid of scales; veins free. Sori following the veins, usually nearly confluent at maturity. Indusia wanting.— About 18 species mainly of the American tropics. The genus was based on *Acrostichum chrysophyllum* Sw.—The name is Greek, referring to the mealy appearance of the lower side of the leaves.

1. **P. calomelanos** (L.) Link. Rootstock short, stout, erect or oblique, clothed with stiff, narrow, fuscous or dark-brown, lustrous scales at the apex: leaves several together, spreading, 1.5 m. long or less; petioles often as long as the blades, stout, dark-brown to dark-purple, brown-scaly at the base; blades coriaceous, dark-green, white-mealy beneath, elongate-deltoid to broadly lanceolate, acuminate, 2-pinnate, with the rachis like the petiole, but often more mealy: leaflets spreading or curved, short-stalked, adjacent or separated, the lower ones the larger, distant, lanceolate, narrowly deltoid; ultimate leaflets separated, spreading, lanceolate, mostly acuminate, the lobes rounded but more or less revolute, finally confluent. [*Acrostichum calomelanos* L.]— (SILVER-FERN.)—Open slopes, banks, and ditches, pen. Fla. Native of tropical America.—(*W. I., Mex., C. A., S. A.*)—Spores mature all year.—Fig. reduced.

Ferns naturalized within our region are few. The present fern represents one of the later invasions from the American tropics. The following information is given in a letter received from a fern student in Florida[1]: "Some distance west of Fort Meade we found quite a large and thriving colony of what I take to be *Pityrogramma calomelanos*. At any rate it is the same plant that nurserymen list under that name in their catalogs and which bears the common name of "silver-fern." This is doubtless an escape but as it covers the bank of a road ditch for several rods it seems to be both thriving and reproducing itself so that you may, eventually, have another naturalized species to add to your list." The species was named in 1753 under the genus *Acrostichum* from Peruvian specimens collected earlier in the eighteenth century.

10. **VITTARIA** Smith.

Slender, tufted, epiphytic plants, with branched and congested rootstocks. Leaves grass-like, crowded on the short rootstock, pendent; blades narrowly linear and elongate, entire, often strongly revolute. Veins obscure, forming a single row of areolae on each side of the

[1] First collected in Florida by W. A. Knight, December, 1931.

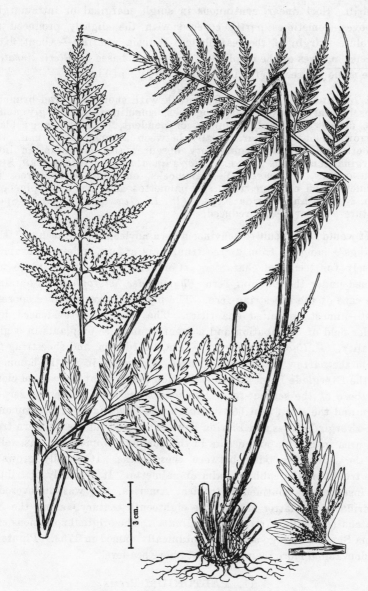

3 cm.

PITYROGRAMMA CALOMELANOS

midrib. Sori linear, continuous in single marginal or intramarginal
grooves, sometimes partly covered with the slightly produced and
revolute margin of the leaf-blade. Indusia wanting.—About fifteen
species, natives of the tropics.—The genus is based on *Pteris lineata* L.
The name is Greek, referring to the narrow leaf-blades.

1. **V. lineata** (L.) SW. Rootstock with short clustered branches,
densely scaly: leaves many together, sometimes exceedingly numerous, densely clustered, drooping, or pendent, 1–12 dm. long; blades
narrowly elongate-linear, usually between 2 mm. and 3 mm. wide,
smooth and shining: veins very obscure: sori borne in an intramarginal continuous groove. [*Pteris lineata* L.]—(GRASS-FERN, SHOE-
STRING-FERN, BEARD-FERN.)—Hammocks, on rough-barked trees and
palmettos, on cabbage-trees, saw-palmettos and live oaks, pinelands,
pen. Florida and Florida Keys.—(*W. I., Mex., C. A., S. A.*)—Spores
mature all year.—Fig. reduced.

It would be difficult to convince a fern novice that a bunch of ''shoe-
strings'' hanging from a tree trunk was a fern, unless he examined
closely for technical characters. Conditions opposite to those mentioned under the climbing-fern, *Phymatodes heterophyllum*, obtain in
the case of the shoestring-fern. The myriad leaves produce spores in
vast—almost unlimited quantities. The results are evidenced by a
wider field of distribution and a great abundance of plants in a given
locality. *V. lineata*, called grass-fern, beard-fern, and shoestring-fern
from the narrow and elongate leaves, is common in all the hammocks
of the Everglade Keys. Its distribution and habitat correspond closely
to those of the serpent-fern, *Phlebodium aureum*. Like the serpent-
fern and the strap-fern (*Campyloneurum Phyllitidis*) it is common on
the Everglade Keys and Florida Keys or throughout the southern tropical area in Florida and occurs in the northern tropical area as well as
in the hammocks lying between these areas. It usually grows on
the trunks of the cabbage-palm or palmetto. It is widely distributed
in insular and continental tropical America, and was discovered in
Florida in the latter half of the eighteenth century,[1] along the Aisa
Hatcha (see under *Acrostichum aureum*). The original specimens came
from Santo Domingo and were botanically named in 1753. Plants are
seldom found more than a few feet above sea-level.

11. **PALTONIUM** Presl.

Relatively small tufted epiphytic plants with short but often
branched rootstocks. Leaves clustered on the creeping rootstock,

[1] First collected in Florida by A. Michaux in 1789.

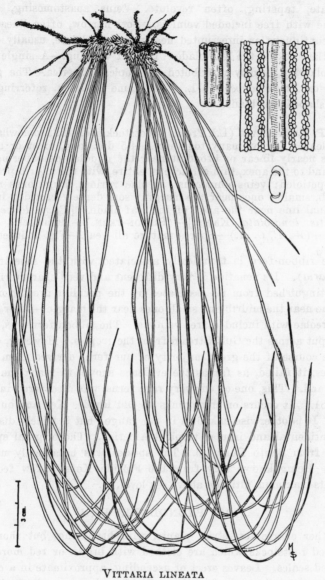

VITTARIA LINEATA

ascending or pendulous; blades entire or at least undivided, narrow, elongate, tapering, often revolute. Veins anastomosing, forming areolae with free included veinlets. Sori narrow, often linear, borne in a continuous or interrupted nearly marginal line, usually crowded near the apex of the leaf-blade. Indusia wanting.—A single species, the following, widely distributed in tropical America.—The genus is based on *Pteris lanceolata* L. The name is Greek, referring to the lance-shaped leaf-blade.

1. **P. lanceolatum** (L.) Presl. Rootstock short, but somewhat creeping: leaves few or many together, 1–4.5 dm. long, erect or arching; blades nearly linear or broadest near the middle and tapering to the base and to the apex, thin-coriaceous, entire, with the midrib prominent, short-petioled: veins numerous; areolae various, large ones near the midrib, smaller ones near the margin: sori densely crowded in a submarginal line near the apex of the leaf-blade. [*Pteris lanceolata* L. *Taenitis lanceolata* Kaulf.]—(RIBBON-FERN.)—Hammocks, Florida Keys.—(*W. I., C. A.*)—Spores mature all year.—Fig. reduced.

The ribbon-fern is technically associated with the shoestring-fern (*Vittaria*). Its venation is very different and very characteristic. It is distinguished from its associates by the peculiar areolation—large areolae near the midrib and small ones near the margin—all or many of the areolae with included free veinlets. The ribbon-fern was, in some way, put across the Gulf Stream from the tropics. However, contrary to the course of the great majority of our ferns derived from tropical sources, it failed, as far as the evidence shows, to reach the Florida mainland. This, one of our very rare ferns, was discovered in Florida in 1881.[1] It occurs on tree-trunks on Old Rhodes Key and on Elliotts Key. It is otherwise unknown in our range; but is widely distributed in continental and insular tropical America. The original specimens came from Santo Domingo. The species was botanically named in 1753. Being known only from the Florida Keys, a few feet represent its maximum altitude above sea-level.

12. **PYCNODORIA** Presl.

Rather coarse terrestrial plants, with branching, but short, often knotted rootstocks which are clothed with brown or red more or less twisted scales. Leaves erect or ascending, approximate in a crown on the short rootstock, or drooping when growing on walls or in sinks: petiole continuous with the rootstock, usually scaly at the base: blades

[1] First collected in Florida by A. H. Curtiss in 1881.

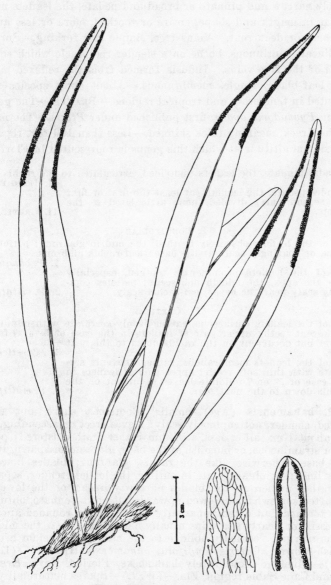

PALTONIUM LANCEOLATUM

relatively narrow and pinnate or broad and pedate, the leaflets narrow, irregular in length and shape, entire or toothed, more or less auricled at the base or decurrent. Veins free, simple and forking. Sori marginal, linear, continuous, borne on a slender receptacle which connects the tips of the free veins. Indusia formed from the reflexed margins of the leaf-blade, single, membranous.—About sixty species widely distributed in temperate and tropical regions.—BRAKES.—The genus is based on *Pycnodoria opaca*, first published under *Pteris*.—The name is from the Greek, meaning thick-skinned.—Less than 100 feet represents the maximum altitude at which this genus is represented in Florida.

Leaf-blades pinnate, the leaflets undivided, articulated to the rachis.
                                                        I. LONGIFOLIAE.
Leaf-blades pedate, the leaflets (at least the first or first
    and second pair) divided, none articulated to the
    rachis.   II. CRETICAE.

I. LONGIFOLIAE

Blades of the leaflets obscurely toothed, the midrib glabrous : petioles glabrous or sparingly scaly at the base : leaf-rachis glabrous.
                                                        1. *P. bahamensis.*
Blades of the leaflets prominently toothed, especially
    near the apex, the midrib pubescent : petioles copi-
    ously scaly near the base : leaf-rachis scaly.   2. *P. vittata.*

II. CRETICAE

Blades of the leaflets coriaceous, rather evenly serrulate with minute hard spinescent teeth : upper pair of leaflets in the case of 5- or 7-foliolate leaves not decurrent on the rachis down to the next pair.   3. *P. cretica.*
Blades of the leaflets membranous, rather unevenly serrulate with thin soft teeth : upper pair of leaflets in the case of 5- or 7-foliolate leaves decurrent on the rachis down to the next pair.   4. *P. multifida.*

1. **P. bahamensis** (Ag.) Small. Rootstock short, but usually branched, slender, not copiously scaly : leaves erect or ascending, light-green, about 1 m. tall or less, stiff, but rather frail, clustered ; petioles green or stramineous, or purplish at the base, glabrous or sparingly scaly at the base, otherwise, like the rachis, glabrous ; blades lanceolate, broadly linear, or oblanceolate in outline, the leaflets tender, separated, often rather numerous, the blades narrowly linear, or the lower ones ovate, often somewhat narrowed upward, but not attenuate, obtuse, obscurely toothed, but often apparently entire, with a rounded auriculate base, sessile or nearly so : veins usually once forked near the midrib or near the margin, decidedly oblique to the midrib : indusium brown or yellowish-brown. [*Pteris longifolia bahamensis* Hieron.]—(LADDER-BRAKE.)—Pinelands and rarely hammocks, Florida Keys, Everglade Keys, and Cape Sable region, Fla.—(*W. I.*)—Spores mature all year.—Fig. reduced.

Our species of *Pycnodoria* fall into two groups of two species each. One has a pinnate and the other a pedate leaf-blade. The pinnate

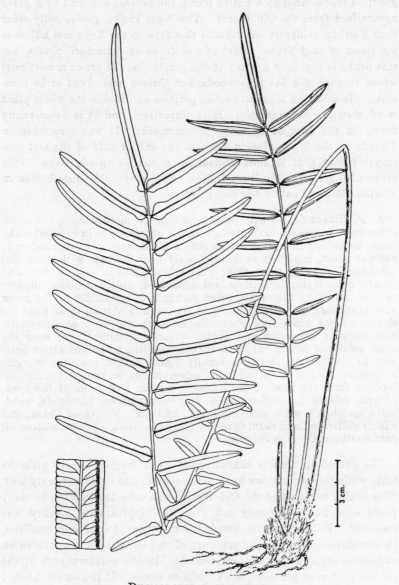

3 cm.

PYCNODORIA BAHAMENSIS

group is represented by a native plant, the present one, and by a plant naturalized from the Old World. The West Indies, geologically older than Florida, evidently contributed this fern to the Keys and adjacent mainland of that State. Most of our ferns are hammock plants, but this brake is typically a plant of the pinelands. It grows almost anywhere through the flat pine woods, but thrives best about or in limesinks. In addition to its straw-like petioles and rachis, the whole plant is of a straw-like character. It is terrestrial, and it is occasionally found on the floor of openings in hammocks. It was discovered in Florida on the lower Florida Keys in the earlier half of the last century;[1] however, it is more abundant on the Everglade Keys. This brake also grows in the West Indies. The geographic distribution in Florida allows of only a few feet altitude.

2. **P. vittata** (L.) Small. Rootstock stout, copiously scaly, branched, often knotted: leaves dark-green, erect or nearly so, or in exposed rocky places spreading in a prostrate rosette, 2–5 dm. long, or more, clustered; petioles green, copiously or densely scaly near the base with the scales extending up along the rachis; blades lanceolate in outline, firm and usually quite rigid, the leaflets firm, separated, widely so below, slightly so near the tip of the rachis, often rather few, the blades of the lower ones lanceolate or ovate and very short, usually obtuse, those near the middle of the blade and above linear-lanceolate to linear-attenuate, acuminate or attenuate and acute, serrate, prominently so near the apex, sessile or nearly so: veins forked near the midrib or about halfway to the margin and occasionally again forked near the margin, somewhat oblique to the midrib: indusium red or brown, usually extending from the base of the leaflet to within 1 or 2 cm. of the apex. [*Pteris vittata* L.]—(LADDER-BRAKE.)—Hammocks, pinelands, roadsides, and brick walls, pen. Fla., Ala., and La. Native of China, and widely cultivated and naturalized in many countries.—Spores mature all year southward.—Fig. reduced.

The preceding fern is characterized by a fragile, almost glabrous leaf, while the present one has a firm, coarse, and copiously scaly leaf. This brake, a native of the Old World, was collected in Florida many years ago, but apparently not even the approximate locality was recorded. Within the past decade it has appeared at several localities, in abundance. In the southern part of the Everglades it appeared on embankments and on hammock islands. In the northern part of the peninsula it even grows on brick walls in towns. It is also established in Alabama and Louisiana, and has invaded the West Indies and South America. It has sometimes been mistakenly identified with *Pteris*

---

[1] First found in Florida by A. W. Chapman.

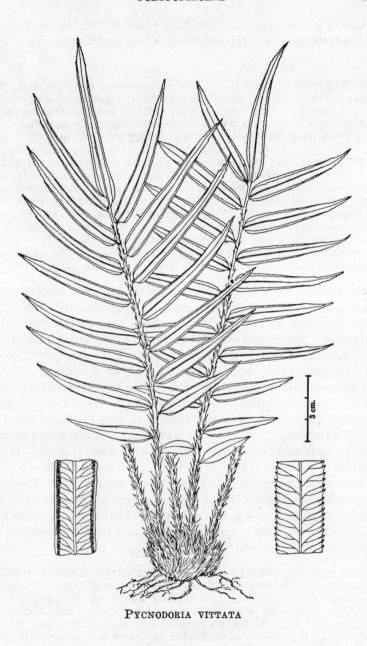

PYCNODORIA VITTATA

longifolia L.   It originally came from China and was named in 1753. Its prostrate rosettes in exposed habitats have suggested the name bird-nest-fern.

3. **P. cretica** (L.) Small.   Rootstock somewhat elongate, leafy and rather sparingly scaly: leaves usually several together or approximate or even clustered, 1 m. long or less; petioles slender, stramineous or pale-brown, sparingly scaly at the base, otherwise glabrous; blades primarily and irregularly pedately divided, very irregular in outline, with the rachis very unevenly winged; leaflets usually 3–7, sessile or nearly so, bright-green (or with a streak of white or pale-green in the middle in *P. cretica albolineata*), the sterile ones considerably broader and spinulose-serrulate, the lower pairs divided into 2 or 3 narrow segments; spore-bearing leaflets with the indusia extending from near the base to within 1–3 cm. of the spinulose-serrulate, acute or acuminate apex: veins parallel, simple or once forked, either near the midrib or near the margin, nearly at right angles to the midrib.   [*Pteris cretica* L.]—(CRETAN-BRAKE.)—Rocky hammocks, N. Fla. and the upper part of the peninsula.—Spores mature in summer and fall.—Fig. reduced.

The question has been raised from time to time, as to whether or not this bracken is a native Florida plant.   Judging from the distribution in the state and the habitats there seems to be little doubt that it is indigenous.   The tropics were evidently the course through which this fern reached Florida in prehistoric times.   It prefers rocky woods, growing best in lime-sinks, in grottoes, and on river-bluffs.   It was first found in Florida before the middle of the last century at Aspalaga Bluff, where it was still growing in 1936.[1]   As the specific name implies, the plant was first found or was thought to have first been found on the island of Crete.   It grows in many places, either native or naturalized, in tropical and subtropical regions around the globe.   It was botanically named in 1767.   As is to be expected in the case of a plant of such wide geographic distribution sports are not rare.   These are common in horticulture.   One of them, *P. cretica albolineata*, which has a streak of white or pale-green in the middle of the leaflets, occurs naturally in Florida.   Some point between 50 and 100 feet represents the maximum altitude of this fern in Florida.

4. **P. multifida** (Poir.) Small.   Rootstock short, but branched, rather copiously scaly: leaves several, many together, sometimes clustered, 1–5 dm. long; petioles glabrous, or sparingly scaly at the base, pale or brownish; blades ovate in outline, pedately divided, with the rachis rather evenly winged: leaflets usually 3–7, mostly lanceolate to narrowly linear, the upper ones undivided, the lower with several elongated

[1] First collected in Florida by J. L. Blodgett about 1838.

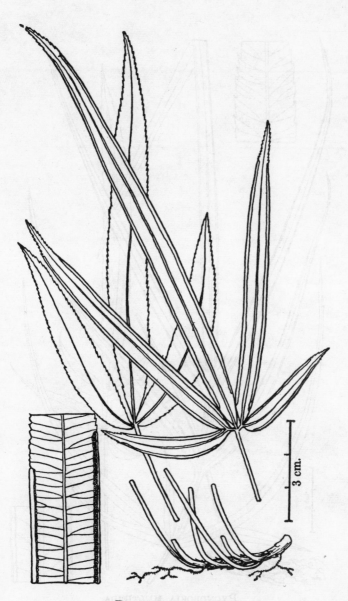

3 cm.

PYCNODORIA CRETICA

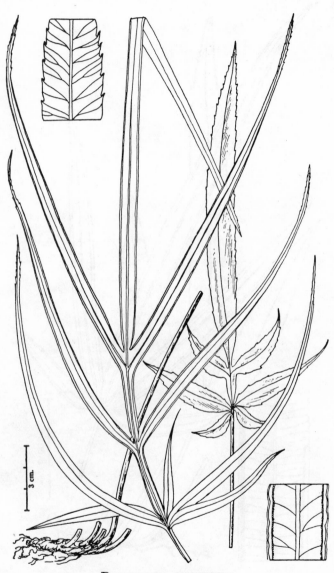

PYCNODORIA MULTIFIDA

linear segments on one or on each side, the sterile ones spinulose-serrate: spore-bearing leaflets narrower, with the indusia extending from the base nearly or quite to the attenuate apex: veins parallel, simple or once forked, obliquely ascending to the margins. [*Pteris serulata* L.f. in part.]—(SPIDER-BRAKE.)—On old walls, rock-pits, and dumps, Fla., La., to N. C., escaped from cultivation. Nativity not known.—Spores mature in summer and fall.—Fig. reduced.

Ferns with leaves of interesting patterns are widely cultivated. Some species are very tender, that is, not well suited to shift for themselves, as it were, outside of their native haunts. In fact very few of the hosts of cultivated ferns become naturalized, at least in temperate regions. The present species was cultivated from an early date. The record of its nativity was lost before it was named in 1804, but it is thought to be a native of China. This fern has long been known in South Carolina and Louisiana. It is often nearly exterminated in South Carolina localities in severe frosts, but usually reestablishes itself. Later it appeared in Florida and may be found on walls in St. Augustine. Referring to its occurrence in St. Augustine, a letter recently received from a fern student contained the following lines: ''If this be the same plant that is known about Charleston as the 'Huguenot-fern,' it is an interesting coincidence that it grows here in the Huguenot Cemetery but not in the Roman Catholic one just around the corner. Both the resurrection-fern and the Venus-hair are common in both places, but this one seems to be a confirmed Protestant.'' How early this fern was introduced into South Carolina we do not know, but it now grows far from habitations as well as in the towns. The finest specimens we have seen were found growing on the remains of the foundation of Thomas Walter's house in his botanic garden along the Santee River.

13. **PTERIS** L.

Coarse terrestrial plants, with elongate branching rootstocks which are clothed with somewhat velvety scales, sometimes vine-like. Leaves borne singly along the elongate rootstock, sometimes greatly elongate and clambering or climbing: petiole continuous with the rootstock, usually naked at the base: blades broad, triangular or pentagonal in outline, ternately decompound, the leaflets entire, toothed, or pinnatifid. Veins free, simple or forked. Sori marginal, linear, continuous, borne on a slender receptacle which connects the ends of the free veins. Indusia double, the outer prominent, formed by the reflexed margin of the leaf-blade, the inner obscure, borne upon the vein-like receptacle and extending beneath the sporangia.—Several species of very wide geographic distribution.—BRACKENS.—The genus is based on *Pteris aquilina* L.—The name is the Greek for fern.—For notes on varieties and forms see Am. Fern Jour. 27: 52–53. 1937.

Ultimate leaflets of the lower pinnae pinnatifid: veins mostly twice or thrice forked.   1. *P. latiuscula.*
Ultimate leaflets of the lower pinnae pinnate: veins mostly once forked.   2. *P. caudata.*

  1. P. latiuscula Desv. Rootstock elongate, stout, woody, horizontal, extensively spreading underground: leaves erect, often in extensive colonies, sometimes 2 m. tall; petioles straw-colored or brownish, more or less velvety scaly at the base; blades 6–12 dm. long, triangular to deltoid-ovate in outline, usually subternate, the three divisions each 2-pinnate, the ultimate segments lanceolate or ovate (linear and more or less elongate as well as glabrous or nearly so in *P. latiuscula pseudocaudata*), usually approximate and connected at their bases: veins mostly twice or thrice-forked.—(BRACKEN.)—Hammocks, woods, and stony hills, exposed sandy places, various provinces, pen. Fla. to Tex. and S. Canada.—Spores mature in summer and fall.—Fig. reduced.

  The texture of the leaves of our ferns varies from the very delicate, even flimsy and translucent to the coarse, opaque and even succulent. The extremes are most evident among the ferns of Florida where filmys and delicate spleenworts occur in company with coarse brackens and leather-ferns. This bracken is one of the common ferns throughout eastern North America, except in the extreme north. By its ruggedness it is able to grow in all the plant provinces and to occur in the extremes of altitude. On dry mountain sides it forms extensive colonies, often appropriating areas almost to the exclusion of other vegetation. On the other hand, this is one of the few northern ferns that approach or really intrude in a typically tropical fern-flora. It occurs fully as far south as the latitude of the Lake Okeechobee region. It appears to grow almost equally well in woods and in open sandy places. In the latter habitat it often takes possession of large areas, spreading extensively by its long and strong rootstocks and growing luxuriantly to the exclusion of all other fern plants. There occurs, nearly throughout the range of the species, a form with narrow segments, particularly an elongate terminal segment. This character suggestive of the leaf of the tropical *Pteris caudata* led to its being designated *pseudocaudata* (see fertile leaflet in upper right-hand corner of figure). Northward the present fern vies with the common polypody for first place in abundance and wide geographic distribution. However, it

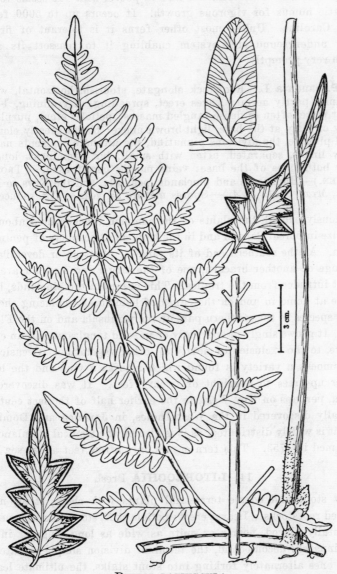

PTERIS LATIUSCULA

usually occurs in drier localities and in poorer soil. It seems to need but little humus for vigorous growth. It occurs up to 5000 feet in North Carolina. Unlike most other ferns it is tolerant of fire, its strong underground stem-system enabling it to reassert its aerial growth very promptly.

2. **P. caudata** L. Rootstock elongate, stoutish, horizontal, woody, sometimes partly aerial: leaves erect, spreading, or reclining, 1–5 m. long or more, often in dense tangled masses; petioles stout, purple and velvety or scaly at the base, light-brown above: blades greatly elongate, 3- or 4-pinnate, the divisions pinnatifid, the ultimate segments narrow, usually linear, separated, often with small, but prominent, lobes on one or both sides of the base: veins mostly once-forked.—(TROPICAL BRACKEN.)—Hammocks and pinelands, pen. Fla. and the Keys to La.— (*W. I., Mex., C. A., S. A.*)—Spores mature all year.—Fig. reduced.

Curiously enough the plants of the common bracken hold about the same size in boreal Canada and in the tropical atmosphere of peninsular Florida. At the southern end of its range it abuts on or dovetails into the range of another bracken, one of the larger ferns of our area, an ancient intruder from the tropics. This occurs in the pinelands, but it is more at home in and on the edges of hammocks, replacing the preceding species in the southern part of the peninsula and on the Florida Keys. It grows singly or sparingly or in solid tangles an acre in extent or more, to the exclusion of nearly all other vegetation. Occasionally in hammocks a variety is found which acts as a vine and the leaves clamber up trees to a height of twenty feet. It was discovered in Florida, perhaps on Key West, in the earlier half of the last century.[1] Originally discovered in the West Indies, in Jamaica and Dominica, where it is widely distributed, as it is also on the tropical mainland. It was named in 1753. This fern occurs only a few feet above sea-level.

14. **LITOBROCHIA** Presl.

Very stout and coarse terrestrial plants with short, stout, much-branched rootstocks. Leaves erect: petiole stiff, stout: blade somewhat horizontally placed, nearly or quite as wide as long, angular in outline, pinnately decompound, the terminal division simple-pinnate, the lateral ones alternately forking into stout stalks, the ultimate leaflets sessile or nearly so. Veins forking and anastomosing. Sori as in *Pteris.*—Several species, tropical.—The genus was based on *Pteris*

[1] First collected in Florida by J. L. Blodgett about 1838.

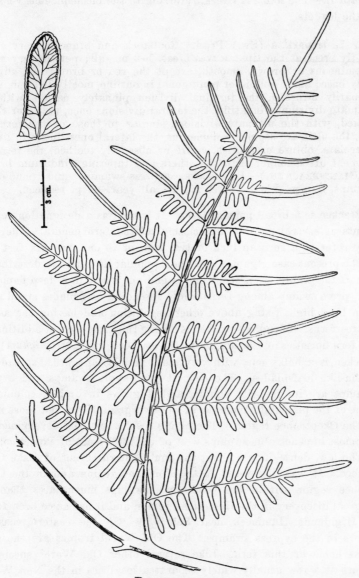

3 cm.

PTERIS CAUDATA

pedata L.—The name is Greek, referring to the inconspicuous venation of the leaflets.

1. L. tripartita (Sw.) Presl. Rootstock and branches very stout, mostly erect at the tips: leaves erect, 1–2 m. tall; petiole very stout, stramineous or brown, smooth, except the red or brown and slightly scaly base; blade deltoid or pentagonal in outline, mostly 1–1.5 m. wide, primarily 3-forked, the terminal division pinnately parted, with the ultimate divisions pinnatifid, the lateral divisions once, twice, or thrice forked, with the ultimate divisions similar to those of the terminal one, the ultimate segments numerous, the lateral ones linear to linear-lanceolate, obtuse or acutish, entire or obscurely toothed, the terminal segment often longer than the others and tapering: indusium brown. —(GIANT-BRACKEN.)—Hammocks, cypress-swamps, and pond-apple swamps, S. pen. Fla.—Spores mature all year.—Fig. reduced.

Bracken is a broad popular term. It is used as a designation for the plants of several more or less closely related fern genera. The term may refer to a fern an inch or two high or to one over six feet tall. In the present case gigantic is the best popular adjective to describe the size of the plant. It is inspiring to find one's self in a deep hammock or cypress swamp among ferns whose spreading leaf-blades stand more than head high, rising above other vegetation and having the aspect of tree-ferns. The giant-bracken is among the rather recent additions to the fern floristics of Florida. Like the leather-ferns (*Acrostichum*) this bracken is a bulky one, with very stout petioles and broad-spread umbrella-like leaf-blades. The deepest pond-apple swamps and cypress swamps are its favorite haunts, and it grows in limited colonies in some of the pineland hammocks of the Everglade Keys, and those north of the Okeechobee region. The plants reach their best development in the most impenetrable swamps west of the settlement of Pompano, and in the low, dense jungle about the southeastern corner of Lake Okeechobee. It was discovered in the Pompano region and in the Okeechobee region within the pond-apple swamps much later than the original discovery in the Homestead region and it has since been found in Highlands Hammock near Sebring.[1] On the eastern coast it grows in the cypress swamps. The Old World tropics are the principal home of this fern. Like several other Old World species, it occurs at a few usually widely separated localities in the New World. It is found only a few feet above sea-level in Florida.—Some Florida specimens were erroneously determined as *Pteris quadriaurita*.

[1] First collector of this fern in Florida is uncertain.

3 cm.

LITOBROCHIA TRIPARTITA

15. **ADIANTUM** L.

Delicate or graceful wood-plants inhabiting rich soil or moist cliffs. Leaves erect or pendulous, single or tufted on the rootstocks, the petiole and its divisions black or dark, shining or dull, sometimes pubescent: blades pinnately or pedately compound, with the petiole continuous into the rachis or forked at the top: leaflets sometimes prominently jointed to the rachis or to the ultimate stalks, very inequilateral, with the midrib wanting or marginal and the veins mostly flabellate, forking, free. Sori short or laterally extended appearing marginal on the back of the leaflets, borne at the ends of the veins. Indusia formed by the more or less altered and reflexed edge or lobes of the leaflets.—(MAIDEN-HAIRS. MAIDENHAIR-FERNS.)—About one hundred and seventy-five species, most abundant in tropical America.—The genus *Adiantum* was based on *A. Capillus-Veneris* L. as the type.—The name is from the Greek and means unwetted, the foliage shedding rain. Extremes of altitude are represented in this genus.—For notes on varieties and forms see Am. Fern Jour. 27: 52. 1937.

Leaf forked at the top of the petiole. 1. *A. pedatum.*
Leaf with the rachis continuous or apparently
  so, from the top of the petiole.
  Petiole and rachis pubescent and dull.
    Leaflets set at right-angles to the rachis;
      blades glabrous beneath, broadly
      rounded at the apex: indusia narrow. 2. *A. melanoleucum.*
    Leaflets set oblique to the rachis; blades
      pubescent beneath, more or less nar-
      rowed at the apex: indusia orbicular
      or reniform. 3. *A. hispidulum.*
  Petiole and rachis glabrous and shining.
    Leaf-blades lanceolate to ovate-lanceolate
      in outline, 1–2-pinnate, or occasionally
      3-pinnate: leaflets continuous with
      their petiolules. 4. *A. Capillus-Veneris.*
    Leaf-blades deltoid to ovate-deltoid in out-
      line, 4–5-pinnate or often 3-pinnate:
      leaflets definitely jointed to their peti-
      olules. 5. *A. tenerum.*

1. **A. pedatum** L. Rootstocks slender, often elongate, mostly horizontal: leaves numerous in colonies; petioles 2–4.5 dm. long, dark chestnut-brown, polished and shining; blades reniform-orbicular to reniform, mostly 2–4 dm. broad, with the larger divisions 1.5–4 dm. long; leaflets rather numerous, various, the blades generally oblong or somewhat lanceolate about the middle of the pinna, obliquely reniform to obliquely deltoid at the base and the terminal one flabellate, all short-stalked, glabrous, the lower margin entire, the upper margin toothed, cleft, or lobed: sori transversely linear-oblong to reniform or linear on the ends of the leaflet-lobes.—(NORTHERN MAIDENHAIR-FERN.)—In rich woods and on damp rocky banks, various provinces, Ga.

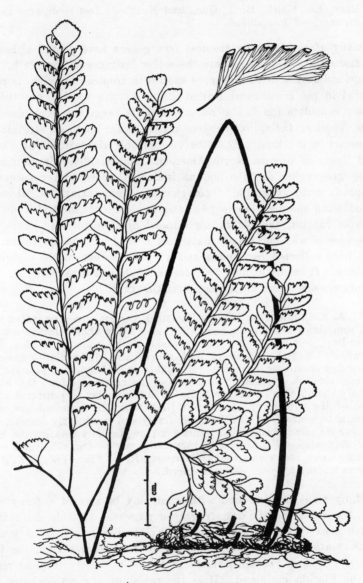

ADIANTUM PEDATUM

to Miss., La., Calif., B. C., Que., and Newf.—(*Asia*.)—Spores mature in summer.—Fig. reduced.

Many of the typically tropical fern genera have pushed either one or few representatives up into the colder latitudes of the north. The genus *Adiantum*, with numerous species in tropical America, is represented in the continental United States by five species, but the one under consideration has alone extended its range into Canada. Another species, *A. Capillus-Veneris*, ranges as far north as Virginia and Missouri in the East. The others reach only the latitude of Florida and Texas in eastern North America. This maiden-hair fern has a wide geographic distribution, as indicated above and consequently occurs in many geographic forms showing slight variations. However, considering the great variety in latitude, longitude, and altitude, and also in habitat, the plants are astonishingly uniform in characters. The species was botanically named in 1753, based on specimens that had been collected in Canada and Virginia earlier in the eighteenth century. It occurs at over 5000 feet altitude in North Carolina. The plants are sometimes known as LOCKHAIR-FERN.

2. A. melanoleucum Willd. Rootstock slender, creeping, often short but sometimes much-branched, with loose fuzzy chaff: leaves erect or spreading, 1–8 dm. long; petioles about as long as the blades, dark-brown or blackish, pubescent with short hairs, dull; blades linear to linear-lanceolate or narrowly triangular in outline, 1–2-pinnate, the pinnae very short-stalked; leaflets few or relatively few, the blades mainly rhombic or rhombic-elliptic, or suborbicular to reniform at the base of the pinnae or obovate at their tips, the terminal one often acuminate, scarcely if at all curved, finely and irregularly serrate, with an obscure joint at the base: indusia narrow, broadly emarginate, laterally elongate.—(FRAGRANT MAIDENHAIR-FERN.)—On sides and edges of lime-sinks, rocky hammocks, Everglade Keys, Fla.—(*W. I., S. A.*)— Spores mature all year.—Fig. reduced.

Many ferns are endowed with what may be termed a ferny odor, but few have the striking fragrance possessed by this maidenhair, which closely resembles that of the well-known sweet-vernal grass— *Anthoxanthum odoratum*. After reaching our shores from the West Indies this fern became isolated in the only strictly tropical region of the Florida mainland. It is the rarest of our maidenhairs, and grows on the sides and on the edges of lime-sinks in a few hammocks isolated in the Long Pine Key pinelands. The plants are less graceful and much less conspicuous than those of the preceding or following

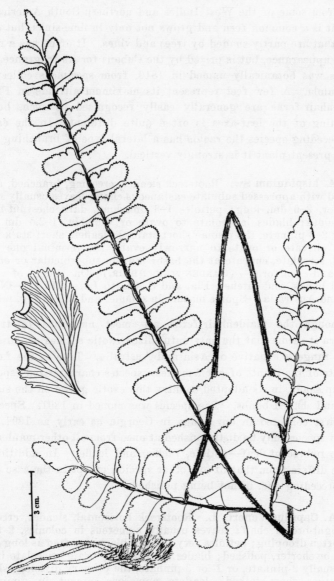

ADIANTUM MELANOLEUCUM

species. It was discovered in Florida in 1916,[1] and is otherwise known only from some of the West Indies and northern South America. In Cuba it is a common fern and grows not only in lime-sinks, but on old walls that are partly shaded by trees and vines. It often has a ragged coarse appearance, but is prized by the Cubans for its fragrance. The species was botanically named in 1810, from specimens collected in Hispaniola. A few feet represent its maximum altitude in Florida. Maidenhair-ferns are generally easily recognized as such, but the branching of the leaf-axes is often quite different. In the case of the preceding species the rachis has a lateral type of branching, while in the present plant it is strongly vertical.

3. **A. hispidulum** Sw. Rootstock slender, creeping, branched, closely covered with appressed subulate castaneous chaff: leaves usually several together, 2–6 dm. long; petioles 1–3 dm. long, dark chestnut-brown, hispidulous; blades lanceolate to ovate or rhombic, 1–2.5 dm. long, mostly 2–3-pinnate, the pinnae short-stalked; leaflets short-stalked, the blades obovate or ovate to narrowly ovate, the terminal one blunt, curved, serrulate, cuneate at the base: indusia suborbicular or emarginate and reniform.—(GARDEN-MAIDENHAIR.)—On sides of walls, shaded banks, and ditches, Fla. and S. Ga. to La.—(*W. I.*)—Nat. of Asia and Australia.—Spores mature in summer and fall.—Fig. reduced.

Although the maidenhair-ferns are most numerous in tropical America it seems that the only naturalized exotic species of *Adiantum* in our range is a native of Asia and Australia. True to the favorite habitats of the plants of our American species characterized especially by deep shade, in its adopted country this exotic grows on the sides of wells and shaded banks. The species was named in 1801. Specimens were first collected in our range in Georgia as early as 1901. The present species may be distinguished at once from all other maidenhairs by the pubescent leaf—petiole, rachis, and leaflet. In addition the petiole differs from that of our other species, except in the case of the next preceding one, in not being polished.

4. **A. Capillus-Veneris** L. Rootstock horizontal, slender, creeping, with light-brown chaff: leaves usually numerous in colonies, 2–5 dm. long, often drooping; petioles very slender, blackish, often as long as the blades or shorter, polished; blades lanceolate to ovate-lanceolate in outline, usually 2-pinnate, or 1- or 3-pinnate, the primary divisions slender but rather short-stalked; leaflets numerous, except in diminutive plants, the blades reniform, suborbicular, obovate, or cuneate, the ter-

[1] First collected in Florida by J. K. Small and C. A. Mosier, January 12, 1916.

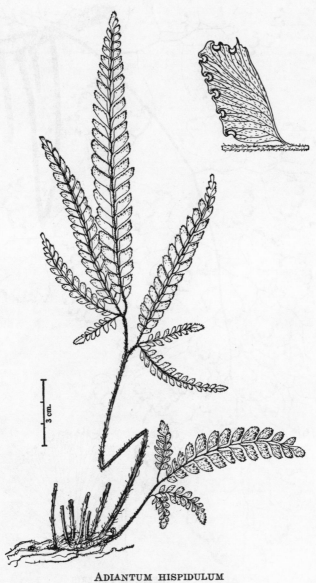

3 cm.

ADIANTUM HISPIDULUM

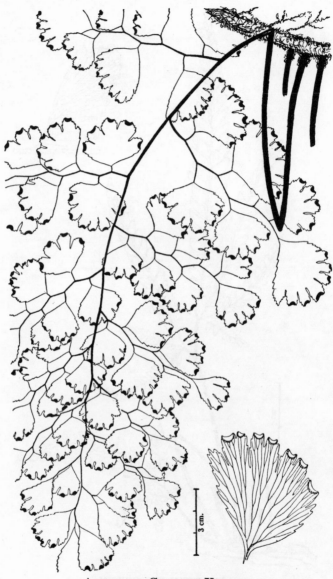

3 cm.

ADIANTUM CAPILLUS-VENERIS

minal one conspicuously cuneate, the sterile ones incised, crenate, or dentate-serrate, often 2–3 cm. long, the sporophyls less prominently so on account of the rolling back of the edges, slender-stalked, not jointed at the base: indusia usually decidedly emarginate.—(VENUS'-HAIR-FERN.)—Hammocks, lime-sinks, river-banks, bluffs, and cliffs; various provinces, Fla. to Tex., Calif., Utah, S. Dak., Mo., and Va.—(*W. I., Mex., C. A., S. A., O. W.*)—Also often on walls in old cemeteries.— Spores mature in summer and fall.—Fig. reduced.

The present species, in various forms, is very widely distributed in nature. Its pleasing leaf and adaptability to artificial habitats, both in the open and under glass, have resulted in its becoming one of the most widely cultivated ferns. Unlike the next preceding and the following species this is a temperate element in our range, extending down into northern Florida and the upper part of the peninsula where it enters the northern tropical area. Curiously enough in this tropical area the plants are mostly diminutive. This is more graceful than either of those just referred to, especially *Adiantum melanoleucum.* The latter has a rather stiff habit of growth; but in the Venus'-hair the pliant leaves often hang in green cascades from the rocks and cliffs on which they grow. The southeast happens to represent just one corner of the geographic range of this plant, which is extremely wide; besides occuring in the United States from Virginia to Missouri, South Dakota, Alberta, and California and southward, it is not rare in parts of tropical America and ranges through the warmer parts of the Old World. It prefers strongly calcareous soils, but also occurs on sandstone (apparently permeated by limy water). The species was named in 1753 from specimens collected in southern Europe. This fern was discovered in our range in the earlier part of the last century. Perhaps this is the only fern named in honor of a star-actress of the ancient celestial movies. Being an attractive fern, popular names are abundant. The more common are LADY'S-HAIR, BLACK-MAIDENHAIR, DUDDER-GRASS, VENUS'-HAIR. Forms resembling plants of *Adiantum tenerum* may easily be distinguished by the lack of a joint between the leaflet and its stalk.

5. **A. tenerum** Sw. Rootstock stout, creeping, or contorted, covered with reddish chaff: leaves erect, several together, mostly 1 m. long or less; petioles often about as long as the blades, sometimes shorter or sometimes longer, polished; blades deltoid or ovate-deltoid in outline, 4-5-pinnate, the primary divisions long-stalked; leaflets very numerous, except in diminutive plants, the blades variable, subreniform, suborbicular, obovate, ovate, or cuneate, mostly 1–2 cm. long, the sterile ones mostly 1–2 cm. long, more prominently lobed or toothed than in *A.*

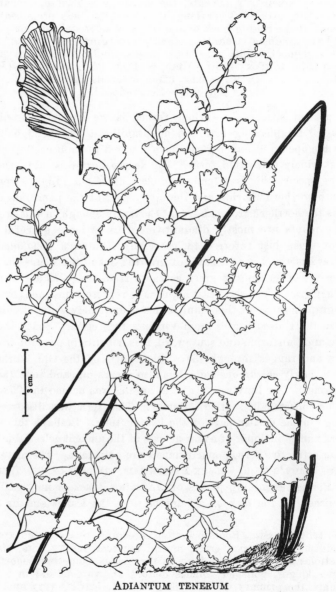

3 cm.

ADIANTUM TENERUM

Capillus-Veneris, slender-stalked, prominently jointed at the base: indusia scarcely emarginate.—(MAIDENHAIR-FERN, BRITTLE-MAIDEN-HAIR, FAN-MAIDENHAIR.)—Rocky floor of hammocks and woods and lime-sinks, pen. Fla.—(*W. I., Mex., C. A., S. A.*)—Spores mature all year.—Fig. reduced.

Like the preceding, this fern is a favorite in cultivation. It may be found in many rock-gardens and glass-houses. In our range it is not only confined to peninsular Florida, but to the two tropical areas within the peninsula. These areas represent the homes of two separate plant immigrations from the tropics. The descendents of the earlier migration from tropical America are now growing in the tropical plant-area in the northern part of the peninsula where they have maintained an existence for many years. Those descended from the later migration from the West Indies are now confined to the Everglade Keys at the southern end of the peninsula. On the Everglade Keys this maidenhair occurs in many high-pineland hammocks, especially in those where arboreous vegetation is so copious as to cause twilight in mid-day and where the floor is honeycombed with small and large lime-sinks. In grottoes of the more northern tropical area the development of this delicate fern is surprising. There are exceptions to this rule of growing so luxuriantly only in dense shade, for in occasional localities where storms have carried away the tops of trees, thus exposing areas of several square rods in extent, this beautiful fern takes almost complete possession of the ground, forming a carpet over the hammock floor, but then usually with smaller leaflets. Curiously enough, although one of the more common tropical ferns in Florida, this was not discovered there until 1875.[1] It is widely distributed in insular and continental tropical America. The original specimens came from Jamaica and Hispaniola. These furnished the material for the original naming which was published in 1788. Each year this fern is becoming more scarce, and where it formerly grew in the greatest abundance it has become rare. Truck loads have been carried away from certain hammocks in recent years by nurserymen. About 100 feet represents its maximum altitude in Florida. Specimens of this maidenhair are frequently but unnecessarily confused with those of *Adiantum Capillus-Veneris,* for the leaflets are conspicuously jointed to their slender stalks. One of its common names, brittle-maidenhair refers to the ease with which the leaflets drop off.

[1] First collected in Florida by S. N. Chamberlin about 1875.

16. **HYPOLEPIS** Bernh.

Large semi-erect or diffuse plants with slender, horizontal, widely spreading, finely scaly or glabrous rootstocks. Leaves apart, at first: petioles elongate, sometimes prickle-armed, erect: blades ample, 1-4 times pinnately compound, the primary leaflets few; pinnules or ultimate segments pinnatifid, the lobes broad. Veins few, simple and forking. Sori small and roundish, marginal, borne at the ends of the lower veinlets of the ultimate segments, sometimes on the upper side, sometimes on both sides of the segments, and occasionally at the ends of adjacent veins, usually indusiate by the turning back of the small marginal lobe.—About three dozen species widely distributed in tropical and subtropical regions.—The genus *Hypolepis* was founded on *Lonchitis repens*, the Linnean name for this species.—The name is from the Greek, referring to the position of the sporangia beneath the indusia.

1. H. repens (L.) Presl. Rootstock elongate, branching, somewhat knotted, minutely brownish scaly-tomentose: leaves 9–60 dm. long or rarely less; petioles stramineous to reddish-brown, smoothish or pubescent and often prickly, the divisions usually similarly pubescent and often armed; blades deltoid to lanceolate in outline, 4–15 dm. long, nearly as wide, 3- or 4-pinnate, the lateral branches opposite or nearly so, spreading, the rachis glabrate or glandular-pubescent, often spinescent; ultimate segments spreading, elliptic to lanceolate, rounded, pinnatifid, somewhat chartaceous, paler below, glabrate to glandular-pubescent, the lobes rounded: veins few, simple or once-forked: indusia distinct scale-like, thin, pale, few and small. [*Lonchitis repens* L.]— Low hammocks and swamps, Oligocene Island region, Fla.—(*W. I., Mex., C. A., S. A.,*)—Spores mature all year.—Fig. reduced.

Although this was one of the later ferns discovered in Florida, it evidently came in during the earlier invasion from the tropics. It still maintains a strong hold on the older tropical area. As time passed it spread southward at least as far as the latitude of Lake Okeechobee. It has not yet been found on the later Florida tropical area, the Everglade Keys. In its migrations it has tended to follow the hammocks lying west of the backbone or lake region, rather than those eastward. In addition to the possibility of this fern's having reached Florida by the wind-carried spores, portions of the fragile leaves or the spinescent leaf-stalks may have clung to the plumage of swamp-birds. Recent exploration has shown the geographical distribution of this fern to be much more extensive than formerly considered. Until quite recently

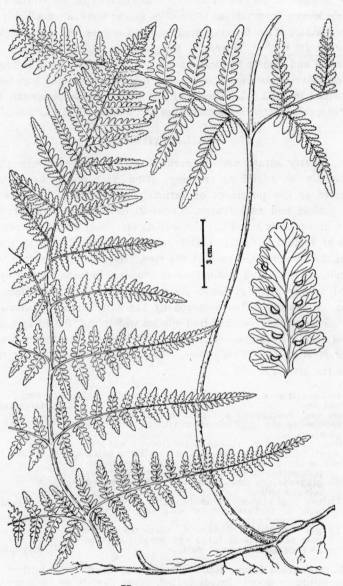

3 cm.

HYPOLEPIS REPENS

it was thought to be one of the very local ferns of the State. It is definitely known from various hammocks, and in some in remarkably prolific abundance, often forming great tangled masses. It was discovered in Florida in 1895.[1] Moreover, the plant is widely known in both continental and insular tropical America. It was discovered in tropical America (Martinique) early in the eighteenth century and was botanically named in 1753. Like some of the other tropical American ferns in Florida, this one reaches a maximum of a hundred feet above sea-level.

17. CHEILANTHES Sw.

Low, mostly small, usually rock-inhabiting and evergreen plants, with usually horizontal or creeping, often wiry rootstocks, typically with more or less pubescent or variously scaly foliage. Leaves uniform: petiole and rachis wiry, blades 2- or 3-pinnate, rather finely divided and usually lace-like; the leaflets relatively broad, deeply pinnatifid or incised with the midrib central. Veins oblique to midrib, forked, the veinlets thickened at the tips. Sori terminal on the veins, marginal, roundish and distinct, or confluent. Indusia formed by the reflexed usually modified leaflet-margins, separated or sometimes continuous. Sporangia often obscured by the hairy or scaly covering.— Comprises more than one hundred species widely distributed in temperate and tropical regions.—The genus *Cheilanthes* was founded on *C. micropteris* Sw. of the West Indies.—The name is from the Greek, referring to the marginal sori.

Indusium continuous around the leaf-segments: foliage brown woolly-tomentose.   1. *C. tomentosa.*
Indusium not continuous around the leaf-segments:
  foliage merely hispidulous or villous, or nearly glabrous.
  Petiole and rachis villous-hispidulous: leaf-segments pubescent on the back with villous hairs.   2. *C. lanosa.*
  Petiole and rachis glabrous or finely appressed-pubescent, except at the base: leaf-segments glabrous on the back or with scattered minute hairs.
    Larger leaf-blades 2-pinnate, with the lower pair of leaflets shorter and smaller than the second pair.   3. *C. alabamensis.*
    Larger leaf-blades 3-pinnate, with the lower pair of leaflets as large and nearly or quite as long as the second pair.   4. *C. microphylla.*

1. C. tomentosa Link. Rootstocks densely chaffy with both striped and bright-brown scales: leaves tufted, often densely so on account of the short-jointed and contorted rootstocks, 1.5–5 dm. tall: petioles stoutish, densely brown woolly-tomentose; blades herbaceous, lanceolate,

[1] First collected in Florida by C. S. Williamson, July, 1895.

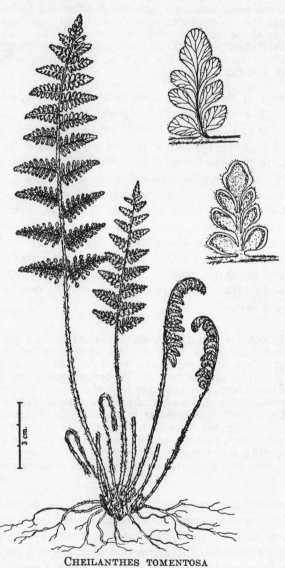

3 cm.

CHEILANTHES TOMENTOSA

varying from linear-lanceolate to oblong-lanceolate, 3-pinnate, mostly longer than the petiole, copiously tomentose, especially lanate beneath, with brownish-white obscurely articulated hairs, the leaflets lanceolate, ovate, ovate-oblong, or oblong-lanceolate, the ultimate lobes about sub-orbicular to ovate, obtuse: indusium continuous, pale, membranous.—(WOOLLY LIP-FERN.)—Rocks and stony soil, cliffs and rocky banks, various provinces, Ga. to Ariz., Mo., and W. Va.—(*Mex.*)—Spores mature in summer and fall.—Fig. reduced.

The plants of the hairy lip-fern, *Cheilanthes lanosa*, and the woolly lip-fern, *C. tomentosa*, are much alike in habit. The former is relatively smaller and less robust looking. Contrary to what these characters would indicate, the former species has extended its range much farther north than the latter. The northern range in the middle states is about equivalent, up to Missouri, while the ranges also coincide to the southeast in Georgia, which state represents the southern geographic limit on the Atlantic seaboard. This fern is really evergreen, but like the resurrection fern (*Marginaria polypodioides*) and some species of selaginella, the leaves become dry and crisp during droughts, then freshen again after rains. The original specimens were collected in Mexico in the earlier part of the nineteenth century and the species was named in 1833. This fern occurs up to 3800 feet in North Carolina and Tennessee.

2. **C. lanosa** (Michx.) D. C. Eaton. Rootstocks copiously chaffy; pale rusty-brown leaves more or less closely tufted on the short-jointed, often contorted rootstocks, 1–3.5 dm. tall; petioles wiry, chestnut-brown, villous hirsutulous; blades herbaceous, linear to lanceolate or oblong-lanceolate, usually longer than the petiole, villous-hirsutulous, gradually attenuate to the apex, 2-pinnate; the leaflets somewhat distant, ovate to ovate-lanceolate or lanceolate-deltoid, usually somewhat glandular, the ultimate lobes close, roundish or ovate, obtuse: indusia interrupted, brown, herbaceous. [*C. vestita* Sw.]—(HAIRY LIP-FERN.)—Ledges, cliffs, rocky ridges, and rocky woods, various provinces, Ga. to N. M., Mo., and Conn.—Spores mature in summer and fall.—Fig. reduced.

Although the lip-ferns delight in the tropics for the most part, more than a dozen species range into or occur in temperate North America. Unlike some of the typically tropical genera such as *Tectaria*, *Nephrolepis* and *Phymatodes*, the extra-tropical lip-ferns have migrated or developed to a greater extent in western North America than on the eastern side of the continent. The species under consideration holds the record for ''far north'' in the eastern United States occurring in

CHEILANTHES LANOSA

Connecticut. As contrasted with *Cheilanthes alabamensis,* another southern species, the plants of the present species seem equally at home in silicious or in calcareous soil. This fern was discovered in the mountains (perhaps the Blue Ridge) of Tennessee and North Carolina about the beginning of the past century and named in 1803. Fully 3800 feet is its altitudinal record in the southern Blue Ridge.

3. **C. alabamensis** (Buckl.) Kunze. Rootstocks horizontal, stout, copiously chaffy with hair-like rusty scales: leaves usually tufted, on the branching contorted rootstocks, 1–5 dm. tall; petioles black, wiry, with a line of short hairs on the upper side and rusty-villous at the base; blades chartaceous, lanceolate to linear-lanceolate, glabrous, longer than the petioles, 2-pinnate, the leaflets ovate to lanceolate, sometimes acuminate, the lower pair usually shorter and smaller than those above, pinnatifid, the lobes mostly acute or acutish, often semi-auriculate: indusia interrupted, pale, membranous.—Rocks, cliffs, ledges, bluffs, usually calcareous, various provinces, Ala. to Ariz., Mo., and Va.—(*Mex.*)—Spores mature in summer and fall.—Fig. reduced.

Instances of rather conspicuous plants escaping attention for long periods, even when growing in regions of botanical activity, are not rare. Although the geographic range of this fern includes much of the southeastern United States except the Coastal Plain, and the contiguous territory to the west as far as Arizona and Mexico, it remained unnamed and undescribed until 1843. It was originally launched under the genus *Pteris,* with the record that it ''grows in tufts on limestone rocks that form the banks of the Tennessee River, at the foot of Muscle Shoals, Alabama.'' This type locality may have been destroyed by the conversion of the shoals into a power dam. Throughout its range this plant seems to prefer a calcareous soil. In the Blue Ridge its maximum altitude is about 1800 feet; while close to 2000 feet is recorded on Lookout Mountain.

4. **C. microphylla** Sw. Rootstock mainly horizontal, copiously chaffy with narrow brown scales when young: leaves sparingly or sometimes densely tufted on the branching rootstocks, mostly 1–4 dm. tall; petioles dark-brown, somewhat rusty-pubescent with very short appressed hairs; blades ovate to lanceolate, as long as the petioles or longer, 3-pinnate or 2-pinnate above the lower leaflets, the leaflets lanceolate to ovate, obtuse to acutish, the lower pair as large and nearly or quite as long as the upper, deeply incised or pinnatifid, the lobes elliptic or ovate: indusia interrupted, or continuous only near the apex. [*Adiantum microphyllum* Sw.]—Shell-heaps and rocky soil in hammocks, Fla.; also various provinces, Tex. to Ariz.—(*W. I., Mex., C. A.*)—Spores mature in summer and fall.

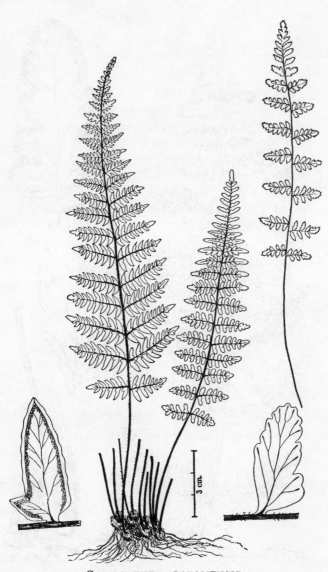

CHEILANTHES ALABAMENSIS

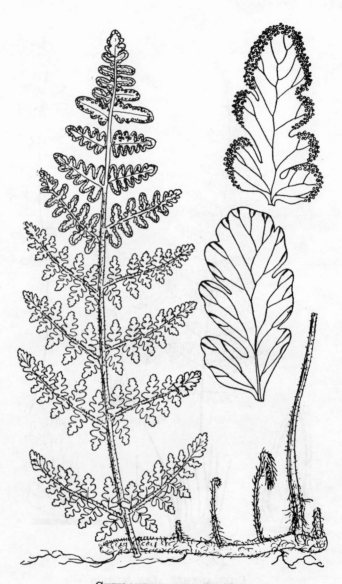

CHEILANTHES MICROPHYLLA

The geographical distribution of *Cheilanthes* in our range lies well north of the Gulf of Mexico, except for the present species. The others adhere to the higher provinces, especially where rocks abound. Northern tropical America is the center of this fern's geographical area. From the West Indies it long ago reached the shores of Florida, and established itself in the coastal regions of the State, and from the tropical mainland it crossed into the states bordering Mexico. A particularly interesting feature in the distribution of this fern, in the southeast, is its habitat. It is well known in Florida as an inhabitant of shell-heaps or kitchen-middens made by the aborigines of that region, and has only rarely been found on the rocky floors of hammocks. The fern was known for many years to grow in Florida on the shell-islands near the mouth of the St. Johns River, in the northeastern portion of the State, although at first confused with a more western species, *C. alabamensis*. It was discovered there in 1878.[1] In recent years it has been found in the southwestern portion on the shell-islands and shell-heaps in the vicinity of Chokoloskee Bay. It has not yet been met with on the Florida Keys. Its occurrence in hammocks in the interior of Florida is a recent discovery. This fern was originally discovered on the islands of Jamaica, Hispaniola, and St. Eustatius before the end of the eighteenth century and botanically named in 1788. It reaches but little altitude in Florida, less than 100 feet on a rocky hill near Lecanto being the maximum.

18. PELLAEA Link.

Stiff, usually low rock-inhabiting plants, relatively small, with stout, often horizontal, densely scaly rootstocks, the foliage glabrous, or inconspicuously pubescent. Leaves uniform on mature plants, often simple or less divided on young plants: petioles usually wiry, often polished: blades 1–3-pinnate, the leaflets commonly jointed at the base, their blades various, entire or hastate-lobed, those bearing spores usually narrower than the others. Veins oblique, forked, the veinlets not thickened at the immersed tips. Sori borne at or near the ends of unconnected veins, intramarginal, at length confluent laterally in a broad submarginal line. Indusium formed by the reflexed margins of the spore-bearing leaflets, these often somewhat modified or even membranous. Sporangia evident or nearly concealed by the revolute leaflet-margins.—Embraces about fifty species of wide geographic distribution. Most abundant in North America.—The genus *Pellaea* was

[1] First collected in Florida by A. H. Curtiss in 1878.

founded on *Pteris atropurpurea,* the Linnean name of the next following species. The name is from the Greek, referring to the dark colored
petiole and rachis of the leaves.—Spores mature late spring, summer
and fall.—For notes on varieties and forms see Am. Fern Jour. 27:
51–52. 1937.

Petiole, rachis, and petiolules more or less clothed with crisped hairs.
                                        1. *P. atropurpurea.*
Petiole, rachis, and petiolules glabrous or nearly so. 2. *P. glabella.*

1. P. atropurpurea (L.) Link. Rootstock short and with short
stubby branches, usually producing numerous fibrous roots, densely
clothed with long-attenuate scales, white at first, rusty in age: leaves
various, the early ones simple, trifoliate, or sparingly pinnate, blades
broad, mostly reinformed, deltoid, or ovate, erose-crenate, rather slender-
stalked; the later leaves larger and copiously pinnate; petioles and
rachis black or nearly so, finely pubescent with brownish hairs; leaflets
thickish, the blades very variable, narrowly ovate to lanceolate, or
nearly linear, 2–5 cm. long, often with scales on the midrib beneath,
short-stalked, pale-green, the spore-bearing ones more or less revolute,
sometimes subulate: veins mostly twice-forked, curved: indusium
hyaline, erose: sori red or brown. (CLIFF-BRAKE.)—Exposed or
sheltered rocks, preferring limestone, various provinces, W. Fla. to
Tex., Calif., B.C., Mack., and Ont.—(*Mex.*)—Fig. reduced.

This cliff-brake is a cool-climate fern, occurring in Canada; it
reaches Florida only by a southern extension of its range along limestone outcrops. It is one of the more widely distributed ferns of North
America. It ranges throughout a large part of the United States, from
the Atlantic Ocean west to California and southern Canada, and has
been collected in Mexico. It has not yet been detected in the West
Indies. Its altitudinal distribution, too, is extensive, as it ranges from
near sea-level to high elevations both in the Appalachian mountain system and in the Rocky Mountains. So far as we definitely know, this
fern was discovered in Virginia on the banks of the Rappahannock
River about the beginning of the eighteenth century. It was well described as early as 1743, and botanically named under the genus *Pteris*
in 1753.

The plants of this fern are evergreen. They thus represent one of
the ferns that may be collected in winter as well as in summer. In
fact, this fern is often more evident during the winter season, because
then there is not as much other growth about the plants to hide them
or divert one's attention. It most frequently grows on limestone
rocks and cliffs, and occurs up to about 4000 feet altitude in the Blue
Ridge. The clusters of leaves are characterized by a glaucous hue.

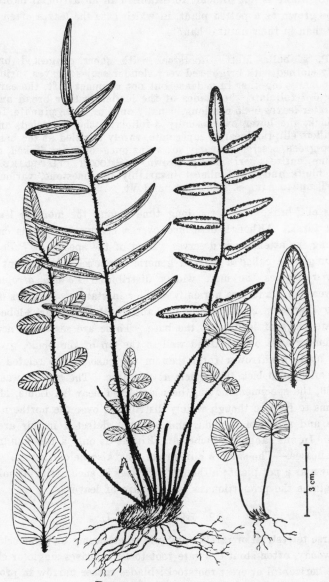

3 cm.

PELLAEA ATROPURPUREA

The cliff-brake is not difficult to establish in an artificial habitat.   It may be grown as a potted plant, in which case the leaves often become larger than in their natural haunts.

2. **P. glabella** Mett.   Rootstock with short congested branches, densely clothed with bright-red very slender scales: leaves various, several or many together in a dense but not compact tuft, the early ones mostly 5–7-foliolate, the blades of the leaflets rather broad and thinnish; later leaves 5–25 cm. long, usually once or twice pinnate, the leaflets thick, the lower ones usually 3-foliolate, short-petioled, and with the leaflets elliptic-linear to lanceolate, rarely auricled at the base, pale- or deep-green, sessile or nearly so: veins once- or twice-forked, curved: indusium entire: sori mostly brown.—(SMOOTH CLIFF-BRAKE.)—Dry rocks, bluffs and cliffs, almost invariably of limestone, various provinces, Tenn. to Ark., S. Dak., Ont., and Vt.

This cliff-brake was for a long time among the more or less unaccepted ferns.   Although described over a century ago, it is only now receiving the attention it deserves.   Most of the species of *Pellaea* have what might be called a marked generic likeness.   The present species closely resembles the more widely distributed *Pellaea atropurpurea*. However, the plants are normally smaller in stature.   A gross differentiating character is frequently at hand in the peculiar 3-lobed or 3-foliolate pairs of leaflets at the base.   These are sessile or nearly so, and similar ones often extend well to the tip of the blade, giving the whole blade a narrower form than in the case of the related species. The leaflets also lack the auricle at the base.   The species was named in 1869, the specimens having been collected near St. Louis, Missouri. It seems to be rare though widely distributed over the northern United States and southern Canada, and was not detected in our area until 1935.[1]   In our range it reaches an altitude of only a few hundred feet in Tennessee.—The smooth cliff-brake may also be cultivated.   It may be grown as a pot plant; although it thrives in such artificial habitat, it still retains the proportionate (small) size of leaves.

19. BLECHNUM L.

Coarse terrestrial or rarely epiphytic erect swamp or hammock plants, with woody, often stout elongate rootstocks.   Leaves single or clustered on the horizontal or erect rootstock: blades rather narrow in proportion to their length, pinnatifid or pinnate, the segments or leaflets callous-margined, entire or toothed. Veins simple, forking, free in non-

[1] Collected near Morristown, Tennessee, by William A. Knight.

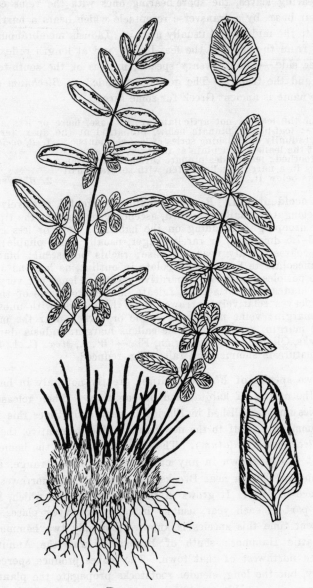

PELLAEA GLABELLA

spore bearing leaves, the spore-bearing ones with the veins connected
near their bases by a transverse receptacle which bears a narrow sorus
parallel to the midrib and usually near it. Indusia membranous, linear,
distinct from the edge of the leaf-blades and at length reflexed from
the inner side.—About twenty species, natives of the south-temperate
regions and the tropics.—The genus is founded on *Blechnum orientale*
L.—The name is ancient Greek for some fern.

Blades of the leaflets not articulate at the base, more or less attenuate,
    entire: leaf-blades pinnate below, pinnatifid at the apex, terminating
    in a gradually diminishing series of leaf-segments.   1. *B. occidentale.*
Blades of the leaflets articulate at the base, not attenu-
    ate, toothed: leaf-blades pinnate throughout, termi-
    nating in a narrow leaflet, often with several small
    leaflets below it.   2. *B. serrulatum.*

1. B. occidentale L. Rootstock mainly horizontal, relatively slender,
greatly elongate, usually branched, ascending or erect at the tip: leaves
erect or drooping (depending on the habitat), more or less clustered,
mostly 3–7.5 dm. long, or rarely longer, usually quite pliable; petioles
slender, coarsely scaly near the base; rachis pubescent; blades narrowly lanceolate to broadly lanceolate in outline, as long as or longer
than the petioles; leaflets comparatively few, at least not very numerous, the blades thin-coriaceous, falcate, lanceolate, those of the spore-
bearing leaves relatively narrower than the others, with uneven fine-
callous margin: veins numerous, simple or forked near the midrib or
near the margin, running into the callous margin: indusia dark-red.—
Hammocks, Oligocene Island region, Fla.—(*W. I., Mex., C. A., S. A.*)—
Spores mature in summer and fall.—Fig. reduced.

Our two species of *Blechnum* differ greatly not only in habit, but
also in the matter of habitat and propagation. When released from
the tropics and established in Florida in very early times this fern did
not accommodate itself to the new habitats like its relative, the swamp-
fern (*Blechnum serrulatum*). The high hammock is the home of this
fern. It is not known in any other habitat in our range, and was
first found in Florida near Brooksville in 1916,[1] and northwest of the
same place in 1933. It grows in shade near streams which, however,
are dry part of each year, usually in rocky or clayey places. Up to
the present time this species is known from only two hammocks, the
Choocohattie Hammock south of Brooksville and the Annuttalagga
Hammock northwest of that town. The leaves produce spores rather
sparingly, but the long, slender rootstocks propagate the plants abundantly in a given habitat. Although apparently rare in Florida, it is
widely distributed in the West Indies and on the mainland of tropical

[1] First collected in Florida by J. B. Norton in 1916.

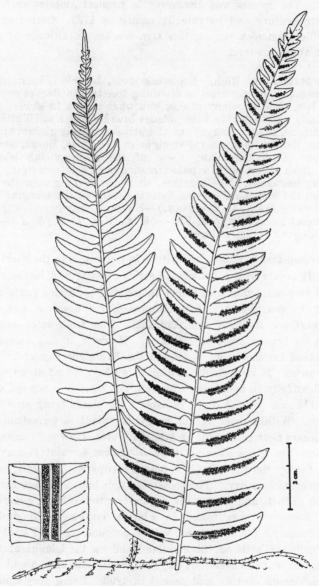

BLECHNUM OCCIDENTALE

America.   The species was discovered in tropical America early in the
nineteenth century and botanically named in 1753.   Occurring in the
Brooksville Hammock region, this fern reaches an altitude of perhaps
150 feet above sea-level.

   2. B. serrulatum Rich.   Rootstock stout, branched, horizontal, and
widely creeping, partly erect or climbing tree-trunks: leaves erect, 2 m.
long or less, rigid in sunny places, somewhat pliable in shade; petioles
rather finely scaly near the base; blades broadly linear to elliptic-lanceolate in outline, mostly longer than the petioles; rachis glabrous; leaflets
numerous, the blades leathery, straight or nearly so, linear, linear-lanceolate, or elliptic-lanceolate, those of the spore-bearing leaves the
smaller, often shiny, with a pale irregularly serrulate margin, sessile:
veins very numerous, close together, simple or forking near the midrib
or beyond the indusium, curving into the teeth at the margin: indusia
red.—(SWAMP-FERN, MARSH-FERN.)—Swamps, marshes, low prairies,
and adjacent hammocks, pen. Fla.—(*W I., Mex., C. A., S. A.*)—Spores
mature all year.—Fig. reduced.

   The swamp-fern is almost ubiquitous in wet places in the Florida peninsula.   It occurs in a considerable series of sizes and leaf-variations.
The vast tropical American fernery thoroughly populated parts of Florida with the swamp-fern.   Its northward course, however, was checked
at the northern limit of the peninsula.   The fresh-water swamp or
marsh is the typical home of this fern.   However, it also occurs in the
low pineland hammocks as well as in the Everglade hammocks and on
moist prairies.   It likes shade, and although best out of direct sunlight,
grows plentifully in open places as well, but there it is always more or
less stunted and quite changed in aspect, the plants being strictly erect
and rigid.   Within most of our range the plant is terrestrial; wherever it occurs near salt water or brackish-water it becomes more or less
epiphytic.   The great abundance of *Blechnum serrulatum* may be ac-
counted for by the fact that the plants occupy wet habitats, many of
which never become dry.   The rootstocks thus have a chance for almost
unlimited growth and the leaves regularly produce vast quantities of
spores.   *Blechnum* was found in Florida before the beginning of
the last century,[1] but it has not yet been found on the Florida Keys.
It is distributed both on the mainland and on the islands of tropical
America.   It was discovered at Cayenne, South America, about the end
of the eighteenth century and named in 1792.   Being very common in
the more southern parts of the Florida peninsula it diminishes in abundance up to its northern limit in Citrus and Hernando counties on the

   [1] First collected in Florida by A. Michaux in 1789.

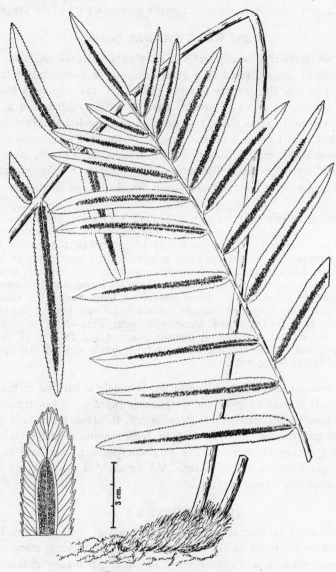

3 cm.

BLECHNUM SERRULATUM

western coast and in St. Johns County on the eastern coast. It has fully 75 feet altitude to its credit in the northern part of its range.

20. **WOODWARDIA** Smith.

Coarse terrestrial swamp or lowland plants. Leaves uniform, arching, more or less clustered on a stout creeping or horizontal rootstock: blades pinnate, the leaflets sharply pinnatifid, the segments toothed. Veins forming a series of areolae parallel to the midrib and another series perpendicular to these, free between these and the margin, simple or forked. Sori borne on veins parallel to the midrib. Indusia opening toward the midrib.—Few species, natives of Europe, Asia, and western North America.—The genus is founded on *Blechnum radicans* L.—The name is in honor of Thomas J. Woodward, an English botanist.

1. **W. radicans** (L.) Smith. Rootstock very stout, scaly: leaves 1–1.5 m. long, coarse, erect-recurving; petioles stout, often clustered on the rootstock; blades 1-pinnate, the rachis glabrous, the leaflets alternate, various, the lateral ones lanceolate, elliptic-lanceolate, or ovate-lanceolate, 1.5–4.5 dm. long, the segments ovate to lanceolate, acute or acuminate, sharply serrate, the terminal leaflet large, deeply pinnatifid, the segments lanceolate to linear-lanceolate, long-acuminate: veins beyond the areolae simple or forked: indusia 2–2.5 mm. long. [*Blechnum radicans* L.]—Swamps and hammocks, pen. Fla.—Nat. of the Old World and cultivated.—Spores mature, summer and fall, or all year S. —Propagates by the rooting of scaly buds borne toward the apex of the leaf-blade.—Fig reduced.

The common Old World *Woodwardia* is widely cultivated in the New World. It is easy to grow and propagates rapidly. When thrown out of gardens in the process of cleaning up, it often takes hold where dumped and thrives. Propagating by both rootstocks and buds it has a double chance to survive. The original specimens are said to have come from Virginia and Madeira. ''Virginia'' is evidently an error. The species was named in 1753.

21. **ANCHISTEA** Presl.

Coarse erect terrestrial swamp or marsh plants, with uniform leaves scattered or clustered on the stout, horizontal or creeping, more or less branching rootstocks. Leaves erect or arching; blades pinnate, the leaflets bluntly pinnatifid, the segments entire. Veins united to form a single series of elongate areolae next to the midrib and its branches in the segments, elsewhere free, simple and forking. Sori borne on

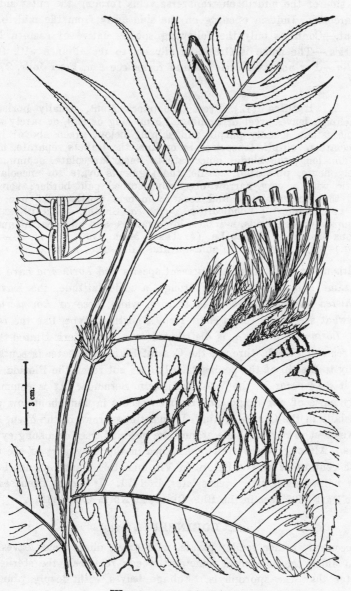

3 cm.

WOODWARDIA RADICANS

each side of the midrib on transverse veins forming the outer sides of the areolae. Indusia opening on the side away from the midrib, persistent.—Contains only the following species native of eastern North America.—The name is Greek, in allusion to the alliance with *Woodwardia*.—For notes on varieties and forms see Am. Fern Jour. 27: 24. 1937.

1. **A. virginica** (L.) Presl. Rootstock stout, usually horizontal, branching: leaves erect or arching, 1.5 m. long or less, or rarely more; petioles stout, usually purple and shining below, green above; blades lanceolate to elliptic-lanceolate in outline, the leaflets separate, mostly 1–2 dm. long, the blades lanceolate to linear-lanceolate, acuminate to merely acute, pinnatifid, sessile, the segments ovate to lanceolate or elliptic with a very narrow obscurely toothed pale border: veins beyond the areolae simple and forked: indusia mostly 2–2.5 mm. long, 1–2 mm. wide. [*Woodwardia virginica* Smith.]—(CHAIN-FERN.)— Swamps, cypress-ponds, marshes, low prairies, and adjacent hammocks, various provinces, Fla. to La. (or Tex.), Mich., Ont., and N. S.—(*Bermuda*.)—Spores mature in summer and fall.—Fig. reduced.

Although the plants of the present species and *Lorinseria* have about the same climatic resistance through a wide latitude, the leaves of *Anchistea* are subcoriaceous in texture, while those of *Lorinseria* are somewhat succulent. This chain-fern, a northern type, like the related fern, *Lorinseria areolata*, is distributed over the eastern United States, and reaches Florida through the Coastal Plain, and extends southward nearly to the tip of the peninsula. It does not reach the Florida Keys, but it does occur in the West Indies, in Bermuda. It is common in many parts of our range, and it often occurs in and about low places especially in the Coastal Plain. It sometimes grows in the open, but it thrives best in partial shade around the bases of trees or among cypress-knees. Although discovered in America in the early part of the eighteenth century or maybe before in Virginia, this plant was not botanically named until many years later, in 1771. It occurs from sea-level to at least 2500 feet in the Blue Ridge, in North Carolina.

22. **LORINSERIA** Presl.

Succulent, rather tender plants, with erect, dimorphous leaves scattered along the horizontal somewhat woody rootstock, the sterile ones shorter than the sporophyls. Foliage leaves with deeply pinnatifid blades, the few segments finely toothed and more or less undulate. Veins copiously anastomosing and forming large transverse areolae along the midrib and smaller oblique areolae gradually diminishing

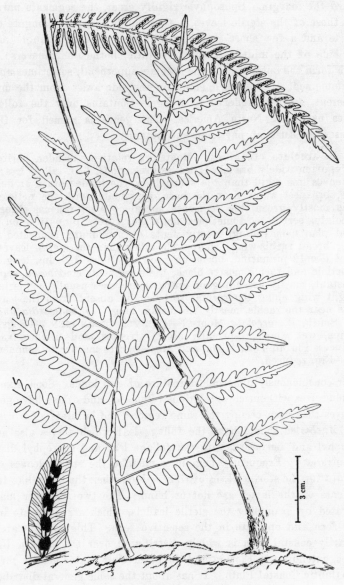

3 cm.

ANCHISTEA VIRGINICA

toward the margin. Sporophyls rigidly erect, the segments narrower than those of the sterile leaves, with a single series of elongate costal areolae and a few short excurrent veinlets. Sori in a single row on each side of the midrib, linear to elliptic, borne on transverse veins which form the outer side of the areolae, superficial, sometimes appearing immersed. Indusium opening on the side away from the midrib, persistent, scarcely reflexed with age.—Contains only the following species native of North America.—The genus is named for Gustav Lorinser, an Austrian physician and botanist.

1. **L. areolata** (L.) Presl. Rootstock relatively slender, horizontal, chaffy, often widely branched: leaves gregarious, 1 m. tall or less; foliage leaves less rigid than the sporophyls, the blades ovate or deltoid-ovate, broadest at or near the base, acuminate, with the petiole and rachis mostly green, the segments succulent membranous, elliptic to lanceolate, serrulate, sometimes undulate, rarely pinnatifid on individual plants, spreading, mostly acute or acuminate, connected by a rather broad rachis-wing; sporophyls taller than the sterile leaves, the blades deeply pinnatifid, borne on brown petioles 3-6 dm. long, with the petiole and rachis mostly black, their segments contracted, separate or distant, mostly ascending or erect, their bases usually connected by a slight wing along the rachis: sori usually absent from the leaf-segments near the rachis, mostly 2.5-6 mm. long. [*Woodwardia angustifolia* Smith. *W. areolata* Moore.]—(NETTED CHAIN-FERN.)—Bogs, and swamps, wet woods, especially along streams, and ditches, various provinces, Fla. to Tex., Mich., and Me.—Spores mature in summer and fall.—Fig. reduced.

Our conspicuously dimorphic ferns are of two kinds. Some stand off by themselves without close relations (*Onoclea*) and others have generic relatives that even occupy the same regions and habitats (*Lorinseria*). Why *Anchistea* should have the foliage leaf which serves also as the sporophyl and *Lorinseria* with the foliage leaf and sporophyl distinct, is a mystery. Frequently beginners mistake the sterile leaves of *L. areolata* for the sterile leaves of *O. sensibilis* when the berry-like fertile segments of the latter are not at hand. The two, however may be separated by examining the sterile leaflets, which are alternate in the chain-fern and opposite in the sensitive fern. This cool-climate and primarily coastal fern is widely distributed over the eastern United States, extending to Florida and the other Gulf States mainly through the Atlantic Coastal Plain. It has about the same general distribution as that of its relative, *Anchistea virginica*, except that it apparently does not grow so far south in the Florida peninsula, but it has been found on Big Pine Key on the Florida Keys. It is apparently most

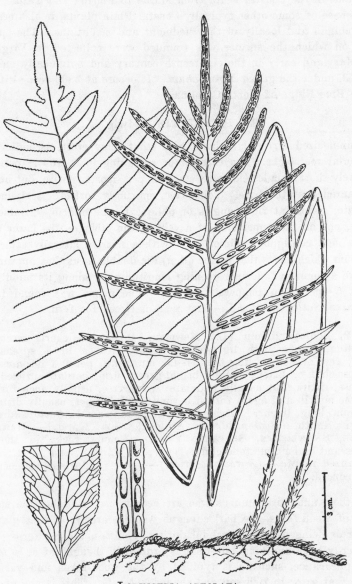

LORINSERIA AREOLATA

abundant in the Coastal Plain from Maine to Florida and Texas. As in the case of some other typically Coastal Plain plants, it also occurs in Michigan and locally in the Piedmont and mountains. The specimens on which the species was founded were collected in Virginia and Maryland early in the eighteenth century and botanically named in 1753, under the genus *Acrostichum*. It occurs at 3800 feet altitude in the Blue Ridge of North Carolina.

23. PHYLLITIS Ludwig.

Medium-sized terrestrial plants with stout scaly erect, ascending or horizontal rootstocks. Leaves erect or spreading in a crown; petioles relatively short: blades elongate, strap-shaped, mostly entire, but undulate, auricled at the base. Veins free, sparingly forked. Sori linear, elongate, almost at right angles or oblique to the midrib, variable in length, one on the upper side of a veinlet, the other on the lower side of the next contiguous veinlet, each with a narrow laterally attached indusium which meets that of the other, the double sorus thus appearing to have a common indusium opening longitudinally along its middle.— About 5 species in temperate regions.—The genus was founded on *Asplenium Scolopendrium* L.—The name is Greek for fern.

1. **P. Scolopendrium** (L.) Newman. Rootstocks short, erect or ascending, chaffy with light-brown scales; leaves in a spreading crown, few or several together, 1–4.5 dm. long, petioles deciduously fibrillose-chaffy; blades simple, bright-green, firm, cordate-auricled at the base, entire, but usually undulate: veins free, usually once forked near the midrib and again forked beyond: sori distinct, usually distant, 4–15 mm. long, linear. [*Asplenium Scolopendrium* L. *Scolopendrium vulgare* Smith. *Scolopendrium Scolopendrium* Karst.]—(HART'S-TONGUE, SNAKE-FERN, SEA-WEED FERN.)—Among rocks in shaded ravines and under limestone cliffs, Tenn.; N. Y., Ont., and N. B.; also naturalized in Md.—(*Eurasia, Africa*.)—Spores mature in summer.— Fig. reduced.

To those amateur botanists who are accustomed to seeing the many kinds of wood-ferns, the hart's-tongue would scarcely, at first glance, appear as being a fern. Rock-inhabiting or cliff-inhabiting ferns very frequently have anything but what is ordinarily thought of as a fern-like appearance, such as is typified by the wood-ferns and various others that grow in rich soil and shaded habitats. This is one of the ferns which have closely allied forms growing in both Europe and America. Across the Atlantic it chooses quite different habitats from

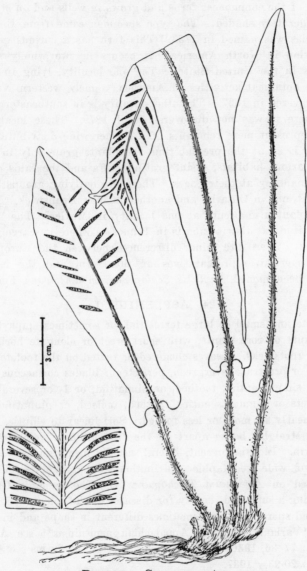

3 cm.

PHYLLITIS SCOLOPENDRIUM

those it favors here. In southern England, especially near London, it is one of the commonest ferns and grows in wells and on stone walls only moderately shaded. The type specimen came from Europe and the species was named in 1753. This fern has a curious geographic distribution in North America. It occurs in two widely separated localities in the United States. The one locality, lying in a region of early botanical activities in America, namely western New York, was discovered in 1807. The other locality is in southeastern Tennessee. There it was not discovered until 1879. These localities evidently represent mere remnants of a former wide distribution of the species. Even at the present time the plants grow only in more or less precarious habitats, disintegrating cliffs and the talus of uncertain permanency at their bases. There are outlying groups or localities for it, one in Ontario, and another in New Brunswick. A closely related plant also occurs at one locality in Mexico. The maximum of its altitudinal distribution is in Tennessee where it scarcely reaches 1000 feet. There are minor differences between the European and North American representatives of this fern, and the latter has recently been named *Phyllitis Scolopendrium americana* Fernald.

24. ASPLENIUM L.

Delicate and small or large terrestrial, or sometimes epiphytic, often wood-plants or rock-plants, with short erect or elongate horizontal or creeping rootstocks. Leaves clustered or tufted on the rootstock, erect, arching, or prostrate, evergreen, persistent: blades coriaceous or membranous, simple, entire, toothed, or pinnatifid, or 1- or several-pinnate, the leaflets or segments entire, toothed, incised, or pinnatifid. Veins free or nearly so, more or less forked. Sori linear to elliptic, or rarely broader, straight, borne apart on the free ultimate veins, oblique to the midrib. Indusia present, lateral, usually membranous.—Fully 600 species of wide geographic distribution.—SPLEENWORTS.—The genus was based on *Asplenium Trichomanes* L.—The name is Greek, the plant being a supposed remedy for diseases of the spleen.—The foliage leaves and sporophyls are sometimes different in shape and in position. —For ''Variants of some Appalachian aspleniums'' see Am. Fern Jour. 26: 77–86, 1936.—For notes on varieties and forms see Am. Fern Jour. 27: 20-23. 1937.

Rachis green and flat nearly throughout.
  Leaf-blades undivided, with very many closely
    placed parallel veins running from the midrib
    to the margin : sori slenderly elongate.   I. SERRATA.

Leaf-blades pinnatifid or pinnate.
  Leaf-blades pinnatifid.   II. PINNATIFIDA.
  Leaf-blades once or twice pinnate, at least
    at the base.
    Leaflets with merely toothed blades.   III. DENTATA.
    Leaflets with incised or pinnatifid
      blades.
      Blades of the leaflets coriaceous.   IV. AURITA.
      Blades of the leaflets membranous.
        Leaf-blades elongate: leaflets
          several to many.   V. VERECUNDA.
        Leaf-blades deltoid to pentag-
          onal in outline: leaflets 3–
          7.   VI. PUMILA.
Leaf-blades at least twice pinnate, with lower
  leaflets once, twice- or thrice pinnate.   VII. MONTANA.
Rachis brown and terete, at least near the base.
  Leaf-blades pinnatifid, or with several leaflets at
    the base: rachis brown below.   VIII. EBENOIDES.
  Leaf-blades pinnate nearly throughout.   IX. PLATYNEURA.

I. SERRATA

Large epiphytic or epipetric humus plants, with
few or several broad ascending or arching leaves
in a crown on a stout rootstock.   1. *A. serratum.*

II. PINNATIFIDA

Leaves clustered, the blades elongate, lanceolate,
with rounded lobes.   2. *A. pinnatifidum.*

III. DENTATA

Leaflets much longer than wide, many-veined, serrate.   3. *A. abscissum.*
Leaflets as wide as long or slightly longer than
wide, few-veined, entire or slightly crenate.   4. *A. dentatum.*

IV. AURITA

Epiphytic humus-plants with clustered leaves:
leaflets toothed, incised or pinnatifid, auricled at
the base by a more or less detached lobe.   5. *A. auritum.*

V. VERECUNDA

Leaf-blades short-petioled: leaflets with very many
small segments.   6. *A. verecundum.*
Leaf-blades long-petioled: leaflets coarser.
  Leaflets as wide as long or nearly so, rather
    equally 5-lobed, or pinnatifid merely at the
    base.   7. *A. subtile.*
  Leaflets much longer than wide, pinnate or pin-
    natifid throughout.
    Leaf-blades linear to linear-lanceolate in out-
      line.
      Leaflets narrowly ovate; segments shal-
        lowly toothed: indusia 2–3 mm. long. 8. *A. biscaynianum.*
      Leaflets broadly ovate: segments deeply
        lobed: indusia 1–1.5 mm. long.   9. *A. scalifolium.*
    Leaf-blades lanceolate to ovate-lanceolate in
      outline.
      Leaflets spaced or approximate, but not
        overlapping, o b l o n g, broadly
        linear, or lanceolate in outline.

Leaflets spaced, opposite or nearly so,
the segments entire or shallowly
notched.   10. *A. suave.*
Leaflets approximate, alternate, the
s e g m e n t s prominently 3–5-
lobed.
Leaves dark-green: leaflets ascending, the larger ones scarcely
narrowed at the tip, the seg-
ments mostly fewer than 10.   11. *A. Curtissii.*
Leaves light-green: leaflets spread-
ing, the larger ones manifestly
narrowed at the tip, the seg-
ments mostly more than 10.   12. *A. cristatum.*
Leaflets crowded, more or less overlap-
ping, ovate in outline.   13. *A. plenum.*

VI. PUMILA

Very small epipetric humus-plant, with few broad
leaflets and leaf-segments, the leaf-blades mostly
3–5-foliolate.   14. *A. pumilum.*

VII. MONTANA

Leaf-blades once pinnate: leaflets toothed or lobed. 15. *A. Trudelli.*
Leaf-blades twice pinnate or primarily pinnate and
secondarily pinnately lobed.
Blades of the leaflets ovate to lanceolate, the
ultimate segments lobed or coarsely toothed.   16. *A. montanum.*
Blades of the leaflets cuneate to cuneate-flabellate, the ultimate segments finely toothed at
the apex.   17. *A. cryptolepis.*

VIII. EBENOIDES

Larger leaves with leaflets or segments tapering
from a more or less dilated base, the tip somewhat elongate and more or less irregularly
toothed.   18. *A. ebenoides.*

IX. PLATYNEURA

Leaflets with toothed or undulate blades.
Plants with uniform leaves, all spore-bearing,
ascending or spreading.
Blades of the leaflets not auriculate.   19. *A. Trichomanes.*
Blades of the leaflets auriculate at the base.
Blades of the leaflets sharply toothed.   20. *A. heterochroum.*
Blades of the leaflets entire or merely
crenulate.   21. *A. resiliens.*
Plants with dimorphic leaves, the foliage leaves
small, spreading or prostrate, the sporophyls
larger: leaflets obscurely or prominently ser-
rate, auriculate, truncate at the base.   22. *A. platyneuron.*
Leaflets with pinnatifid blades.   23. *A. Bradleyi.*

1. **A. serratum** L. Rootstock short, erect, stout: leaves few or
several in a crown, ascending and arching, 3–8 dm. long; blades undivided, linear-oblanceolate, usually short-acuminate, serrate or serrate-
crenate at least above the middle, and sometimes irregularly incised,
paler and less shining beneath, tapering to a short stout somewhat scaly
petiole, the midrib keeled, often purplish beneath: veins very numerous
and closely placed, once-forked near the midrib: sori pale, slenderly
elongate, following the veins on the upper half of the blade from near
the midrib at least half-way to the margin.—(WILD BIRDNEST-FERN.)—

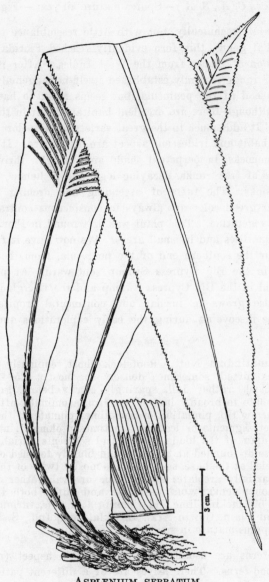

ASPLENIUM SERRATUM

3 cm.

Hammocks, mostly on trees, logs, and rocks, southern peninsular Fla.
—(*W. I., Mex., C. A., S. A.*)—Spores mature all year.—Fig. reduced.

An *Asplenium* technically, but with little resemblance to our other
species of that genus, this fern evidently reached Florida during the
second invasion of plants from the West Indies. After reaching the
shores of our range it firmly established itself in congenial habitats at
the southern end of the peninsula, but seems never to have advanced
northward, although there are excellent habitats for it in the Oligocene
Island area. It adds much to the great variety of fern flora of Florida.
Its peculiar habit and iridescent aspect are distinctive. It grows best
in dense hammocks, in perpetual shade and twilight, thriving equally
well on bases of tree-trunks, decaying logs, and in humus, particularly
about lime-sinks. The tufts of ascending and arching leaves with
their peculiar green color are always in conspicuous contrast with the
surrounding vegetation. This plant was first found in Florida in 1877[1]
in limited quantities and in small areas. We now have it from various
localities near the southern end of the peninsula, from the latitude of
Deep Lake in the Big Cypress Swamp southward. At present it is
most plentiful in the Big Cypress Swamp and the Everglades National
Park. It also grows in insular and continental tropical America,
where it was discovered during the early explorations and named in
1753.

2. **A. pinnatifidum** Nutt. Rootstock short, copiously chaffy and
leafy; leaves tufted, sometimes densely so, mostly 0.5–4 dm. long;
petioles blackish, rather dull, sparingly chaffy below, green above;
blades lanceolate to broadly lanceolate, firm, acuminate, often tapering
to a long narrow tip, pinnatifid or sometimes pinnate at the base; one
or more lower segments or leaflets sometimes prolonged into a slender
tip like the apex of the blade, the typical segments variable in shape,
usually obtuse or rounded at the apex and bluntly toothed or lobed and
bluntly auricled at the base, sessile: veins mostly twice or thrice forked,
sometimes partially areolate: sori elliptic or oval, rather close to the
midrib.—(LOBED-SPLEENWORT.)—Rocks and cliffs, both igneous and
sedimentary but lacking lime and yielding acid soils, various provinces,
N. of Coastal Plain, Ga. to Ark., E. Okla., Mo., Ind., S. E. Pa., and
W. N. J.—Spores mature in summer.

The rock-ferns are usually quite different in aspect (appearance)
from the wood-ferns. Their leaves are of a different pattern, usually
less divided, and smaller. The lobed-spleenwort belongs with the more
unusual rock-ferns. It is also to be classed among the rarer ones.

[1] First collected in Florida by A. P. Garber in 1877.

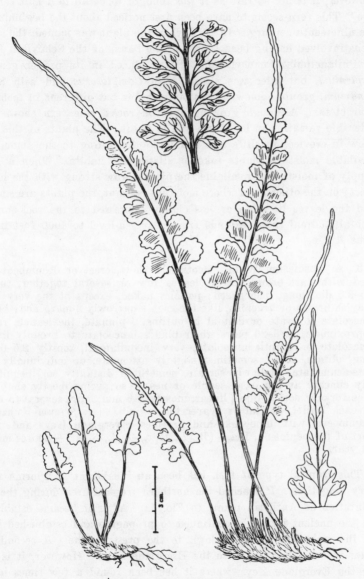

ASPLENIUM PINNATIFIDUM

However, it it not so rare as it was thought to be up to a half century ago. This fern seems to have been first noticed about the beginning of the nineteenth century. In 1818 when the plant was named, the specimens involved having been found on the banks of the Schuylkill River at Philadelphia, Pennsylvania, it was placed in its proper genus— *Asplenium*, but later was classed with *Camptosorus* and with *Scolopendrium*, groups somewhat similar in habit but different in technical characters. Although growing only on rocks, this fern shows considerable variation in leaf-form and in habit. The plants of this fern grow in crevices in cliffs and boulders. According to the amount of available moisture plants take on distinctive habits. When a good supply of moisture is available the plants grow strong with the leaves erect; on the other hand where moisture is scant, the plants are smaller and the leaves lie more or less closely appressed to the rock-surface. The altitudinal range extends from near sea-level to 4000 feet in the Blue Ridge.

3. A. abscissum Willd. Rootstocks short, erect or decumbent covered with dark-brown scales: leaves few or several together, tufted, 1.5–3.5 dm. long, deep-green; petioles naked, except at the very base, grayish-brown or greenish, like the rachis narrowly 2-margined: blades lanceolate to ovate or deltoid in outline, 1-pinnate, the leaflets rather approximate, in 8–20 pairs, their blades lanceolate to broadly linear-lanceolate or elliptic-lanceolate, very inequilateral, mostly 2.5–6 cm. long, obtuse, acute, sometimes slightly attenuate, or individually caudate-acuminate, shallowly serrate, sometimes distantly so, inequilaterally cuneate at the base, sessile or nearly so: veins mostly simple or once forked: sori oblique, linear, mostly 2–6 mm. long, several to many on each leaflet, medial or nearer the midrib. [*A. firmum* Kunze.]— Hammocks, with lime-sinks and grottoes, Everglade Keys and upper part of the peninsula, Fla.—(*W. I., Mex., C. A., S. A.*)—Spores mature all year.

This tropical type of fern has been an inhabitant of Florida for a very long time. It reached the northern tropical area during the first migration of Antillean plants to Florida. After it became established on the ancient island, it continued to propagate and established itself in the rocks and grottoes down to the present time. A second and later invasion brought it to the Everglade Keys. However, it is rare on the Everglade Keys, where it has been found a few times in the much eroded hammocks of the Biscayne pineland and where it grows only in limited quantities. It is more plentiful in the hammocks of the Oligocene island area of the peninsula, where it was discovered for the

ASPLENIUM ABSCISSUM

first time this side of the Gulf Stream in 1878,[1] near Ocala. The plants thrive best in rocky hammocks, and grow usually in much-eroded places, especially about lime-sinks. This plant is widely distributed in continental and insular tropical America. It was discovered in the West Indies in the eighteenth century and named in 1810. The Florida plants show considerable variation in the shape of the leaflets. These may be reasonably uniform in size and shape, or the terminal one may be decidedly caudate-acuminate. A similar elongation is sometimes seen in some of the lateral leaflets, especially the basal ones.

4. A. dentatum L. Rootstock short, erect or ascending, not creeping, brown-scaly: leaves few or many together, tufted, erect or prostrate, 0.5–2.5 dm. long, bright-green; petioles minutely scaly at the base or naked, dark-brown below, green above, like the rachis flat or flattish; blades narrowly elliptic to linear in outline, 1-pinnate, the leaflets distant, 5–12 pairs, their blades obovate, rhombic, suborbicular or often cuneate, 4–11 mm. long, very inequilateral, the dilated upper edge and the apex coarsely and irregularly few-toothed, the straight lower edge and the cuneate base entire: veins mostly simple or once forked: sori few, very oblique, pale, linear, mostly 2–4 mm. long, rather near the midrib.—Eroded rock in hammocks, Everglade Keys and local rock outcrops a little north of them, Fla.—(*W. I., Mex., C. A.*)—Spores mature all year.

This, the smallest of our tropical spleenworts, evidently did not effect a landing on the old tropical island now isolated in the northern part of the Florida peninsula along with the other often associated ferns during the earlier invasion from the Antilles. However, it was successful in establishing itself during the second invasion after the Everglade Keys were elevated and made habitable for fern growth. As far as our evidence goes, it is now widespread in the hammocks of the Everglade Keys. Although occurring in most of the high-pineland hammocks, it is exceedingly abundant in only a few of them. Its favorite habitats are perpendicular rock walls, not, however, those of the well-like lime-sinks, but the shelving irregular rocks in grottoes. This plant reaches its greatest development in the Deering Hammock at Cutler, where its growth is extraordinary. There in many places the plants are so thickly placed that the leaves completely hide the rocks. This spleenwort was discovered in Florida after the middle of the last century.[2] It grows in many of the West Indian islands, where it was discovered early in the eighteenth century and named in 1753.

[1] First collected in Florida by W. H. Shockley in 1878.
[2] First collected in Florida by A. P. Garber in 1877.

ASPLENIUM DENTATUM

5. A. auritum Sw. Rootstock small, erect or nearly so, brown-scaly: leaves few or numerous, tufted, 2–6 dm. long, the old petioles often long persistent, splitting into fibrous tufts; petioles as long as the blades or shorter, brown to grayish-green, slender, naked, except the sparingly scaly base; blades elliptic-lanceolate or deltoid to deltoid-ovate in outline, acuminate, 1-pinnate, the leaflets spreading or ascending, commonly lanceolate or linear-lanceolate, spaced, short-stalked, more or less falcate, with a single elliptic to obovate basal segment or several such segments, very obliquely incised, sometimes tapering to a long-caudate tip, the margins obliquely crenate to incised-pinnatifid, or in simpler forms the leaflets oblong-elliptic, auriculate, subentire: veins several times forked in the larger segments or lobes: sori numerous, linear-elliptic, medial or irregular, very oblique.—Hammocks near Hillsborough River, Oligocene Island region, Fla.—(*W. I., Mex., C. A., S. A.*)—Spores mature all year.—Fig. reduced.

Considered as migrants, our typically tropical spleenworts of relatively restricted geographic distribution fall into two groups: *Asplenium pumilum, A. cristatum,* and *A. auritum* represent a migration to the early tropical area; *Asplenium serratum* and *A. dentatum* a migration to the later tropical area. Furthermore the early area has yielded five endemic species, namely *Asplenium Curtissii, A. subtile, A. plenum, A. suave,* and *A. scalifolium.* The later area has so far yielded only one endemic, *Asplenium biscaynianum. Asplenium auritum* is one of our very rare ferns. For over four decades it was thought to be restricted in our range to Cedar Hammock in Sumter County,[1] where it was discovered in 1895. Later it became extinct at that locality, but was found elsewhere. *Asplenium auritum* may grow on either trees or rocks in the tropics. In Florida it is more restricted in its habitat. It has been found on the north side of giant live oaks that lean sharply to the south. At its best, it produces a colony extending from the ground to a height of twenty feet. As a resurrection fern it has a remarkable ability to fold opposite leaflets together and roll up the entire leaf as a protection against loss of moisture. It is very loosely rooted and plants are easily dislodged from the tree trunk by climbing animals or storms. On falling to the ground they retain the ability to revive for a long time but never seem to root where they fall. In the fern garden, however, if supplied with abundant moisture, they grow luxuriantly and attain a size unequaled in the hammocks. In Florida it was first mistaken for *A. erosum* L. The original specimens came from Jamaica and were named in 1801.

[1] First collected in Florida by F. L. Lewton and C. S. Williamson in 1895.

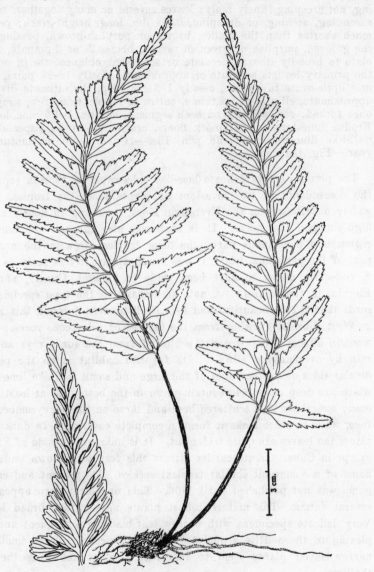

3 cm.

ASPLENIUM AURITUM

6. A. verecundum Chapm. Rootstock very short, erect or ascending, not creeping, finely scaly: leaves several or many together, tufted, ascending, arching, or drooping, 0.5–4 dm. long, bright-green; petioles much shorter than the blades, brown or purplish-brown, passing into the grooved, purplish or greenish rachis; blades 2- or 3-pinnate, lanceolate to broadly linear-lanceolate or somewhat oblanceolate in outline, the primary leaflets separate or approximate, mostly 12–22 pairs, ovate or elliptic-ovate in outline, mostly 1–3 cm. long, the ultimate divisions approximate, elliptic or spatulate, entire or lobed: veins few, simple or once forked: sori solitary on each segment, elliptic, 1–1.5 mm. long.— Eroded limestone on hammock floors, crags, and rocks, especially in well-like lime-sinks, N. and pen. Fla.—(*Cuba.*)—Spores mature all year.—Fig. reduced.

The plants of this delicate lace-like spleenwort in Florida represent the descendents of two invasions of plants from the tropics. It is widely distributed on the Everglade Keys, occurring in nearly all the high-pineland hammocks. It is scattered also through the lime-sink region and contiguous parts, the older tropical area in the northern part of the peninsula, where it was found apparently as early as 1855. A collection seems to have been made in Jackson County, northern Florida, in the forties.[1] A note accompanying the type specimen records that ''This beautiful and delicate little fern I found this winter in West Florida, growing from the fissures of calcareous rocks. They were in almost every instance protected from the sun's rays and the rain by overhanging cliffs.'' Its favorite habitat is on the perpendicular sides or on the edges of the large and small well-like lime-sinks, which are deep enough to contain water in the bottom or at least moist mud; sometimes it is scattered here and there on the honeycombed surface, while in other sinks it forms a complete covering. In dark moist places the leaves are quite iridescent. It is unknown outside of Florida except in Cuba. In its earlier history this fern was known under the name of a somewhat similar tropical species. Its present and correct name was not published until 1906. This fine lacey fern appears in several forms. The mature robust plants have rather broad leaves. Very delicate specimens with narrow leaf-blades are frequent and perplexing to those little acquainted with the species. These small and narrow-leaved plants seem to represent a stage following the prothallium.

[1] First collected in Florida by A. W. Chapman, about 1840.

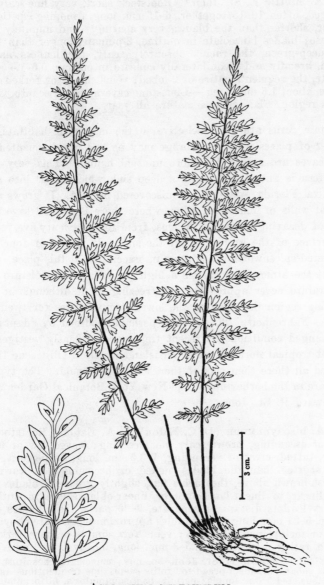

3 cm.

ASPLENIUM VERECUNDUM

7. A. subtile E. St. John.[1] Rootstock short, very fine-scaly: leaves clustered, often 10–15 together, 6–15 cm. long, drooping; petioles very slender, shorter than the blades, very sparingly and minutely scaly at the base; blades lanceolate in outline, 2-pinnate, longer than the petioles, deep-green, the rachis obscurely scaly, the leaflets ascending, spaced, broadly and inequilaterally cuneate in outline, 0.6–1.4 cm. long, pinnate, the segments entire or 2-lobed: veins simple or forked: indusia fragile, about 1.5 mm. long.—Limestone cavern, near Lecanto, Oligocene Island region, Fla.—Spores mature all year.

Certain ferns are quite selective in the matter of habitats, but all manner of places where anchorage may be had are frequented. However, caves are among the more unusual haunts. This very graceful little fern is known only from a deep sink which opens into a cavern in central Florida, where it was discovered in 1934. It grows upon the vertical walls of limestone, often where there is no soil save the thin layer of decaying mosses or lichens, from ten to twenty-five feet below the surface of the ground about the sink. It is one of four recently discovered spleenworts which grow in association at this place. In their habitat the atmosphere carries a high percentage of moisture and the temperature never approaches the freezing point although in the surrounding region the mean of the lowest temperatures for twenty years is 24° + Fahrenheit. These ferns, perhaps modified by adaptations to the changed conditions of recent times, are evidently vestiges of the ancient tropical flora of the small island which in Oligocene time constituted all there then was of the Florida peninsula. The type specimens are in the herbarium of the New York Botanical Garden and that of Edward P. St. John.

8. A. biscaynianum (D. C. Eaton) A. A. Eaton. Rootstock short, erect or ascending, brown-scaly, not creeping: leaves few or many together, tufted, erect or ascending, 1–3.5 dm. long, deep-green; petioles much shorter than the blades, naked or becoming so, brown below, greenish-brown above, the rachis flat, slightly grooved; blades 1–2-pinnate, linear to linear-lanceolate or linear-oblanceolate in outline, the primary leaflets distant or separate, 9–20 pairs, their blades ovate in outline, 5–21 mm. long, the pinnules approximate, cuneate-obovate, few-lobed or incised near the apex: veins few, simple or once forked: sori oblique, rather pale, linear, 2.5–3 mm. long, mostly 1 or 2 on a pinnule.

[1] *Asplenium* **subtile** E. St. John, sp. nov., rhizomate caespitose squamis minutis subarachnoideis praedito : foliis saepissime frequentibus aggregatis, nutantibus, 1–1.5 dm. longis ; petiolis basi squamulosis, filiformibus, nigris ; lamina lanceolata, delicatissima, foliolis distantibus, subtilissimis, inaequaliter pinnatifidis margine inferiori subintegri, speriori profunde loba, foliolis distalibus apice 3-lobis : soris paucis in vena simplici vel in distali venae dichotomae. In oris lapideis in antro ad Lecanto, Florida, Decembri 8, 1934, E. P. St. John, typus in herb. Hort. Bot. Noveboracensis.

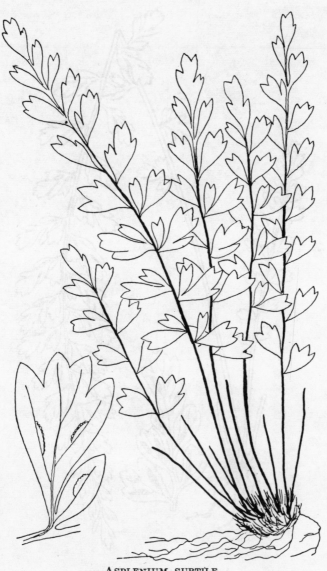

Asplenium subtile

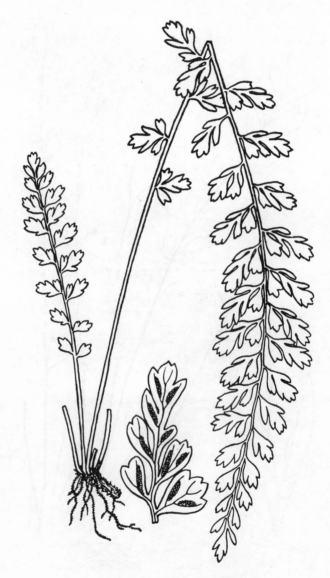

ASPLENIUM BISCAYNIANUM

—Eroded limestone, hammock floors, lime-sinks, and cliffs along the water, Bay Biscayne and few inland hammocks, Everglade Keys, S. pen. Fla.—Spores mature all year.—Fig. reduced.

The present spleenwort represents a case where notwithstanding an abundance of sporiferous leaves the plants have been quite rare, at least in historic times, and grow mainly in a locality which will soon be wiped out of existence as a natural habitat for plants. It is most abundant in the largest of the hammocks within its range—Brickell Hammock, now within the limits of the city of Miami—where it was discovered in 1887.[1] It occurs in many parts of the hammock, ranging from the bay shore on the east to near the pinelands on the west. It thrives on the face of bluffs and in recesses and on detached boulders in and about shallow lime-sinks. It prefers low moist situations and grows with *Asplenium verecundum* and *A. dentatum*, from which fern students formerly believed it had arisen as a hybrid. Although it usually occurs in company with its supposed parents it has been found in extensive patches in depressions near the middle of the hammock where *Asplenium dentatum* was scarce and *A. verecundum* absent. In the northern tropical region in central Florida where the closest relatives of *A. biscaynianum* grow—the cave aspleniums and *A. Curtissii*, ferns far more like *A. biscaynianum* than either *A. verecundum* or *A. dentatum*—*A. dentatum* has never been found. It is not probable, therefore, that *A. biscaynianum* is a hybrid, unless the species originated in that way ages ago. This is a very beautiful plant; but unfortunately, it is destined, apparently, to be exterminated at an early date, for, aside from the locality referred to above, it occurs in sparing growths in only a few other hammocks on the Everglade Keys.

9. **A. scalifolium** E. St. John.[2] Rootstock stout, copiously scaly: leaves clustered, few together, 15–30 cm. long, drooping; petioles brown, slender, shorter than the blades, sparingly and minutely scaly; blades nearly linear in outline, 2-pinnate, twice as long as the petioles or less, deep-green, the rachis minutely scaly like the petiole, the leaflets ascending, mostly approximate, especially on the upper part of the blade, ovate in outline, mostly 1–2 cm. long, pinnate, the segments 2–5-lobed,

[1] First collected in Florida by Isaac Holden in 1887.
[2] *Asplenium* **scalifolium** E. St. John, sp. nov., rhizomate caespitoso, squamulis arachnoideis rubidis induto : foliis plerisque congregatis, nutantibus 1.5–3 dm. longis; petiolis tenuissimis brunneis; laminą elongata, lineari, delicata, foliolis numerosis congestis, in lamina inferiori discretis, subtilissimis, unipinnatis, ultimis saepissime 7 usque ad 9 subinaequilateraliter cuneatis : soris paucis in vena simplici vel in distali venae dichotomae. In oris lapideis in antro ad Lecanto, Florida, Martio, 1934, E. P. St. John, typus in herb. Hort. Bot. Noveboracensis.

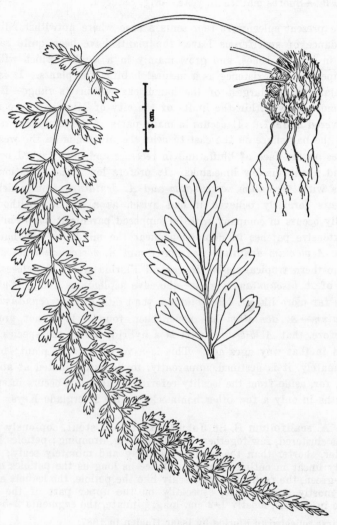

ASPLENIUM SCALIFOLIUM

obtuse or acutish: veins mostly forked: sori fragile, 1–1.5 mm. long.—
Limestone cavern, near Lecanto, Oligocene Island region, Fla.—Spores
mature all year.—Fig. reduced.

A host of caverns doubtless exist beneath the surface in the porous
limestone strata of the Florida peninsula. Many of the ''sinks'' are
evidently the result of the roofs of these caverns falling in. The sinks
have become ferneries, but their species are largely the same. Where
a small portion of a roof has fallen in leaving a well-like opening, unusual ferns are to be expected where anchorages are available on the
walls of the well. This endemic fern, discovered in 1934, resembles
Asplenium biscaynianum in general appearance, but significant peculi-
arities indicate that it should have specific rank. It is found with three
related endemic species in a sink that opens into an extensive cavern
in central Florida. It grows upon a shelf of the limestone wall about
twenty feet below the ground level and about the same distance above
the floor of the cave at that point. It is most closely associated with
Asplenium scalifolium; Asplenium subtile occupies a place above it, and
A. suave below it. *Asplenium verecundum* and *A. abscissum* grow on
walls having a different exposure at about the same height.

10. A. suave E. St. John. Rootstock short, fine-scaly: leaves
clustered, often 6–10 together, 10–20 cm. long, drooping; petioles
brown, very slender, almost filiform, sparingly and minutely scaly at the
base, about as long as the blades or slightly shorter; blades lanceolate
in outline, 2-pinnate, about as long as the petioles or slightly longer,
deep-green, the rachis very minutely scaly, the leaflets spreading or
slightly ascending, spaced, oblong in outline, 1–2 cm. long, pinnate, the
segments entire or slightly 2-lobed, mostly obtuse: veins mostly simple:
indusia not seen.—Limestone cavern, near Lecanto, Oligocene Island
region, Fla.—Spores mature all year.

Caves with surface openings are unusual in Florida. As in the case
of other places of unusual geological features, ferns different from the
wide-spread species of the region are to be expected there. This fern,
discovered in 1934, is one of four mentioned in notes under *Asplenium
subtile,* which are known only from a cave in central Florida, a habitat
which approaches tropical conditions of humidity and temperature far
more nearly than the surrounding country. It has been found only on
slightly shelving walls of limestone from twenty to thirty-five feet
below the surface of the ground about the sink. In addition to its
endemic associates, *Asplenium abscissum* and *A. verecundum* grow near
it at a somewhat higher level.

11. A. Curtissii Underw. Rootstock short, erect, with few brownish scales: leaves often numerous, clustered, 2.5–5 dm. long; petioles stoutish, grayish-brown, sometimes sparingly scaly at the base; blades lanceolate to elliptic-lanceolate in outline, 1–3.3 dm. long, 1–2-pinnate, scarcely or only slightly narrowed at the base, the leaflets ascending, elliptic to elliptic-lanceolate, or lanceolate, the larger ones with few to several close very oblique cuneate segments, the larger of these usually rather coarsely 2–5-cleft or deeply pinnatifid or divided: sori short, tumid.—Hammocks, on cliffs, crags, in lime-sinks, and grottoes, Oligocene Island region, Fla.—Spores mature all year.—Fig. reduced.

For many years this was the only known endemic species of *Asplenium* in the hammocks of the old tropical area in northern peninsular Florida, as is *Asplenium biscaynianum* in the hammocks of the later tropical area or the Everglade Keys. Both, however, are real tropical types of spleenworts. It was discovered in 1879,[1] but was for many years confused with or associated with several West Indian species, such as *Asplenium myriophyllum,* and nearly three decades elapsed before it was properly named. This species occurs only where there is greatly eroded limestone. In several large grottoes the plants line the perpendicular faces of cliffs and cañons, forming cascades of iridescent green. It grows either in pure colonies, or mixed with other spleenworts and the creeping-fern (*Goniopteris reptans*). Its distribution is not as limited as that of the preceding or following spleenworts. The mature plants are very distinctive, but in the stage following the prothallium the leaves may be narrow, closely simulating the mature leaves of *Asplenium biscaynianum.*

12. A. cristatum Lam. Rootstock erect or ascending, rather stout, fibrous-scaly: leaves several or many, clustered, 2–4 dm. long, bright-green; petioles quite short or sometimes nearly or quite as long as the blades, greenish to brown, greenish-margined; blades 1- to 2-pinnate, elliptic to ovate-lanceolate or elliptic-oblanceolate in outline, more or less attenuate above, at the base truncate or abruptly narrowed, or frequently gradually reduced with few or several pairs of smaller leaflets, the leaflets spreading, numerous, often approximate, sessile, the larger ones lanceolate to oblong-lanceolate, 3–10 cm. long finely pinnatifid or 2-pinnatifid, the basal divisions often flabellately divided and overlying the rachis: veins simple or once-forked: sori copious, linear or elliptic-linear, oblique to the midrib: indusia pale, thin. [*A. cicutarium* Sw.]—Hammocks, rocky places, Oligocene Island region, Fla. —(*W. I., Mex., C. A., S. A.*)—Spores mature all year.—Fig. reduced.

[1] First collected in Florida by A. H. Curtiss in 1879.

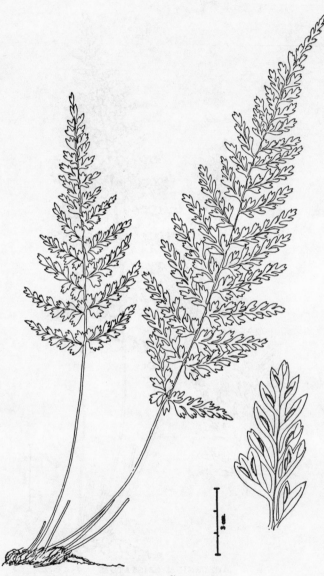

ASPLENIUM CURTISSII

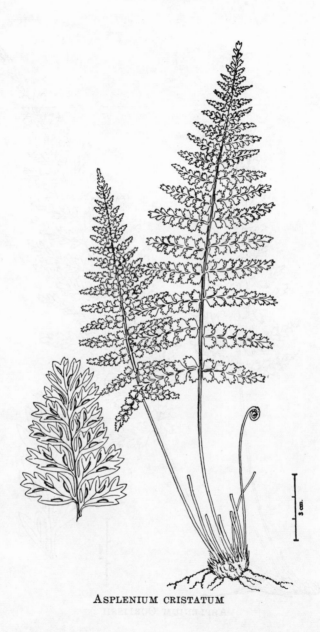

ASPLENIUM CRISTATUM

Color alone will distinguish this from our other spleenworts. The peculiarly bright-green leaves and the almost excessive cutting of the blades are unique among our species. It was evidently among the earlier arrivals from the West Indies and is now, apparently, strictly isolated far northward of its tropical home in the more ancient tropical area of Florida along with similarly stranded ferns. It is also widely distributed in tropical America, but has not yet been found on the Everglade Keys where it is to be expected. It was first collected in Florida in 1878.[1] The original specimens came from the West Indies and were named in 1786. In Florida this spleenwort seems to have settled down as an inhabitant of Citrus and Sumter Counties, in a restricted area not far from the Withlacoochee River. On account of its habitat it is in great danger from forest fires. As it is an attractive and rare fern it might be the unfortunate victim of attempts to exploit it commercially.

13. A. plenum E. St. John.[2] Rootstock short, fine-scaly: leaves sparingly clustered, often 8–14 together, 15–25 cm. long, drooping; petioles brown, rather slender, about as long as the blade or shorter, minutely scaly especially at the base; blades lanceolate or ovate-lanceolate in outline, 2-pinnate, about as long as the petioles or longer, deep-green, the rachis minutely scaly, the leaflets spreading or ascending, mostly approximate or overlapping, especially on the upper part of the blade, ovate in outline, 1.5–4 cm. long, pinnate, the segments entire or 2–8-lobed, obtuse: veins simple or forked: indusia fragile, nearly 2 mm. long.—Limestone cavern, near Lecanto, Oligocene Island region, Fla.— Spores mature all year.—Fig. reduced.

Ferns are usually not suspected of being inhabitants of caves and so often long elude the searcher. This fern was discovered in 1936. It was at first considered a form of *Asplenium Curtissii*, from which it differs in similar ways and to about the same extent as that fern differs from *A. verecundum*. It is associated with *Asplenium subtile, A. suave,* and *A. scalifolium,* all endemic species, in a limestone cavern in central Florida. It grows in a thin accumulation of leaf mold on a shelf of the vertical rock wall of a deep sink, about twenty feet below the ground level.

[1] First collectd in Florida by W. H. Shockley, in 1878.
[2] *Asplenium* **plenum** E. St. John, sp. nov., rhizomate caespitoso, squamis pusillis brunneis induto: foliis parcius aggregatis, saepe 4–14, nutantibus, 1.5–2.55 dm. longis: petiolis tenuibus, brunnels: lamina lanceolata ovato-lanceolata, delicata, foliolis plerisque approximatis, vel inferioribus discretis imbricatisve, laminis pinnatifidis, segmentis saepissime 9–15 obtusis emarginatisve; soris paucis in vena simplici vel in distali venae dichotomae. In oris lapideis in antro ad Lecanto, Florida, Aprili, 1936, E. P. St. John, typus in herb. Hort. Bot. Noveboracensis.

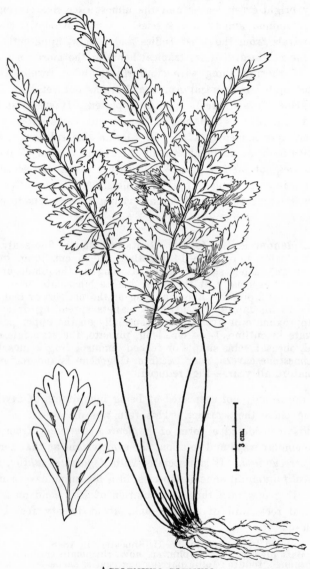

ASPLENIUM PLENUM

14. A. pumilum Sw. Rootstock short, erect or nearly so, fine-scaly: leaves few or several together, tufted, erect or spreading, 0.3–2 dm. long, bright-green: petioles as long as the blades or longer, becoming naked, brown below, greenish and greenish-margined above; blades 1-pinnate, or merely 3-lobed in small forms, those of the foliage leaves suborbicular or deltoid-ovate in outline, often 3-foliolate, the leaflets frequently subreniform, more or less lobed and shallowly toothed, those of the sporophyls triangular-ovate to pentagonal in outline, 3- to 7-foliolate, the leaflets deltoid-ovate to ovate, but inequilateral (the basal pair stalked), deeply lobed below or both edges with the first proximal lobes nearly or quite free, all obtuse, acute or somewhat acuminate: veins mostly twice or several times forked: sori oblique, linear to linear-ellipsoid, up to 1 cm. long, pale, several or numerous on each leaflet.— Limestone boulders and ledges, hammocks, Oligocene Island region, Fla.—(*W. I., Mex., C. A., S. A.*)—Spores mature in fall.

The various species of *Asplenium* have elongate copiously pinnatifid or pinnate leaf-blades. However, *Asplenium serratum* has uncut leaves; the present species is unique with its deltoid or pentagonal 3–7-foliolate leaf-blades about as wide as long. In this way it stands out sharply from all our other spleenworts. The tropical complexion of the fern floristics of Florida is emphasized by the possession of many West Indian species. Curiously enough, this species has not been found in the more typical West Indian portion of the state, the Everglade Keys, but far up in the northern part of the peninsula, on the ancient tropical area there. If it once grew in the intervening region apparently it has become extinct. It occurs on many of the West Indian islands and from Mexico to Brazil. The fern was discovered in Florida in 1929.[1] The first specimens were found in Jamaica and named in 1766. Except for *Asplenium auritum* and *A. cristatum*, the present species was for many years the most geographically localized spleenwort in our range, being, as far as known, confined to a single hammock in Alachua County. Recently, 1935, exploration on the ancient Oligocene Island disclosed two additional localities. One of these localities is within several miles of the one that had previously been known near the northern end of the Oligocene Island. The other is well over a hundred miles toward the south and nearer the southern end of that ancient island. Should one or two of the three known stations be destroyed through ''improvement'' developments, we will still have this interesting fern as a member of the Florida floristics.

15. A. Trudelli Wherry. Rootstock short, chaffy: leaves tufted, mostly 1–4 dm. long, often ascending or even erect; petioles dark-brown or blackish and sparingly scaly at the base, green above; blades lance-

[1] First collected in Florida by Hugh O'Neill and Fred Walker, 1929.

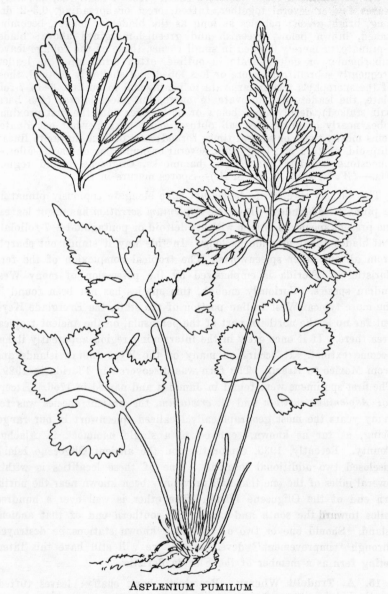

ASPLENIUM PUMILUM

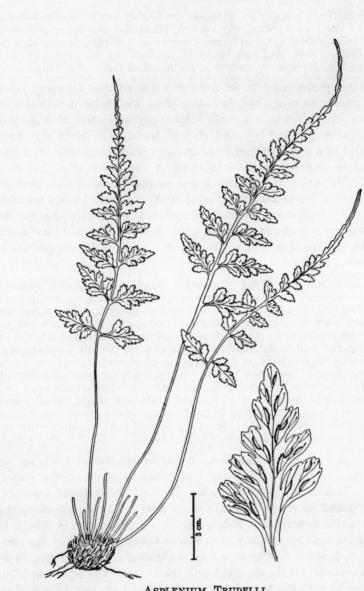

ASPLENIUM TRUDELLI

olate, sometimes broadly so, pinnate, the leaflets ovate, mostly 1–3 cm. long, the lower ones manifestly stalked, pinnatifid, the upper pinnately lobed: veins mostly twice or thrice forked: sori elliptic, mostly close to the midrib.—Cliffs, rocks on banks of streams, various provinces, Ala. to Ill. and N. J.—Spores mature in summer and fall.—Fig. reduced.

This fern posed as a form of *Asplenium pinnatifidum* for many years. It can usually be recognized as distinct from the plants of that species. However, the leaves have a build suspiciously suggestive of a mixture of *Asplenium pinnatifidum* and *A. montanum*. The plant may have originated as a cross between those species. They frequently are found growing in close proximity with those of the two species just mentioned. The habit and general aspect is that of *Asplenium pinnatifidum*, but the leaves are usually more erect; the lower leaflets resemble those of *A. montanum*. Plants were collected many years ago, but the plant was not named and described until 1925. There seems little doubt that this fern is of hybrid origin, but it appears to be self-perpetuating in some localities.

16. A. montanum Willd. Rootstock short, the congested branches dark-brown, scaly: leaves tufted mostly 0.5–2 dm. long, evergreen; petioles naked, slender, dark-brown on the lower portion, naked or sparingly scaly at the base; blades lanceolate to ovate-lanceolate or deltoid-lanceolate, 1–2-pinnate, firm, the primary divisions short-stalked or sessile, the leaflets deltoid to ovate in outline, pinnate or pinnatifid, the lobes or segments ovate or oblong: veins obscure, simple or twice or thrice forked: sori few, short, elliptic, more or less confluent at maturity: indusia thin-membranous. — (MOUNTAIN - SPLEENWORT.) — Rocks in woods, banks and bluffs, and cliffs and crags, igneous and sedimentary, and giving rise to acid soils, various provinces, except Coastal Plain, Ga. and Ala. to Ark., Mich., and W. Mass.—Spores mature in summer and fall.

Although not a conspicuous fern, the mountain-spleenwort was among those discovered in the early days of botanical study in the United States. Thus it is unlike *Asplenium Bradleyi*, its frequent associate, which escaped detection until a century later. Like its associate, the mountain-spleenwort has a wide geographic distribution. Although it grew in the vicinity of many of the older towns and cities of the eastern states, it seems first to have been recognized in the high mountains of the Carolinas, late in the eighteenth century, and was named in 1810. As compared with the following species the leaf-form may be described as a fine lace-work. This is especially pronounced in well-developed leaves. The altitudinal range extends from near sea-level to about 5000 feet in the Blue Ridge.

ASPLENIUM MONTANUM

17. A. cryptolepis Fernald. Rootstock short, the branches congested, brown-scaly: leaves tufted, mostly 0.5–1.5 dm. long, evergreen; petioles naked or minutely scaly at the base, green or brown; blades rhombic to deltoid-ovate in outline, glabrous, 2–3-pinnate, or pinnatifid above, lax, the primary leaf-divisions slender-stalked, the leaflets stalked, variable, cuneate to cuneate-flabellate and commonly rhombic or obovate, mostly obtuse, finely toothed at the apex: veins flabellate, few, simple or twice or thrice-forked: sori few, linear-oblong; strongly confluent at maturity: indusia membranous, delicate. [*A. Ruta-muraria* Michx., not L.]—(RUE-FERN.   WALL-RUE.)—Cliffs, bluffs, and rocks in woods, almost exclusively on limestone, occasionally on sandstone, various provinces, Ala. to Ark., Mo., Mich., and Vt.—Spores mature in summer and fall.

As a result of the geographic position and the geologic structure of the Southeastern States a much varied fern association has been established and maintained there.   The highlands at the North and the tropics at the South combine to give the fern student a more abundant assemblage of species and a greater variety in pattern of leaf than is to be found in any area of similar extent in North America.   The leaf of the present fern forms a rather coarse lace-work.   Up to a few years ago this fern was confused with the European *Asplenium Ruta-muraria*. It received its present name in 1928.   The altitudinal range extends from near sea-level to about 2500 feet in the Appalachians.

Asplenium cryptolepis ohionis Fernald.   A plant recently described from Ohio but rather widely distributed in the Eastern States is characterized by staghorn-like lobes and segments to the leaf blades. Further study will doubtless prove this plant to be much more common than it is thought to be at present.

18. A. ebenoides R. R. Scott. Rootstock short or somewhat elongate, chaffy, sometimes copiously leafy: leaves tufted, mostly 1–3 dm. long; petioles purplish-brown, shining, sparingly chaffy at the base; blades lanceolate to deltoid-lanceolate, often irregular and variable, firm, tapering to a slender acuminate apex, pinnatifid, or commonly pinnate near the base, the segments lanceolate to deltoid-ovate, frequently irregular on the same leaf, obtuse, acute or long-acuminate at the apex, entire or irregularly and shallowly toothed, more or less broadly auricled at the base, sessile: veins mostly once to thrice forked: sori linear to elliptic, rather close to the midrib.—Rocks, and rocky banks, various provinces, Ala. to Mo., Va., and Vt.—Spores mature in summer and fall.—Fig. reduced.

Most of our spleenworts were known to botanists before the middle of the past century.   Some, however, escaped detection or recognition until the latter half of the nineteenth century.   Scott's-spleenwort, like the pinnatifid-spleenwort, belongs with those of the less usual kinds.

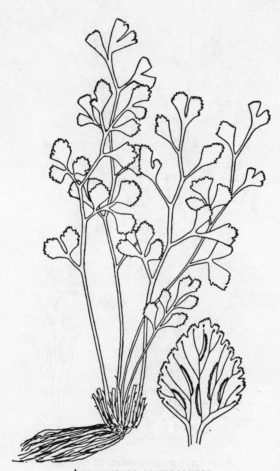

ASPLENIUM CRYPTOLEPIS

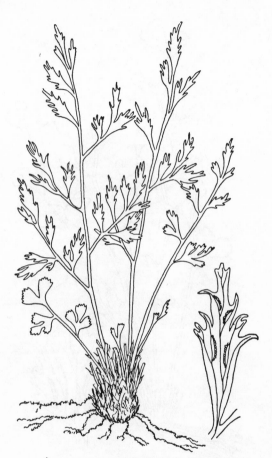

ASPLENIUM CRYPTOLEPIS OHIONIS

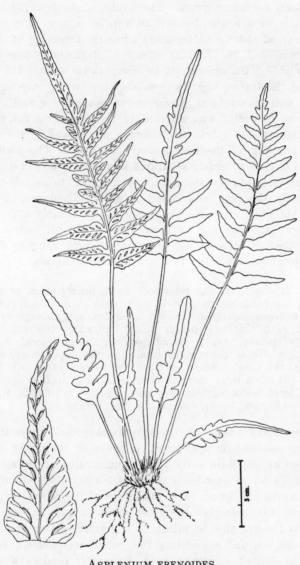

ASPLENIUM EBENOIDES

Its habit and habitat have caused quite an unusual reaction among fern students for many years. The banks of the Schuylkill River at Philadelphia were again destined to furnish a new fern. This discovery occurred about a half century after the launching of *Asplenium pinnatifidum,* and the fern in question, *Asplenium ebenoides,* was named in 1865. On account of its comparative rarity, the irregular pattern of the leaves, and its invariable occurrence only in company with two well-known ferns, *Camptosorus rhizophyllus* and *Asplenium platyneuron,* hybridity was assumed to be responsible for its origin. The possible natural hybrid origin finally was proved by the successful artificial crossing of the two presumable parents. The plants found from time to time at widely separated localities, either as single specimens or at the most few individuals, seemed not to be self-perpetuating. Finally the fern was found in great abundance in glens at Havana, Alabama, where the plants are unquestionably self-perpetuating both proliferously and by their spores. The altitudinal range is less than that of some of our other spleenworts, ranging from near sea-level to about 3000 feet in the southern mountains.

19. A. Trichomanes L. Rootstock short, nearly erect, or ascending, branched, the branches congested, with blackish scales: leaves densely tufted, numerous, mostly spreading, 0.5–3 dm. long, evergreen: petioles purplish-brown, shining; blades linear, pinnate, the rachis purple-brown, the leaflets oval or roundish-oblong, inequilateral, rounded at the apex, crenate or dentate, especially on the upper edge, cuneate to truncate at the base: veins mostly once or twice forked: sori 2–6 pairs, elliptic.—(MAIDEN-HAIR SPLEENWORT.)—Rocks, preferring limestone, rarely on brick walls, various provinces, Ga. to Tex., Calif., B. C., Ont., and Que.—(*Eurasia.*)—Spores mature summer and fall.

As a result of its very wide geographic range and its relative abundance, the maiden-hair spleenwort, in spite of its rather diminutive size, is one of the more early fern acquaintances of young botanists generally. In North America it has a much wider distribution, east and west and north and south, than any others of the related small leaved spleenworts, for example *Asplenium resiliens* and *A. heterochroum.* The plants too are able to withstand a greater variety of adverse climatic conditions, and considering their small root-systems, small rootstocks, and limited supply of food, frequently produce a prodigious number of leaves. The name of the species published in 1753, referred to the plants growing in Europe. The species ranges in altitude from near sea-level to 5000 feet in the Blue Ridge.

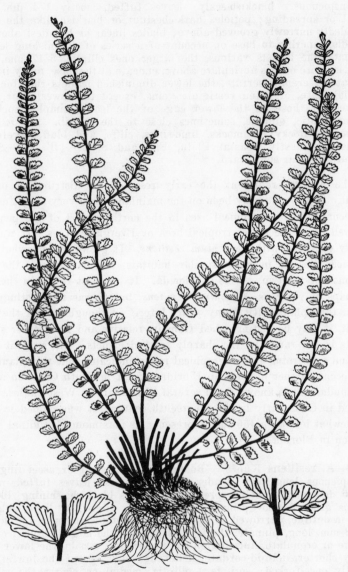

ASPLENIUM TRICHOMANES

20. A. heterochroum Kunze. Rootstock short, erect or ascending, inconspicuously blackish-scaly: leaves tufted, mostly 1–4 dm. long, erect or spreading; petioles dark-chestnut or blackish, like the rachis decidedly narrowly grooved above; blades linear or broadest about the middle, tapering to base on account of a series of diminishing leaflets, pinnate, the leaflets various, the larger ones elliptic, 5–17 mm. long, obtuse, more or less auriculate above, cuneate at the base, finely incised-serrate or crenate-serrate, the lower diminished leaflets rhombic-ovate to flabellate, or often vestigial: veins, except the lowest pair, once-forked, or those on the lower edge of the leaflet simple; sori few, linear-elliptic, oblique, sometimes close to the midrib. [*A. muticum* Gilbert.]—Rocky hammocks, lime-sinks, cliffs, and bluffs, preferring limestone, mostly Coastal Plain, Fla. and S. C.—(*W. I.*)—Spores mature all year southward.

The Antilles represent the early reservoir of distribution of this plant. It has evidently been on the mainland for a very long time, for it occurs in the old tropical area in the northern part of the peninsula as well as in the newer tropical area or Everglade Keys. It was formerly confused with *Asplenium resiliens*. It grows in somewhat similar localities or in quite similar habitats, and is perhaps the more common of the two species in Florida. It was first found in the state perhaps as early as *Asplenium resiliens*, but it was not distinguished from that plant until many years later. Although it has the same habit, it may be distinguished from its relative and from other spleen-worts in our range by the sharply toothed leaflets. The present information concerning its geographical range indicates that this plant does not occur further north than Florida, except in South Carolina and in Bermuda. It is known from several islands of the West Indies. Collected in Cuba early in the nineteenth century, it was named in 1834. Somewhat less than 150 feet represents its maximum altitudinal distribution in Florida.

21. A. resiliens Kunze. Rootstock short, erect or ascending with conspicuous long very slender blackish scales: leaves tufted, mostly 1–3.5 dm. long, erect or spreading; petioles blackish, shining, like the rachis grooved above; blades linear, linear-elliptic, or linear-oblanceolate in outline, narrowed at the base by a diminishing series of leaflets 8–12 mm. long, pinnate, the leaflets various, the larger elliptic, obtuse, entire or crenulate, auricled on the upper side, sessile, the lower gradually shorter, deltoid-cordate, deflexed: veins, except the lowest pair, mostly once-forked: sori few, elliptic, medial or nearer the margin, straight or nearly so. [*A. parvulum* Mart. & Gal. not Hook.]—(BLACK-STEM SPLEENWORT. LITTLE-EBONY SPLEENWORT.)—Rocky river-bluffs, rocky hammocks, boulders, and lime-sinks, preferring limestone, but

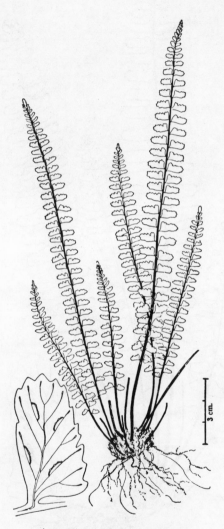

ASPLENIUM HETEROCHROUM

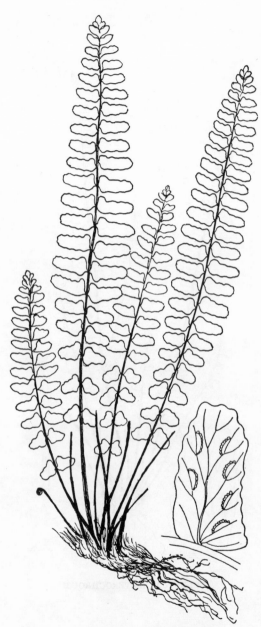

ASPLENIUM RESILIENS

also on igneous rocks, various provinces, Fla. to Tex., N. M., Kans., and
S. Pa.—(*W. I., Mex.*)—Spores mature in summer and fall, or all year
southward.

The course of migration of this spleenwort is not altogther clear.
Its range may once have covered more of the mainland even further
northward than now. The ice age may have pushed it southward even
to some of the West Indian islands and Mexico, or its course of migration may have been northward from the tropical parts. The black-stem
spleenwort inhabits the same kind of places as *Asplenium platyneuron*,
but also prefers even more rocky soil, and it is particularly fond of
growing on cliffs. It was first collected in Florida in the earlier half
of the nineteenth century. This plant is not typically a tropical fern,
although it grows in some of the Antilles and in Mexico. Aside from
growing in the Coastal Plain, it extends northward to the mountain
valleys of southernmost Pennsylvania, preferring to grow in limestone,
and also into the interior as far as Kansas and New Mexico. About
2000 feet represents its maximum altitude in the southern highlands.
Mexico furnished the original specimens. It was first named, although
improperly, in 1842. The present name dates from 1844.

22. **A. platyneuron** (L.) Oakes. Rootstock short, erect or ascending, scaly: leaves tufted, one or several, erect sporophyls however accompanied at the base by a rosette of small spreading leaves; petioles
purplish-brown, shining, like the rachis slightly grooved above; blades
linear or linear-oblanceolate in outline, or gradually narrowed at the
base, firm, pinnate, the rachis chestnut-brown, the leaflets 20–40 pairs,
lanceolate or linear-lanceolate, or the diminishing ones below the middle
of the blade gradually smaller and broader, elliptic, ovate or triangular, subfalcate, alternate or partly so, crenate, serrate, or incised,
sessile, auricled on the upper side at the base and sometimes below:
veins simple or once-forked, or the basal pair several times forked:
sori 8–12 pairs, elliptic, crowded or rather approximate. [*A. ebeneum*
Ait.]—(EBONY-SPLEENWORT. BROWN-STEM-SPLEENWORT.)—Woods,
roadside-banks, sand-dunes, and shell-mounds, various provinces, and
hammocks, Fla. to Tex., Calif., Colo., Ont., and Me.—Spores mature
in summer and fall or all year southward.—Fig. reduced.

Two outstanding characters may be assigned to this fern—a very
extensive geographic range and great variability. One would expect
variability over such a wide range, but much variation is evident in
limited areas. In natural rocky habitats and artificial ones, such as
brick or stone walls, the plants often closely resemble those of *Asplenium resiliens* and *A. heterochroum*. The ebony-spleenwort may well be

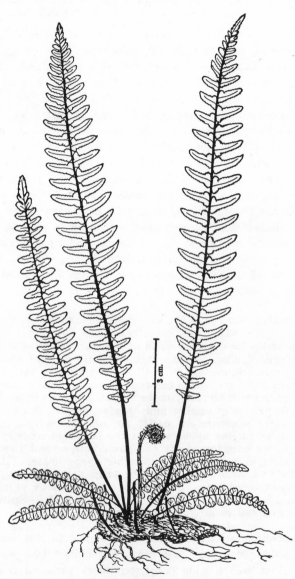

ASPLENIUM PLATYNEURON

considered a northern type. Nowhere does it reach the Tropic of Cancer. However, its range extends southward to the old tropical area in northern peninsular Florida and there it associates with various tropical ferns. It has not been found on the Everglade Keys which lie three hundred miles further south. It is widely distributed and usually common in North America, except the extreme north, mostly east of the Rocky Mountains. However, it is larger in the Coastal Plain than in the higher regions. It is less abundant perhaps in the Gulf States than in other states northward, and there it also differs somewhat in the form and toothing of the leaflets from the plants growing further north.[1] Within our range it grows from sea-level to over 4500 feet altitude in the Blue Ridge. It prefers to grow in partial shade. This fern was first found in Virginia in the early part of the nineteenth century, and named in 1753.

23. A. Bradleyi D. C. Eaton. Rootstock short, erect or ascending, with narrow dark-brown scales: leaves tufted, 0.5–2.5 dm. long, mostly spreading; petioles stoutish, like the rachis grooved above, rich chestnut-brown; blades lanceolate, oblong-lanceolate or broadly linear in outline, acuminate, scarcely if at all narrowed at the base, the rachis brown for the lower two thirds of its length, but green terminally, the leaflets short-stalked or sessile, ovate to deltoid-ovate, or rarely oblong or the lower leaflets often deltoid, mostly 1–2.5 cm. long, all pinnatifid or the lower ones pinnate, with obtuse lobes, segments or leaflets which are toothed at the apex: veins except the basal ones simple or once or twice forked: sori few, near the midrib.—(BRADLEY SPLEENWORT.) Precipitous cliffs, igneous, metamorphic, or sedimentary, but not limestone, and giving rise to intensely acid soils, various provinces, Ga. to Ark., Mo., and N. Y.—Spores mature in summer and fall.

Several of our more interesting ferns, now known to have a wide geographic range, escaped detection for many years. Curiously enough this fern is widely distributed in the regions where active botanical collecting was in progress during many years preceding its discovery. Well known localities for the Bradley-spleenwort are in the vicinity of large cites—Baltimore, Maryland and Little Rock, Arkansas—and historic spots of Revolutionary and Civil War activities, such as Kings Mountain and Crowders Mountain, North Carolina, and Lookout Mountain, Tennessee. The first collection seems to have been in the Cumberland Mountains of Tennessee, in 1870. The species was named after the discoverer in 1873. No great altitude has been recorded for this

[1] One southern form has been named by Featherman variety *bacculum-rubrum*.

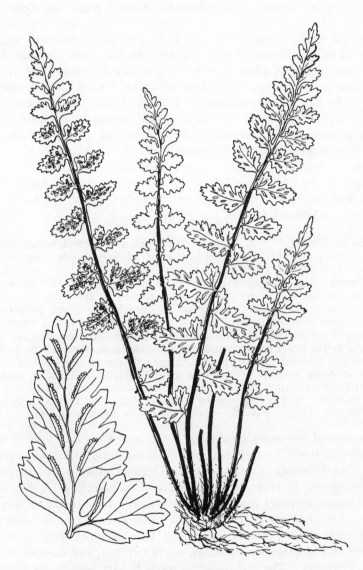

ASPLENIUM BRADLEYI

fern. It ranges from about 2000 feet on Lookout Mountain to near sea-level on the Atlantic seaboard. The size and dividing of the leaf-blades depend largely on the supply of moisture available. Plants growing in crevices of rocks where water is scarce or the supply irrregular have small once-pinnate leaves that lie flat against the rock, while plants that have a steady and generous water-supply grow with the leaves erect, the blades often more or less completely twice-pinnate.

25. **ATHYRIUM** Roth.

Relatively large terrestrial plants with horizontal or creeping root-stocks. Leaves erect or arching, not evergreen: petioles greenish, succulent: blades herbaceous, 1–3-pinnate or 1–3-pinnatifid, the ultimate segments herbaceous-membranous, irregularly toothed or incised, relatively broader and blunter than the leaflets. Veins free, simple or sparingly forked, running nearly or quite into the teeth of the leaf-segments. Sori usually curved when young, elliptic to linear-elliptic, or crossing the vein and recurved, sometimes unequally horseshoe-shaped. Indusia shaped like the sori and opening along the side facing the midrib, or rarely vestigial and concealed.—Comprises about eighty-five species, most abundant in the tropics.—The genus is founded on *Polypodium Filix-foemina* L. The name is Greek, meaning without a shield, of doubtful application here.—The following species have usually been treated as conspecific with *Athyrium Filix-foemina* (L.) Roth.—The spores mature from July to September.—The number of vaulted sori is variable. Sometimes they are scattered on the leaflets, other times their development is essentially complete.—Spores mature summer and fall.—For notes on varieties and forms, see Am. Fern Jour. **26:** 132–135. 1936.

Rootstock creeping, not densely clothed with old petiole-bases: leaf-blades broadest near the base: indusia with gland-tipped cilia: spores blackish.   1. *A. asplenioides.*
Rootstock horizontal or somewhat oblique, completely covered with the bases of spent petioles: leaf-blades broadest near the middle: indusia with lobes or glandless cilia: spores yellow-brown.   2. *A. angustum.*

1. **A. asplenioides** (Michx.) Eaton. Rootstock relatively slender, copiously chaffy: leaves 3.5–11.5 dm. tall; petioles tufted, stramineous, brownish, or reddish, coarsely scaly at the base; blades broadly elliptic-ovate to elliptic-lanceolate, or lanceolate, broadest near the base, acuminate, 2-pinnate, except towards the apex (or pinnate and with pinnatifid segments in depauperate forms), the leaflets lanceolate, acuminate, short-stalked or the upper ones sessile, 1–2 dm. long, the ultimate divisions elliptic, oblong-lanceolate, or lanceolate, coarsely

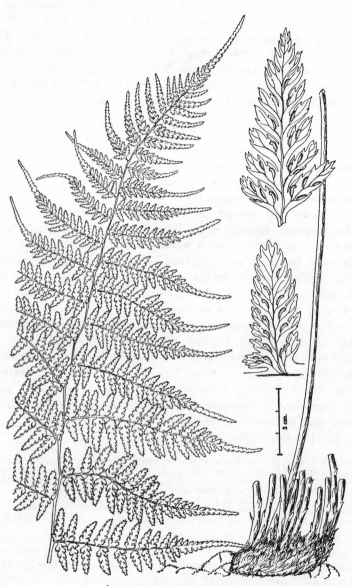

3 cm.

ATHYRIUM ASPLENIOIDES

toothed, serrate, incised, or pinnatifid with their lobes or teeth often again toothed, sometimes decidedly auricled at the base: sori short, curved when young, oblique to the midrib: indusium with gland-tipped cilia. [*Nephrodium asplenioides* Michx.]—(LOWLAND LADY-FERN.)— Moist hammocks, wet woods, creek-banks, and shaded bluffs, various provinces, but less common in the Coastal Plain, Fla. to E. Tex., Kans., Minn., Ont., and N. S.—Fig. reduced.

The temperate and boreal parts of the Northern Hemisphere are girdled by the geographic range of this species and its near relatives, Europe and Asia as well as nearly all parts of the United States and southern Canada being in their range. It is a cool-climate plant, common in the north and reaching only as far south as northern Florida. The present sparse representation southward may be the mere relic of a more generous growth when the climate was cooler. Where this plant is more plentiful than in the Gulf States it presents numerous forms. In the southern mountains it occurs nearly or quite to the summits of the higher peaks and often grows luxuriantly on the moist, often cloud-bathed mountain tops. Within our range it is quite constant in its form of growth and in the technical characters which set it off from *A. Filix-foemina* of Europe, with which it has often been confused. When this species was named in 1803, it was said to range from New England to Canada. However, it actually grows chiefly further south. The wide range helps to account for much minor variation in the cutting of the leaf-blade. Some plants show much more lacy patterns than others. The altitudinal distribution is extensive, reaching from sea-level to about 6600 feet in the Blue Ridge.

2. **A. angustum** (Willd.) Presl. Rootstock short, horizontal or somewhat oblique, completely covered with the bases of spent petioles: leaves 4–11 dm. tall, sometimes dimorphic; petioles somewhat tufted, stramineous, the scales with narrow dark-walled cells; blades somewhat elliptic in outline, at least broadest near the middle, 2-pinnate, the leaflets lanceolate, acuminate, sessile or nearly so, mostly 1–1.5 dm. long, the ultimate divisions lanceolate to elliptic-lanceolate or ovate-lanceolate, doubly serrate, not auricled at the base: sori rather short, often strongly curved, oblique to the midrib: indusium with glandless cilia. [*Aspidium angustum* Willd.]—(UPLAND LADY-FERN.)—Wet woods, moist banks, wooded hillsides, rocky streams, and sandy bogs, various provinces, Pa. to Tenn., Mo., S. Dak., and Newf.—Fig. reduced.

As noted under the preceding species, this plant and its relatives girdle the globe. The several species now recognized as distinct were formerly included under the Linnaean specific name *Filix-foemina*.

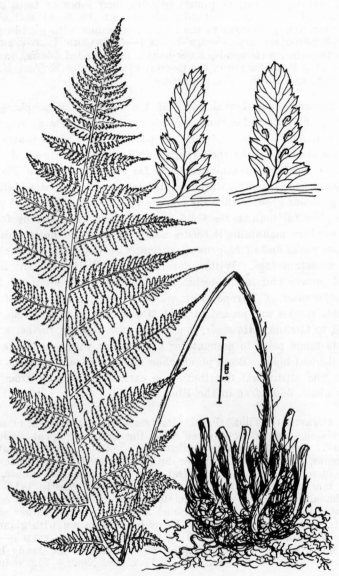

ATHYRIUM ANGUSTUM

Some of the present-day segregations grow as far south as the Gulf of Mexico, but prefer a cool climate and are more wide-spread north of the latitude of the Mason and Dixon line. When the species was named in 1810, it was said to grow in Canada. Today it is known to range from Pennsylvania to Tennessee, Arkansas, South Dakota, Ontario, Quebec and Newfoundland. Its altitudinal distribution in our range seems to be limited by the 4000-foot contour.—Several varieties and forms of this unstable species have been proposed and described. They seem fall into two primary groups: one with dimorphic leaves, the blades of the sporophyls coriaceous, contracted, with the sori confluent and thus covering the segments. Here belong the typical form and *A. angustum elatius.* The leaflets of the former are relatively small (5–12 cm.), with the segments of the foliage leaves obtuse, and only slightly toothed or lobed. The leaflets of the variety *elatius* are larger (12–25 cm.) with the segments strongly toothed or pinnatifid. *Athyrium augustum rubellum* represents the second form, that with uniform leaves whose blades are membranous and not contracted, the sori spaced and not confluent at maturity. In some cases this seems to pass into the preceding species.

26. DIPLAZIUM Sw.

Large terrestrial plants, with horizontal or erect rootstocks which are scaly at the tips. Leaves in a crown, resembling those of *Athyrium* but less divided, and like them not evergreen: petioles succulent, more or less scaly at the base: blades 1-pinnate (in our species), broad, the leaflets numerous, rather broad, pinnatifid, the ultimate segments toothed or incised. Veins free, simple or sparingly forked, running almost or quite into the teeth of the leaf-segments. Sori elongate, double, at least in part, borne back to back on a vein, but not crossing it. Indusium covering the sorus, opening in opposite directions when double.—Consists of about three hundred and fifty species, mostly tropical.—The genus is based on *Asplenium plantagineum* L.—The name is Greek, alluding to the double indusia.

1. **D. acrostichoides** (Sw.) Butters. Rootstock sinuous, copiously chaffy: leaves 6–12 dm. tall; petioles ultimately stramineous, coarsely scaly at the base; blades lanceolate, acute or acuminate, decidedly narrowed at the base, 1-pinnate, the leaflets lanceolate to linear-lanceolate, mostly 0.5–1.5 dm. long, sessile, acuminate, deeply pinnatifid into numerous oblong, obtuse or subacute, finely crenate or serrate-crenate segments: sori crowded, slightly curved or straight, the lower ones often appearing to be double: indusium light-colored, lustrous when

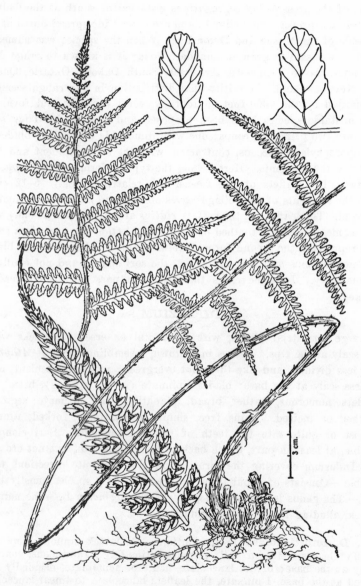

3 cm.

DIPLAZIUM ACROSTICHOIDES

old. [*Asplenium acrostichoides* Sw. *A. thelypteroides* Michx.]—(Sɪʟ-
ᴠᴇʀʏ Sᴘʟᴇᴇɴᴡᴏʀᴛ.)—Rich moist woods, shaded banks, river-flats, and
swamps, Ga. to La., Minn., and N. S.—(*Asia.*)—Spores mature in summer and fall.—Fig. reduced.

There are two relatively large ferns that the young plant collector
and the amateur in almost any wooded region in southeastern North
America encounters. One of them is this plant commonly called sil-
very spleenwort and the other its relative, the so-called lady-fern. The
plants of these two species have the same general habit, but by the more
compound leaf structure of *Athyrium asplenioides* and the less compound
structure of *Diplazium acrostichoides* the two may be distinguished
from each other at a glance. The present fern is much less lace-like
than the *Athyria*. The simply pinnate blade and the little-cut segments give the leaf a less elegant appearance. The plant has nearly as
wide a geographic distribution in eastern North America as the following species, but the altitudinal distribution seems to be less extensive.
About 5500 feet in the Blue Ridge seems to be the maximum. The
plant was named *Asplenium acrostichoides* in 1801; locality was given
for the origin of the specimens. The plant was again named *Asplenium
thelypteroides* in 1803, the specimens being said to have come from the
mountains of Virginia and North Carolina.

27. **HOMALOSORUS** Small.

Large terrestrial plants with horizontal or creeping rather stout rootstocks. Leaves in a crown, resembling those of *Nephrolepis*, partly
foliar, partly spore-bearing: petioles succulent, more or less scaly at the
base: blades 1-pinnate, the leaflets numerous, narrow, undulate or
shallowly toothed, sometimes slightly auricled at the base. Veins free,
forked near the midrib and sometimes beyond, or partly simple in
sporophyls, the branches running into the sinuses of the teeth. Sori
slightly curved, linear, becoming somewhat turgid, extending mainly
on upper branch of the vein from the midrib to near the margin.
Indusia closely covering the sori, opening toward the midrib.—Consists
of the following species.—The name is from the Greek, alluding to the
regular lines of sori.

1. **H. pycnocarpus** (Spreng.) Small. Rootstock stoutish, creeping:
leaves in a crown, the sporophyls usually taller than the foliage leaves,
4–13 dm. long; petioles 2–3 dm. long, slightly scaly at the brownish
base, green above; foliage-blades lanceolate to elliptic-lanceolate, pin-

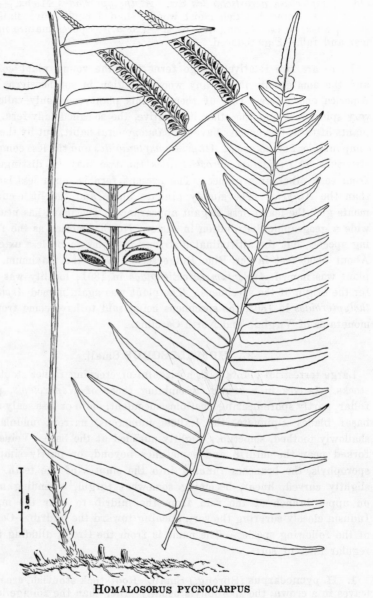

3 cm.

HOMALOSORUS PYCNOCARPUS

nate; leaflets numerous, the blades lanceolate to linear-lanceolate, acuminate or attenuate at the apex, entire or crenulate, obtuse or truncate or subcordate at the base, with or without basal auricles; sporophyls and their leaflets narrower than the foliage leaves: sori 20–40 pairs, linear, approximate or crowded. [*Asplenium angustifolium* Michx., not Jacq. *Asplenium pycnocarpum* Spreng. *Athyrium pycnocarpum* Tidestrom.]—(GLADE-FERN.)—Moist rich woods, shaded ravines, rocky hillsides, wooded cliffs and swamps, various provinces, Ga. to La., Kans., Wis., and Que.—Spores mature in summer and fall.—Fig. reduced.

The glade-fern may be associated with either *Asplenium* or *Athyrium* by technical characters, or the two genera just mentioned might likewise be united, as they often are. However, this fern is so different in general habit and in the leaf-structure, gross and minute, that if *Athyrium* may be held generically distinct from *Asplenium* there is no good reason why the present fern should not be likewise separated from both its former generic associates. It is a woods-plant with annual foliage, and in various other respects unlike the spleenworts with which it usually is associated. The even branching of the veins in the leaflets and the termination of the veinlets in the sinuses on the leaflet edge, together with the numerous oblique sori arranged in almost perfectly parallel order set it off distinctly from its former associates. The altitudinal distribution appears not to be wide—the 3300 foot contour seems to be its limit in the southern mountains. The original specimens came from the banks of the Ohio River, and the plant was first named in 1803.

28. CAMPTOSORUS Link.

Slender plants with short erect or ascending, somewhat scaly rootstocks. Leaves approximately clustered, diffuse: petioles very variable in length, naked or nearly so: blades narrow and tapering, simple, entire or lightly sinuate, truncate or cordate at the base. Veins forking and anastomosing. Sori linear or oblong, several times as long as broad, irregularly scattered on either side of the reticulate veins or sometimes crossing them, partly parallel to the midrib and partly oblique, the outer ones sometimes approximate in pairs, with the two indusia opening face to face, or confluent end to end thus forming crooked or bent lines of sori. Indusium thin, narrow.—Two species, the following and one in Asia.—The genus is based on *Asplenium rhizophylla* L.—The name is Greek, alluding to the curved or bent sori. —For notes on varieties and forms see Am. Fern Jour. 27: 22. 1937.

1. C. rhizophyllus (L.) Link. Rootstock short, chaffy: leaves diffuse, prostrate or arching, mostly 1–4 dm. long; petioles light-green above the brown or purple base, tufted; blades thin, but somewhat coriaceous, lanceolate, simple, prolonged at the apex into a caudate-attenuate tip which often takes root at the apex, undulate to sinuate, usually cordate and auriculate, sometimes hastate, with the basal auricles occasionally much elongate and caudate-attenuate: veins slender, some of the veinlets running to the margin, others vanishing in the tissues: sori irregular in size, shape, and position. [*Asplenium rhizophylla* L.]—(WALKING-LEAF. WALKING-FERN.)—On damp, often mossy rocks and stony banks, preferring limestone, but frequent on many other kinds of rock, various provinces, Ga. to Okla., Kans., Ont., and Que.—Spores mature in summer and fall.

As in the case of some flowering-plants, some ferns have made doubly sure of holding their own not only through sexual reproduction, but by vegetative propagation as well. The walking-leaf is an unusual fern in the general and varying pattern of the leaf. It is well designed for spreading and increasing away from the parent plant, by a series of short leaps, as it were. The much elongated tip of the leaf arches to the ground and there takes root; from this point a new plant arises; then the tip of each leaf on the resulting growth may give life to new plants. Thus in a few generations vegetative propagation produces a great many plants. This fern shows considerable instability in its leaf-form. Whether this is the result of innate characteristics assumed in its ancestral history or due to modern individual chance hybridization cannot be determined. Of course, we do know that, at times, the walking-fern hybridizes with the ebony-spleenwort to make *Asplenium ebenoides*. The species was named in 1753, as *Asplenium rhizophylla*, the specimens being said to have come from "Virginia and Canada." The altitudinal distribution range is from about 3000 feet in the Blue Ridge to near sea-level.

29. TECTARIA Cav.

Elegant terrestrial plants, variable in size, usually growing on rock, with mostly short or sometimes elongate, creeping or horizontal scaly rootstocks. Leaves erect and arching or pendent, more or less clustered on the rootstock: petiole not jointed to the rootstock: blades broad, membranous, usually of a deltoid, ovate, or hastate type, lobed, pinnatifid or 1-pinnate, i.e. 3-foliolate, the leaflets opposite, again lobed or pinnatifid. Veins branching and freely anastomosing, thus forming numerous areolae with free included veinlets. Sori orbicular or reni-

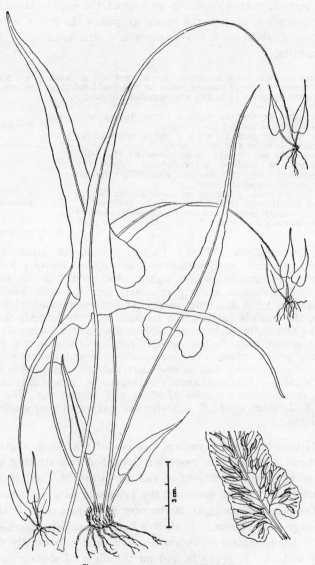

3 cm.

CAMPTOSORUS RHIZOPHYLLUS

form, scattered over the back of the leaf-blade or its segments.
Indusia peltate, flattish, opening all around the edge.—About twenty-
four species widely distributed in the tropics.—The genus is based on
Polypodium trifoliatum L.—The name is Latin, alluding to the pro-
tective indusia.

Sori borne in two rows between the lateral veins, with some sori often
    irregularly placed : basal lobes of the leaf-blades, or leaflets, usually
    nearly or quite equaling the terminal or some-
    what smaller.
    Basal lobes or leaflets with a large, long-acumi-
      nate auricle on the lower side.   1. *T. heracleifolia.*
    Basal lobes or leaflets with a more rounded or
      obtuse lobe on the lower side.   2. *T. minima.*
Sori irregularly scattered : basal lobes of the leaf-
    blades, or leaflets, much smaller than the
    terminal one, the former decidedly distant
    from the terminal leaflet.
    Petioles grooved, glabrous or nearly so : leaves
      not proliferous in the axils of the leaflets.   3. *T. Amesiana.*
    Petioles nearly terete, copiously pubescent : leaves
      proliferous in some of the axils of the leaf-
      lets.   4. *T. coriandrifolia.*

1. **T. heracleifolia** (Willd.) Underw. Rootstock stout, elongate,
decumbent or nearly erect, with dark-brown scales: leaves 4–6 dm. long
or rarely more; petioles reddish, light-brown, or dark-brown, somewhat
shining, with deciduous scales particularly near the base; blades dark-
green, hastate, 1.5–5 dm. long, somewhat coriaceous, undivided or 3–5-
foliolate, the leaflets various, the terminal one the largest, the blades
acuminate, and undulate, incised, or lobed, those of the lower pair stalked
or nearly sessile, more or less curved: sori numerous, in two rows between the lateral veins, with some often irregularly placed, about
2–2.5 mm. in diameter: indusia orbicular, peltate. [*Aspidium heracleifolium* Willd.]—(HALBERD-FERN.)—Hammocks, lime-sinks and grottoes, on the floor or on sides of sinks and ledges, pen. Fla. and S.
Tex.—(*W. I., Mex., C. A., S. A.*)—Spores mature all year southward.—
Fig. reduced.

The halberd-ferns show various degrees of travelling ability. The
vast tropical America fern reservoir furnished this striking plant to
Florida on two waves of migration and established it where rocky sinks
and grottoes in various parts of the peninsula have sheltered it for
ages. The perpetual twilight of the very dense hammocks is the home
of this large halberd-fern. It thrives best in habitats suitable to the
growth of maiden-hair (*Adiantum tenerum*) and it is usually found in
company with it. It grows in and on the edges of shallow lime-sinks,
sometimes almost carpeting the hammock floor, and it thrives best in
the well-like lime-sinks, particularly in the smaller ones, where it often
grows a foot or two below the orifice with the large leaf-blades sup-

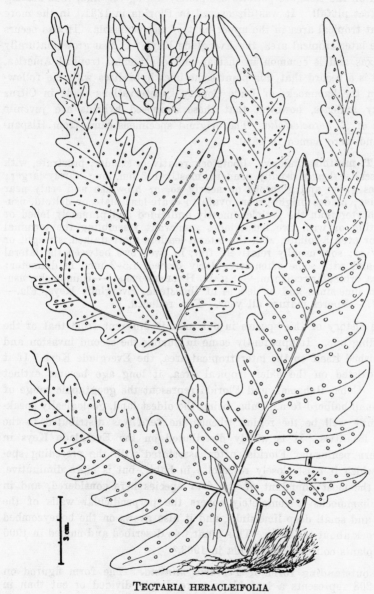

3 CM.

TECTARIA HERACLEIFOLIA

ported on the elongate petioles completely hiding the sink, thus making a perfect pitfall. It was discovered in Florida in 1881,[1] in the more ancient tropical area in the upper part of the peninsula. It also occurs on the later tropical area, the Everglade Keys. It also grows naturally in Texas and is common in insular and continental tropical America. There is a record that this plant sometimes hybridizes with the following, in the hammocks of Dade County. Observations made in Citrus County indicate, however, that these supposed hybrids are juvenile forms of *T. heracleifolia*. The original specimens came from Hispaniola and were named in 1810.

2. **T. minima** Underw. Rootstock relatively slender, prostrate, with dark scales: leaves usually pendent, mostly 1–3 dm. long, rarely larger; petioles green and glabrous or nearly so, or brownish and scaly near the base; blades bright-green, ovate to ovate-lanceolate or deltoid, usually shorter than the petioles, mostly undivided and pinnately lobed or pinnatifid or with two basal lobes somewhat resembling the terminal lobe, or even 3-foliate, with the lateral leaflets short-stalked, straight or nearly so: sori usually relatively few, in two rows between the lateral veins and with some often irregularly placed, 1.5–2 mm. in diameter: indusia orbicular-reniform.—(SMALL HALBERD-FERN.)—Hammocks, usually in lime-sinks and on ledges of limestone, Everglade Keys, Fla.—(*W. I.*)—Spores mature all year.—Fig. reduced.

The history of this species in our area is different from that of the preceding one. It apparently came in during the second invasion and established itself on the later tropical area, the Everglade Keys. If it once existed on the older tropical area, it long ago became extinct there. Cuba, Bahamas, and Florida represent the geographic range of this small halberd-fern. Cuba, being the oldest land, geologically speaking, may well be the region whence the fern was distributed to the other localities. It is widely distributed on the Everglade Keys in southern peninsular Florida, often associated with the preceding species, which it most closely resembles in habit, but is more diminutive. It is the most abundant of the four species here considered, and in some hammocks it completely covers the perpendicular walls of the large and small deep lime-sinks, and it also grows on the honeycombed lime-rock about the sinks. This plant was described and named in 1906 from plants collected in Florida in 1903.[2]

An outstanding form of *Tectaria minima*. The form figured on page 208 represents a leaf blade more deeply divided or cut than in

[1] First collected in Florida by A. H. Curtiss in 1881.
[2] First collected in Florida by J. K. Small, J. J. Carter, and A. A. Eaton in 1903.

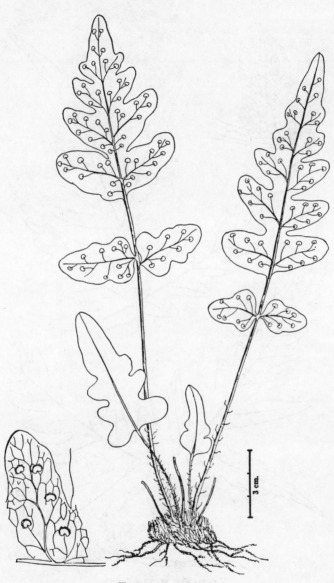

TECTARIA MINIMA

TECTARIA MINIMA var.

the typical form.   It occurs mainly in the hammocks of the Everglade Keys.

3. **T. Amesiana** A. A. Eaton.   Rootstock rather stout, short, but creeping, with brown scales: leaves erect or ascending, or pendent, fully 3 dm. long or less; petioles yellowish-brown, glabrous or with few hairs on the upper side and scattered scales; blades membranous, narrowly ovate or elliptic-ovate in outline, mostly shorter than the petioles, merely pinnatifid or pinnate and with a pair of lateral leaflets and a larger pinnatifid terminal leaflet, the leaflets short-stalked, with deltoid-ovate obtuse blades and lobes: sori few, scattered, about 1 mm. in diameter: indusia reniform, persistent.—Hammocks, in and about lime-sinks, Everglade Keys, S. pen. Fla.—Spores mature all year.—Fig. reduced.

The halberd-ferns in Florida run in pairs as to abundance.   The two preceding species are common where they grow, this one and the following are very rare.   The present one is the rarer of the two and is endemic.   It seems to have originated north of the Gulf Stream.   The present species like *T. coriandrifolia* grows only in the Hattie Bauer Hammock on perpendicular rock walls deep down in the large lime-sinks or about their edges.   It was discovered in 1903[1] and described and named in 1906.   It is, as yet, unknown outside of Florida, except for a doubtful record for the Bahamas.

4. **T. coriandrifolia** (Sw.) Underw.   Rootstock rather stout, short, with fine scales: leaves spreading or ascending, 0.5–2 dm. long or more; petioles light-brown, softly scaly-pubescent throughout; blades membranous, elliptic or elliptic-lanceolate in outline, mostly longer than the petioles, with one or two pairs of small lateral leaflets and a very large pinnatifid terminal leaflet, the blades of the leaflets and the lobes obtuse, the lower leaflets slightly stalked with mostly ovate or deltoid-ovate rounded or obtuse blades: sori few, scattered, not in rows, about 1 mm. in diameter: indusia reniform, deciduous.—Hammocks, lime-sinks, Everglade Keys, S. pen. Fla.—(*W. I.*)—Spores mature all year. —Fig. reduced.

In spite of its very limited distribution and scarcity in Florida this delicate fern seems to be holding its own against great odds.   The sole locality has been ravished by hurricanes, fire, and vandalism.   Its small size and habitat in lime sinks may be its salvation.   It evidently came to Florida during the second tropical fern invasion.   It is now known only from the Hattie Bauer Hammock, where it occurs low down on the rough perpendicular walls of the well-like lime-sinks.   It was discovered in our range in 1903;[2] but was previously known from the West Indies, particularly Cuba and Jamaica.   The original specimens were collected in Jamaica and the species was named in 1801.

[1] First collected in Florida by A. A. Eaton in 1903.
[2] First collected in Florida by A. A. Eaton, December 1903.

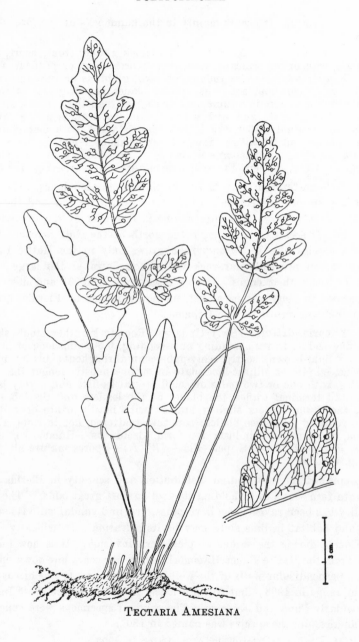

TECTARIA AMESIANA

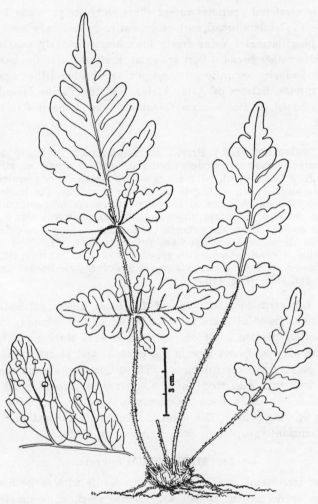

TECTARIA CORIANDRIFOLIA

30. CYRTOMIUM Presl.

Coarse terrestrial plants, usually growing on banks or rocks, with firm, horizontal, very scaly rootstocks. Leaves erect or spreading, sparingly clustered: petioles rather short, very scaly: blade 1-pinnate, elongate, the leaflets broad, coriaceous, entire or shallowly toothed, more or less inequilateral. Veins freely branching, copiously anastomosing, the areolae rather broad. Sori orbicular, scattered over the back of the leaflets. Indusia, centrally peltate, opening all around the edge.—Four or five species, natives of Asia, Africa, and the Pacific Islands.—The genus is based on *Polypodium falcatum.*—The name is Greek, meaning bow.

1. **C. falcatum** (L.f.) Presl. Rootstock stout, copiously brown or black scaly: leaves more or less clustered, erect or nearly so, stiff, 1.5–5 dm. long: petioles stout, very shaggy with broad, brown scales; blade 1-pinnate, dark-green, oblong to lanceolate in outline, the leaflets alternate, inequilaterally ovate to falcate-ovate, acute or acuminate, 5–10 cm. long, entire or undulate, short-stalked, glossy above: sori numerous, borne on connected or free veins in the areolae. Indusia circular, about 1 mm. in diameter.—[*Polypodium falcatum* L.f. *Aspidium falcatum* Sw.]—HOLLY-FERN.—Old walls, especially at Fort Marion, St. Augustine, Fla.—Native of Asia, Africa, and Polynesia.—Spores mature in summer and fall.—Fig. reduced.

It is not surprising that one of the more widely cultivated ferns should make itself at home in the mild climate of Florida. This one has definitely planted itself on the walls of Fort Marion in St. Augustine[1] and may be found also in old gardens and places where surplus garden plants have been dumped. The original specimens came from Japan, and were described under the genus *Aspidium* in 1801. Our illustration was made from specimens growing on the walls of Fort Marion, St. Augustine. The plant is frequent in cultivation and often grows luxuriantly, especially under glass or in shade.

31. MENISCIUM Schreb.

Coarse terrestrial or epiphytic swamp plants with large horizontal, creeping, or decumbent rootstocks. Leaves erect, approximate on the horizontal rootstock: petiole not jointed to the rootstock: blades rather broad, 1-pinnate; leaflets spreading, entire or toothed. Primary veins connected by numerous parallel transverse arcuate veins. Sori elliptic, or somewhat curved, borne about the middle of the transverse veins.

[1] First collected in Florida by Wm. A. Knight in 1932.

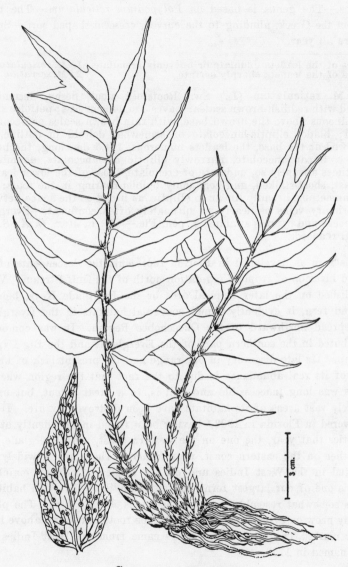

3 cm.

CYRTOMIUM FALCATUM

Indusia wanting.—About fifteen species, widely distributed in the tropics.—The genus is based on *Polypodium reticulatum.*—The name is from the Greek, alluding to the curved, crescent-shaped sori.—Spores mature all year.

Blades of the leaflets undulate or unevenly crenulate.   1. *M. reticulatum.*
Blades of the leaflets sharply serrate.   2. *M. serratum.*

1. M. reticulatum (L.) Sw. Rootstock stout, fleshy, decumbent, clothed with reddish-brown scales: leaves 3 m. long or less; petioles stout, stramineous above the brown base, with thin brown scales or becoming naked; blades elliptic-lanceolate or somewhat deltoid in outline, not narrowed at the base, the leaflets numerous, 1–4.5 dm. long, the blades narrow, linear-lanceolate, narrowly elliptic or lanceolate, acuminate, sometimes abruptly so, undulate or crenulate, those of the lower leaflets, at least, short-stalked, and commonly bulblet-bearing in the axils: sori very numerous, broadly linear to elliptic, as broad as the space between the primary veins or nearly so, ultimately often confluent.—Everglade hammocks and cypress swamps, S. pen. Fla.—(*W. I., Mex., C. A., S. A.*) —Fig. reduced.

This fern as developed in Florida represents the descendents of the second invasion of tropical vegetation north of the Gulf Stream. When established on the later tropical area or the Everglade Keys, being a lowland fern, it evidently found congenial habitats in the Everglades and spread northward to the Okeechobee Region. It was commonly distributed in the southern part of the Everglades and the Big Cypress Swamp. Its late discovery in our range and the present lack of knowledge of its real abundance is due to the fact that the region where it grows was long inaccessible and still is, to a great extent, but unfortunately vast areas of its habitats have been destroyed by fire. It was discovered in Florida in 1903,[1] having been found independently at two localities that year, the one on the western coast, near Everglade, and the other on the eastern coast, near Miami. The plant is widely distributed in the West Indies and on the tropical American mainland. This is one of our largest ferns and an epiphyte at that. In habit the leaves somewhat resemble those of the genus *Acrostichum.* The plants usually grow on cypress-knees, to which the rootstocks cling above high-water mark. The original specimens came from the West Indies and were named in 1759.

2. M. serratum Cav. Rootstock stout, mostly horizontal, clothed with brownish or reddish scales: leaves usually 1.5–2 m. long; petioles
[1] First collected in Florida by J. E. Layne, spring 1903.

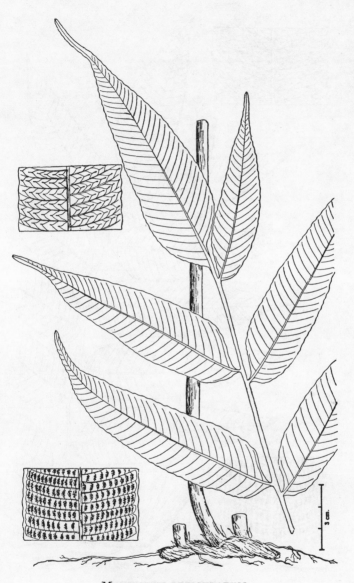

MENISCIUM RETICULATUM

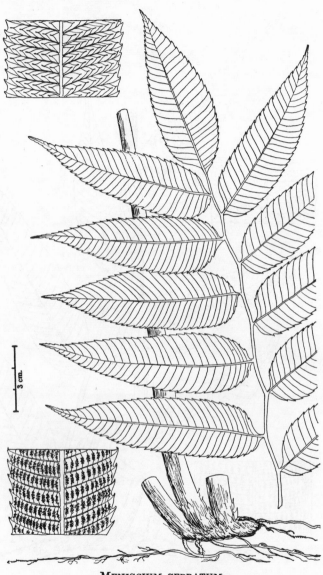

3 cm.

MENISCIUM SERRATUM

stout, often pale-stramineous above, usually sparingly scaly near the
base, at least when young; blades broadly lanceolate to elliptic-lanceolate or deltoid-lanceolate in outline, slightly narrowed at the base, the
leaflets numerous, 1–2.5 dm. long, the blades narrowly lanceolate to
linear-lanceolate, mostly acute, sharply serrate, otherwise as in *M. reticulatum:* sori very numerous, linear-arcuate, usually confluent.—Pond-
apple hammocks, about Lake Okeechobee, Fla.—(*W. I., Mex., C. A.,
S. A.*)—Fig. reduced.

The prehistory of this large fern may be stated as was that of the
preceding species, but it apparently proved itself a better traveller and
became abundant in the deep swamps of the Lake Okeechobee Region.
Whether this or the preceding species of *Meniscium* came into our range
from tropical America first, we do not know. This species, although
found in Florida later than the preceding, is apparently the more abundant of the two. It occurred in the vast and almost impenetrable
pond-apple hammocks which once comprised many thousand acres along
and near the southern shores of Lake Okeechobee, only fragments of
which are now left, and it may be expected in the hammocks on some
of the larger Everglade islands. It was not discovered in Florida until
1912,[1] nearly nine years after the preceding species was first found
in the state. The original specimens came from Cuba and were named
in 1803.

32. GONIOPTERIS Presl.

Small or medium sized, wood or rock plants with short erect or somewhat elongate horizontal rootstocks. Leaves often clustered, erect,
spreading, or drooping, rather tender, long-petioled, sometimes dimorphic: petioles more or less stramineous, sometimes scaly at the
base: blades 1-pinnate, the leaflets coarsely toothed. Veins more or
less branching and some joined to form a few areolae. Sori borne on
the backs of the veins: indusia wanting.—Several species, mainly tropical.—The name is Greek, alluding to the angles made by the joining of
the veins.

1. **G. reptans** (J. F. Gmel.) Presl. Rootstock short, mostly erect or
ascending: leaves clustered, spreading, arching, or procumbent, often
rooting at the tip or along the rachis, about 1–9 dm. long; petioles slender, yellowish, glabrous or with very fine scales; blades ovate to lanceolate, oblong-lanceolate or linear-lanceolate in outline, softly pubescent
with simple and branched hairs, 1-pinnate, the leaflets several to many,
the blades thin, crenate or crenate-pinnatifid, sometimes broad, sometimes narrow, those bearing sori usually much narrower than those with-

[1] First collected in Florida by J. W. Harshberger, January 22, 1912.

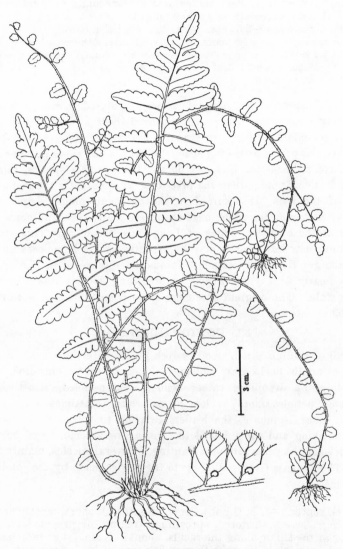

3 cm.

GONIOPTERIS REPTANS

out them, the lobes rounded or obtuse: veins simple, the basal ones of adjoining segments united, the resulting vein running into the sinus: sori
rather few, medial or nearly so: indusia wanting or vestigial. [*Polypodium repens* Sw. not Sw. Prodr. 130. 1778. *Polypodium reptans* J.
F. Gmel. *Dryopteris radicans* Maxon, not L.]—(CREEPING-FERN.)—
Hammocks and grottoes, usually in rocky places or lime-sinks, pen. Fla.
—(*W. I., Mex., C. A., S. A.?*)—Spores mature all year.—Fig. reduced.

The creeping-fern has been a traveller far beyond its creeping ability,
which moreover stands it well for maintaining itself when once established in one of its rocky habitats. Its first long journey was from the
West Indies to the ancient tropical area in northern peninsular Florida.
In the tropic fern region of Citrus, Sumter, and Hernando Counties it
almost invariably grows under overhanging rock faces, in grottoes,
sinks, and very similar rock formations. It seems to prefer a drier
habitat than any of our other rock ferns. There the leaves hang pendent and very often take root at the tip. The leaves are variable in
size and shape, some being short and blunt, others elongate and acuminate. Its second journey from the south was to the southern tropical
area, the Everglade Keys. The greatest development of this fern observed during our studies was in the Goodburn hammock on the Everglade Keys. There the lime-sinks are very shallow and exposed to the
sunlight, altogether a combination that one would not expect to be conducive of the growth of this fern. However, it was there that an excep-
tionally fine development was once observed and in many places the
rocks were densely and deeply carpeted with the leaves, most of which
had also rooted at the tip and were thus giving rise to new plants.
The species was first found in Florida in 1883[1] in the northern part of
the peninsula. It is widely distributed in the West Indies and in continental tropical America. It was named in 1791.—A form with uniform
leaves has been named *Goniopteris reptans conformis*.

33. THELYPTERIS Schmidel.[2]

Rather slender, typically wood, marsh, or bog plants. Leaves erect
or nearly so, or sometimes spreading, usually clustered or colonized on
the rootstock, often dimorphic, not evergreen in regions of frost: petioles not jointed to the rootstock, slender, usually scaleless or nearly so:
blades narrow or broad, 1-pinnate, the leaflets membranous, herbaceous,
or papyraceous, pinnatifid, the segments usually entire or crenate.
Veins usually simple or once-forked, the tips running to the margin or

[1] First collected in Florida by J. Donnell Smith in 1883.
[2] Text prepared by Robert P. St. John.

near it. Sori nearly or quite orbicular, borne on the back of the somewhat modified leaf-blade or a division of it. Indusium orbicular or
reniform-orbicular, attached near the center. [*Aspidium* Sw. in part.]
—SHIELD-FERNS.—About one hundred species of wide geographic distribution. The genus is based on *Acrostichum Thelypteris* L.—The
name is Greek, meaning female-fern.—Spores mature in spring and fall
or all the year southward.—For notes on varieties and forms, see Am.
Fern Jour. 26: 94–99. 1936.

Rootstock, petiole, rachis, and bases of costae not shaggy with long, fine,
    reddish scales.
    Basal veins of adjacent leaf-segments running
      toward or into the sinus, but not united.   I. THELYPTERIDES.
    Basal veins or a pair of veins uniting in the
      tissue below the sinus, the resulting vein
      running into the sinus.   II. DENTATAE.
Rootstock, petiole, rachis, and bases of costae
    shaggy with long, fine reddish scales.   III. SUBMARGINALES.

I. THELYPTERIDES

Leaf-blades conspicuously narrowed at the base, the lower leaflets more or
    less reduced in length and widely spaced.
    Rootstock erect or decumbent: leaflets very
      numerous, minutely and softly fine-pubes-
      cent on the midrib on both sides, the lower
      ones with much enlarged basal segments.   1. *T. panamensis.*
    Rootstock horizontal: leaflets relatively few,
      pilose on the midrib on both sides, the
      lower ones with slightly enlarged basal
      segments.   2. *T. noveboracensis.*
Leaf-blades not conspicuously narrowed at the
    base, but the lower leaflets sometimes
    slightly shorter than those above.
    Sori medial or supramedial.
      Veins of the foliage leaves forked or with
        simple ones intermixed.   3. *T. Thelypteris.*
      Veins of the foliage leaves simple.
        Leaflets not conspicuously widened at
          base.
          Leaflets short, elliptic, with few
            segments.   4. *T. macilenta.*
          Leaflets elongate, linear, with many
            segments.
            Without a conform terminal
              leaflet; most segments long-
              est toward the base of the
              leaflet.   9. *T. augescens.*
            With a conform terminal leaf-
              let; most segments longest at
              the middle of the leaflet.   10. *T. Serra.*
          Leaflets conspicuously widened at base.
            Rootstock erect.   11. *T. patens.*
            Rootstock horizontal.   12. *T. unca.*
    Sori marginal or submarginal.
      Leaflets more or less elliptic in outline.
        Usually more than five pairs of veins
          to a segment: leaf-blades with short
          pinnatifid tips.   5. *T. simulata.*

Usually fewer than five pairs of veins
to a segment : leaf-blades with elon-
gate pinnatifid tips.   8. *T. saxatilis.*
Leaflets not elliptic in outline.
Rootstock more or less succulent and
branched,   producing   scattered
leaves : leaflets mostly approximate.   6. *T. ovata.*
Rootstock woody, simple, producing
leaves in a distichous series :
leaflets mostly separated.
The lower two pairs of leaflets conspicuously narrowed at their
bases ; segments   separate
more than two-thirds to
midrib.
Texture thin : leaflets not distant, the lowest leaflets some-
what reduced.   6a. *T. ovata Harperi.*
Texture firm ; leaflets distant,
the lowest leaflets scarcely re-
duced.   9a. *T. augescens*
                                                     Lindheimeri.

The lower two pairs of leaflets not
conspicuously narrowed at their
bases ; segments separate not
more than two-thirds to midrib.   7. *T. normalis.*

II. DENTATAE

Leaf-segments with rather numerous veins : sori
thus approximate or contiguous and ultimately
confluent forming a continuous medial row on
each side the midrib.   13. *T. gongylodes.*
Leaf-segments with few veins : sori separated, not
confluent.
Leaf-blade not terminating in a lobe distinct
from the lateral leaflets.
Mature leaflets light-green : petiole and
rachis light-stramineous : basal veins
meeting near the sinus.   14. *T. versicolor.*
Mature leaflets dark-green : petiole and
rachis reddish : basal veins meeting
considerably below the sinus.
Lower leaflets not much reduced.   15. *T. dentata.*
Lower leaflets, few or several, much
reduced and more or less auriculate.   16. *T. reducta.*
Leaf-blade terminating in a lobe separated
from the lateral leaflets by a distinct stalk.   17. *T. tetragona.*

III. SUBMARGINALES

Rootstock large, erect, high-crowned ; petiole-
bases nearly straight ; leaves ascending and
arching.   18. *T. submarginalis.*

1. **T. panamensis** (Presl) E. St. John. Rootstock stout, erect, at
least partly so, 2–4 dm. high, sparingly scaly : leaves in a close crown,
up to 1.5 m. long, erect or nearly so ; petioles short below the rudimentary leaflets, scaly at base ; blades lanceolate above the narrowed
base ; leaflets very numerous, firm-membranous, sessile, usually contiguous except the lower ones, the blades narrowly lanceolate from a
broader base to linear-lanceolate, acuminate, deeply pinnatifid, the
middle ones 7–12 cm. long or rarely more, the lower ones greatly re-

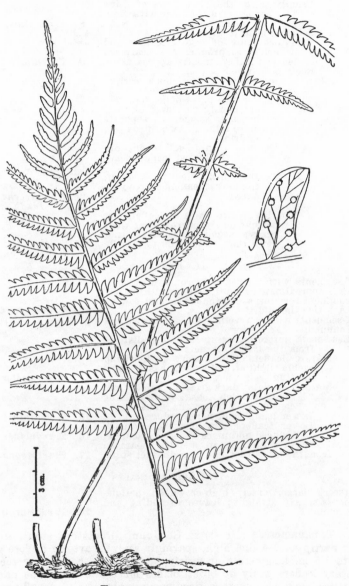

THELYPTERIS PANAMENSIS

duced, hastate and auriculate, distant, the segments obtuse, oblique, strongly revolute and falcate, entire, the basal ones decidedly enlarged: veins simple, in 7–9 pairs, oblique: sori submarginal, scarcely confluent: indusia minute, ovate-reniform, glandular and slightly pilose, evanescent. [*Dryopteris contermina* of most authors, in part.]—Swamps and wet hammocks, lower Oligocene Island region, pen. Fla.—(*W. I., Mex., C. A., S. A.*)—Fig. reduced.

One word describes the habit of this fern, *i.e., plumose.* The erect or nearly erect cluster of narrow elongate pinnate leaves makes it a different object from our other wood-ferns. It is one of our rarer plants. Its distribution in Florida renders it a puzzle. Did it first appear north of the Gulf Stream a pioneer to the ancient Oligocene Island area or did it come with the second invasion of tropical vegetation to the Everglade Keys? Today its distribution lies in or near the water-shed of the Peace River. Considering the southward flow of the river, one would naturally be inclined to consider it a very early pioneer, and that the plant followed the river valley southward as even the climate of the ancient tropical area proved too inclement for its growth northward. It was first found in Florida only near Fort Meade, where it was collected in 1881.[1] In more recent years it has been found at several localities in the middle part of the peninsula. The plant is quite characteristic on account of its long and narrow leaves with a small gland on the rachis below each leaflet and the greatly reduced and distant lower leaflets. This fern has a counterpart in the more elevated plant provinces north of Florida, namely *Thelypteris noveboracensis.* Like the latter plant its leaves are very tender and sensitive to frost. Continental and insular tropical America is the true home of this fern. Florida represents an outlying station to which the species migrated long ago. The original specimens came from Panama and were named in 1825.

2. **T. noveboracensis** (L.) Nieuwl. Rootstock slender, wide-creeping, somewhat scaly: leaves erect, mostly 3–6 dm. long; petioles rather long; blades lanceolate or elliptic-lanceolate, tapering both ways from near the middle, long-acuminate; leaflets membranous, the blades lanceolate or linear-lanceolate, sessile, long-acuminate, deeply pinnatifid, pilose on the midribs and veins, especially beneath, 3–7 cm. long, the lower ones gradually shorter, distant, and deflexed, the segments flat, oblong, obtuse, entire or crenate, the basal often slightly enlarged: veins simple, or those of the basal lobes forked, in 4–8 pairs: sori submarginal, not confluent: indusia minute, delicate, glandular.—(NEW YORK FERN.)—Rich woods, bogs, ravines, and moist pastures, various provinces, Ga. to Ark., Minn., Ont., and Newf.—Fig. reduced.

[1] First collected in Florida by J. Donnell Smith in 1881.

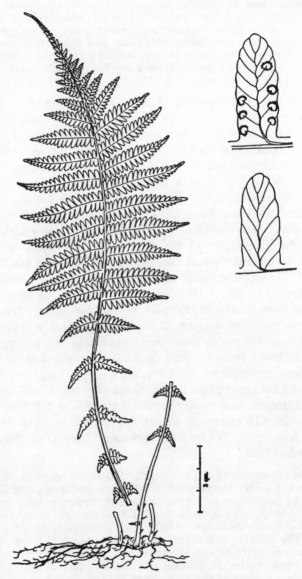

THELYPTERIS NOVEBORACENSIS

For some reason comparatively few ferns have states for name-sakes. In the range of this work there are nine species, exclusive of fern-allies, distinguished by state names. These states are Florida (one), Alabama (three), Louisiana (one), Virginia (three), and New York (one). In addition, one of our ferns is named for Panama and another for a minor geographic area, the Bay Biscayne region in southern Florida. Linnaeus inaugurated the geographic designation of species by states by the publication of the fern under consideration and also *Lycopodium carolinianum*. This shield-fern is characteristic of the inland and more elevated plant provinces, and occurs as high as 5000 feet in the Blue Ridge. It may be recognized at once as it is the only small *Thelypteris* in this range which has very much reduced and distant leaflets on the lower part of the rachis. Although it is curiously unlike its large counterpart in the Coastal Plain of peninsular Florida, *Thelypteris panamensis*, the technical characters that separate the two relatives are slight. The original specimens of *Thelypteris noveboracensis* are said to have come from Canada. The species was named in 1753.

3. **T. Thelypteris** (L.) Nieuwl. Plants more or less colonized; rootstock rather slender, horizontal and widely creeping, black, glabrous or nearly so: leaves erect, 1.5 m. long or less, in colonies; petioles slender, glabrous or nearly so, purple or purplish toward the base; blades lanceolate or elliptic-lanceolate, with the rachis glabrous, or finely pubescent, short-acuminate; leaflets membranous, numerous, the larger ones 4–8 cm. long, the blades lanceolate to linear-lanceolate, slightly acuminate, sessile, or nearly so, pinnatifid, the segments ovate to ovate-lanceolate or ovate-elliptic, obtuse, more or less revolute: veins once-forked or twice-forked: sori about medial, numerous, sometimes slightly confluent: indusia small, delicate, glabrous. [*Acrostichum Thelypteris* L. *T. palustris* Schott.]—(MARSH-FERN.)—Marshes, swamps, bogs, damp woods, and ditches, various provinces, Fla. to Tex., Man., Ont., and N. B.—(*O. W.*)—Fig. reduced.

Various ferns show the results of environmental experiences in the past ages. There are great differences in their geographic distribution. The area occupied by some species is vast; that of others is very localized. The former may represent a species that has reached its maximum development in geographic distribution, while the latter may be a species that has had its maximum geographic development long ago and is now on the wane, or it may be just starting on its career. How many ferns have thus reached their acme and then gradually passed out of existence we shall never know. The present fern is distributed in

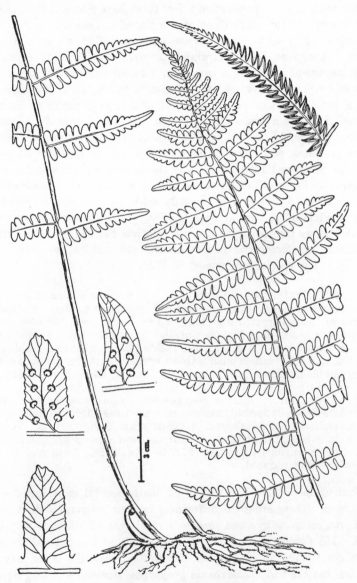

THELYPTERIS THELYPTERIS

Europe and in North America. In Atlantic North America it ranges from southern Florida to southern Canada, reaching the 2500-foot contour in North Carolina. It is not among those ferns, paired as it were, that have a counterpart southward or northward as the case may be. It is somewhat distinctive among ferns of similar habit by its general port, but it may be known definitely by its forked veins in foliage leaves. The original specimens were from Europe and were named in 1753. It seems to produce sporophyls very rarely in the winter in Florida.

4. **T. macilenta** E. St. John. Rootstock horizontal: scales numerous, small, of similar appearance on rootstock, lower petiole, and croziers, glossy, lanceolate with clasping bases and long, brittle tips, with numerous setae which are deciduous, simple and stout, with about fourteen longitudinal slender opaque septa and moderately translucent lumina commonly four times as long as broad and having truncate rather than acute ends: leaves few, clustered, erect, 1.5–5 dm. long; petioles stramineous, finely pubescent with pale hairs, copiously scaly at the base; blades narrowly elliptic to elliptic-lanceolate in outline, acuminate at the tip, like the rachis sparingly pilose, grayish-green, herbaceous; leaflets 10–20 pairs, the blades elliptic or nearly so, decidedly narrow toward the base, 1–3.5 cm. long, slightly separated or somewhat spaced on the lower part of the rachis, mostly spreading or slightly ascending on the upper part of the rachis and strongly deflexed below the middle, pinnatifid, with the midrib (and the midvein) of the segments often sinuous, the segments irregular in length, separate two-thirds toward the midrib, mostly ovate, obtuse, entire, the basal segments somewhat reduced and the distal basal segment somewhat broadened, with the sinus open, acute and but very little callous membrane: veins only 2–4 pairs in a segment, simple, oblique, the proximate basal vein entering the apex of the sinus, the distal one entering side of sinus much above the apex: sori very few, usually 2 or 3 to a segment, medial: indusia sparingly pilose.—Rocky places, Annuttalagga Hammock, Oligocene Island region, Fla.—Fig. reduced.

A colony of three or four plants of this interesting fern was found in Annuttalagga Hammock, near Brooksville, Florida, in 1934.[1] Intensive search in this area for two years has failed to discover additional plants. The associates of the colony are *Thelypteris versicolor* and *T. normalis*. It represents a very distinct species and seems to have no close relatives in continental North America. The species was named and described in 1936.

5. **T. simulata** (Davenp.) Nieuwl. Plants more or less colonized: rootstock slender, widely creeping, sparingly if at all scaly: leaves

[1] Discovered by Edward P. St. John, May 6, 1934.

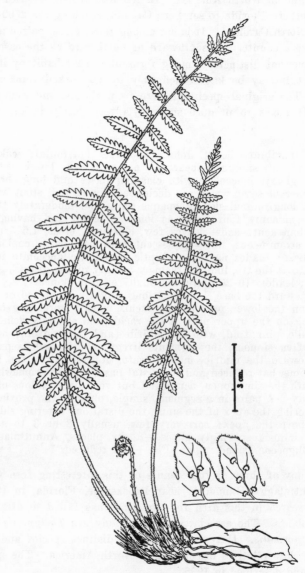

THELYPTERIS MACILENTA

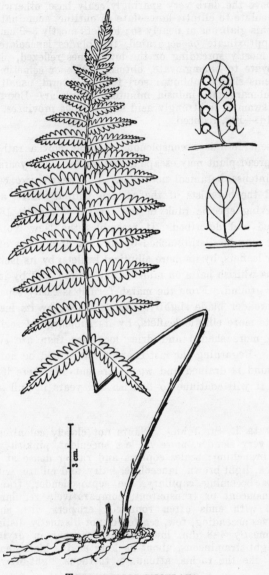

THELYPTERIS SIMULATA

erect, mostly 3–11 dm. long, sometimes clustered; petioles slender, stramineous above the dark very sparingly scaly base, otherwise glabrous;
blades lanceolate to elliptic-lanceolate in outline, acuminate at the tip,
like the rachis glabrous or nearly so; leaflets mostly 3–9 cm. long, membranous, approximate or separated, the blades lanceolate to elliptic-
lanceolate, mostly spreading or the lower ones reflexed, pinnatifid, the
segments ovate to oblong-ovate, obtuse, entire or sometimes obscurely
crenate: veins simple, oblique: sori few to several, usually 4–12 on a
segment, submarginal: indusia minutely glandular.—Bog-fern.—Moist
woods and swamps, in strongly acid soil, various provinces, Ala. to Pa.,
Me., and Md.—Fig. reduced.

The present fern is a conspicuous example how a rather abundant
and wide-spread plant may escape attention for many years in a region
of rather intense botanical activities. For nearly two centuries this
fern eluded the botanists of the eastern United States, at least as a
plant deserving specific rank in the ferns. Not until 1894 was this
plant named and described. It resembles the New York fern very
closely, but may be distinguished by its lack of a series of greatly reduced lower leaflets, by its more elliptical leaflets, by its lack underneath
of numerous whitish hairs on midribs and costae, and by its preference
for moister ground. From the marsh fern it is easily separated by its
relatively broader blade slightly reduced below, by its lack of forked
veins, by its more elliptic leaflets, by its submarginal sori, and by its
growing in more shaded and drier locations than are suited to the
marsh fern. Regarding the last character it should be noted, however,
that if ground is drained and woods are cut off where it has become
established it will continue to flourish for years in full sun and dry
ground.

6. **T. ovata** R. St. John.[1] Plants not closely colonized: rootstock
horizontal, very slender, more or less succulent, pinkish when young,
repeatedly branching: scales copious and rather dense at the apex of
the rootstock, light-brown, lanceolate, hairy and ciliate, with attenuate
twisted tips becoming capillary, the septa slender, translucent, the
lumina translucent or transparent, comparatively regular in outline,
broad, and with ends often rounded: croziers with short-stemmed
glands: leaves ascending, few, scattered, not distinctly distichous on the
rootstock, mostly 4–8 dm. long, often fragrant in drying; petioles
slender, bright-stramineous, about as long as the blade, having on the
upper part like the rachis, attenuate, tortuous, light-brown deciduous

[1] *Thelypteris* **ovata** R. St. John, sp. nov., rhizoma furcata, tenue: folia
dispersa: lamina ovata, apice abrupte acuminato-caudata: pinnae diver-
gentes; pinnae infimae ad basem angustae, deflexae: sori parvi, submarginales.—In colle lapidose ad Lecanto, Florida, Martio 26, 1934, R. P. St.
John, typus in herb. Hort. Bot. Noveboracensis.

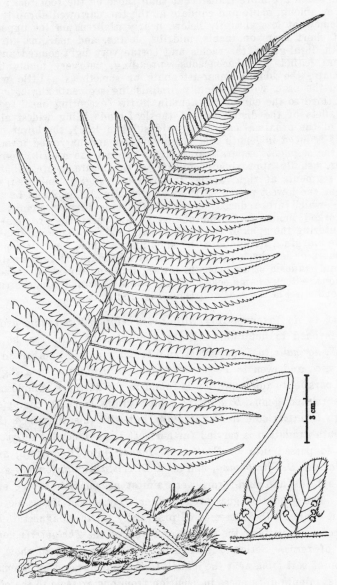

3 cm.

THELYPTERIS OVATA

scales, which are more translucent than those on the rootstock; blades ovate or oblong, acute and caudate at the tip, narrowed abruptly above and somewhat less abruptly below, nearly glabrous on the upper side, except short hairs on rachis, midribs, costae, and margins, hirtellous beneath, light-green, the rachis and costae very light-colored and very slender; leaflets thin-herbaceous, spreading, not very numerous, approximate, the blades linear-attenuate or sometimes a little widened toward the base, with gradually diminishing segments throughout the distal third to the end of the acuminate tip (excepting basal segments the leaflets of the distal half of the leaf-blade being widest at base, those of the proximal half being widest at middle), the lower pair of leaflets reduced in length and much reflexed and narrowed toward the base, the segments separate four fifths toward the midrib, numerous, slender, usually approximate, falcate or subfalcate, acute, ciliate, the basal segments at right angles to costa and slightly enlarged, except those of the lowest pair of leaflets—especially the proximal basal segments—which are reduced or wanting: veins usually simple, rarely once-forked, moderately prominulous, in 5–8 pairs, the proximal basal vein entering the apex of the slender, obtuse sinus, the distal one reaching the margin a little above the apex of the sinus, the pair separated by a more or less keeled cartilaginous membrane: sori few, small, submarginal: indusia stramineous to brown, thin and somewhat evanescent, hirtellous.—Rocky hammocks and lime-sinks, Coastal Plain, central pen. and northern Fla. to Ala. and Ga.—Fig. reduced.

What to do taxonomically with the *Thelypteris normalis* group of ferns is hard to determine. Every gradation of form can be found from *T. normalis* to *T. augescens* and *T. Serra* and in another direction to *T. unca* and even to *T. versicolor* and *T. dentata*. To a slight extent a parallel to this condition is found in the northern spinulose ferns of the related genus *Dryopteris*, which grade from *D. campyloptera* through *D. intermedia* to *D. spinulosa*, but with this difference, that in the South gradation is carried further. It is as if northern *Dryopteris spinulosa* passed into *D. Boottii*, *D. Boottii* into *D. cristata*, and *D. cristata* into *D. Clintoniana*, and as if *D. cristata* × *Clintoniana* and the other hybrids and mid-forms were almost as common as the specific types. The gradation goes even further. By almost insensible differences it connects the extremes of practically all the diagnostic characters used in describing the species or forms of the *Thelypteris normalis* group of ferns. Series of specimens can be arranged to show every position of sori from near the midrib to the margins and in like manner the most minute differences in venation from one extreme to the other—and so with structure and habit of rootstock, shape of blade, leaflets, segments, color, texture, structure of scales, and pubescence.

Such conditions present an interesting problem. Perhaps the warm humid climate and the rock-filled soil of Florida and other similar regions facilitate fertilization and stimulate fertility so favoring repeated hybridization in susceptible groups, or in some other way set in motion processes that nature uses when species are making. However that may be, persistent field study has brought to notice more intergrading forms in this group than it is wise to attempt to describe.

In this text only those intermediate forms have been described which possess distinctive characters of recognized taxonomic importance, which have one or more characters carried to an extreme within the group, which are conspicuous because of frequency of occurrence and comparative stability, which occur in widely separated localities, and which have been found somewhere in nearly pure stands. Such a fern is *Thelypteris ovata*. It lies between *T. augescens* and *T. normalis*. Its characteristic rounded, broad blade with spreading or radiating approximate leaflets—a compromise between the abruptly reduced *T. augescens* and the more or less lanceolate *T. normalis*—is found in most of the rocky hammocks and on most of the shaded stony hills in central and northern Florida. Its segments are more deeply cut and more falcate than those of either *T. normalis* or *T. augescens*. The rootstock is slender and succulent and in the typical form branches erratically, scattering the petioles, rather than producing them in a bilinear series as do its closest relatives. *Thelypteris ovata* does not thrive in tangled masses as *T. normalis* and *T. augescens* often do. Although *T. ovata* is abundant over a wide area it is described in this text for the first time. The type specimen, in the herbarium of The New York Botanical Garden, was collected on a rocky hill at Lecanto, Florida, March 26, 1936; similar specimens were collected in Metz's Grotto, five miles southeast of Floral City, Florida, January 20th, 1935, Robert P. St. John 362.

6a. T. ovata Harperi (C. Chr.) R. St. John. This plant is related to *T. ovata*, but as Christensen's description is incomplete[1] and the cited specimens differ among themselves in several characters, it is not possible to make a close comparison of *T. ovata* and *T. normalis Harperi*. The most obvious distinction between the two probably lies

---

[1] *Dryopteris normalis Harperi* "Lower pair of pinnae rather reduced and, like the following pair conspicuously narrowed toward the base, the upper basal segment still not very reduced. Pinnae incised nearly to rachis, the segments oblique, acute, the edges often revolute. The basal anterior vein only runs to sinus, the posterior one reaching the margin about 1 mm. above sinus. Sori small, near the edge; indusium subglabrous."— C. Chr. Vidensk. Selsk. Skr. VII. **10** : 182, 1913.

in the habit of growth of rootstock and leaves, in the reflexion and greater reduction of the lower pairs of leaflets, and in the position and structure of scales.

7. **T. normalis** (C. Chr.) Moxley. Plants colonized: rootstock woody, horizontal, bearing leaves in a distinct bilineal series on the sides, the apex sparsely covered with scales: scales thin, lanceolate or linear-attenuate, castaneous, setose, and ciliate, having slender, not very prominent half-opaque septa and short and broad translucent lumina which are unequal in size with angular ends: leaves erect or ascending, mostly 8–15 dm. long; petioles about as long as the blades, moderately scaly at the purplish arcuate base; blades elliptic-lanceolate to ovate-elliptic in outline, more or less gradually narrowed to a short, pinnatifid apex, a little narrowed below, medium-green, decidedly pubescent throughout and glandulose beneath; leaflets numerous, herbaceous, horizontal or slightly ascending, the blades about even in width except the attenuate, serrate tip, or rarely tip gradually becoming entire, the lower ones more or less reflexed but little reduced in length, and in some forms slightly narrowed toward the base, especially on the proximate side, the segments lanceolate to elliptic, obtuse or obliquely acutish, separate about two thirds toward the midrib, not falcate, revolute only when senescent, usually ciliate, the basal segments not much enlarged, the proximate one usually forming an angle of 45° with the rachis: veins in 7–10 pairs, simple, except rarely in basal segments of very large specimens, very oblique, not prominent, the proximal basal one entering the apex of the sinus (which has little or no cartilaginous membrane), the distal basal vein reaching the margin slightly above the apex: sori numerous, close, supramedial to submarginal: indusia somewhat persistent, pilose.—Hammocks, moist woods, cypress-heads, lime-sinks, bluffs, gullies, and ditches, Coastal Plain, Fla. to Tex. and S. C.—(*W. I.*)—Fig. reduced.

Even before Carl Christensen in 1910 distinguished and named this fern, G. S. Jenman called attention to its creeping underground root-stock "upon which the fronds are arranged in a bilinear series." As Christensen observed, this character is usually sufficient to distinguish it from the ferns that most resemble it except *Thelypteris augescens.* From the latter it may be separated by its much thinner texture, more gradual distal narrowing of the blade, broader segments, broader leaf-lets, and lack of persistent scales on the rachis. There are, nevertheless, intergrading forms, for *T. normalis* has a wide range of variability.

Its tendency to depart from typical form may be due partly to its extensive habitat and geographic range. It is the most widely distributed wood-fern of Florida. It grows in nearly all the hammocks of the mainland, but perhaps not on the Florida Keys. It occupies the

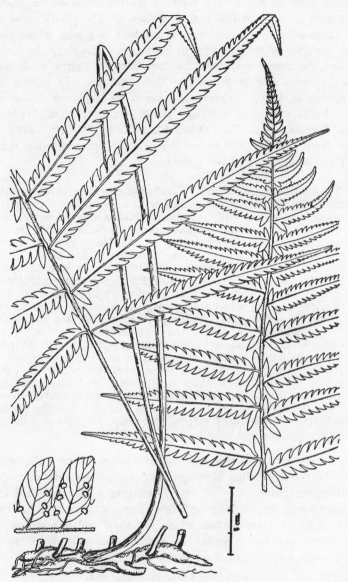

THELYPTERIS NORMALIS

hammock floor as well as the sides of the lime-sinks and flourishes in the borders of fields and in roadside ditches. The plants occur singly or in large crowded colonies and thrive best in glades where the sun strikes the floor of the hammock at least part of the day. In favorable locations the leaves may measure four feet in length while on dry rocks specimens may be found less than foot tall. In distinguishing this species in 1910, Christensen based it on *Aspidium patens* D. C. Eaton, Ferns of North America, *pl. 70* (in part) and *Nephrodium patens* Jenman, Bull. Bot. Dept. Jam. II. 3: 165 (in part) [*"N. patens* Desv.*"*]. In 1913 he reverses his citation and takes the Jenman plant as the type of the species.

8. **T. saxatilis** R. St. John.[1] Plants not closely colonized: rootstock slender, decumbent, the apex clothed with brown scales: scales lanceolate, setose, and ciliate with translucent lumina of various shapes and sizes and somewhat opaque septa: leaves clustered on the rootstock, erect or ascending; petioles as long as the blade, slender, light-stramineous, scaly near the base, pilose near the blade; blades 7–15 cm. long and 3–7 cm. wide, lanceolate or ovate-lanceolate in outline, broadest a little below the middle, tapered slightly below and gradually above into an apex that extends through one third or one half of the length, whitish-pilose beneath and on the margins, midribs, and rachis, light-green, herbaceous; leaflets spreading or ascending, the blade elliptic below, elliptic-lanceolate above, the tips entire and obtuse, the segments few, broad, oblique, separate about one half toward midrib, the basal segments mostly parallel to the rachis and rarely enlarged: veins not prominent, simple, 2 to 5 pairs, the proximate basal vein entering the apex of the sinus below which is a pilose short keeled cartilaginous membrane, the distal vein reaching the margin considerably above the apex: sori relatively large and near the margin: indusia persistent, whitish-pilose.—Cliffs, rocky slopes, lime-sinks, throughout Fla. except the Keys.—Fig. reduced.

Depauperate unfruited specimens of *Thelypteris normalis* may frequently be found growing in sun or half shade in crevices of rock and with them sometimes a similar fern which may be distinguished by the presence of sori, by the long leaf-tip—often nearly as long as the rest of the blade, by lower leaflets which are short and nearly oval, by a short obtuse and entire leaflet-tip, and by decidedly fewer pairs of veins in segments. All of these distinctions except the presence of sori

[1] *Thelypteris* **saxatilis** R. St. John, sp. nov., saxatilis, rhizoma breve, decumbens: folia fasciculata, apicibus acuminato-caudatis longitudine dimidian vel tertiam partem laminae aequantibus; pinnae lanceolatae vel elliptico-lanceolatae, apicibus integris: venae 2–5-jugae; sori magni submarginales.—In lapidosis, Suwanee River, Ellaville, Florida, R. P. St. John, Novembri 12, 1934, typus in herb. Hort. Bot. Noveboracensis.

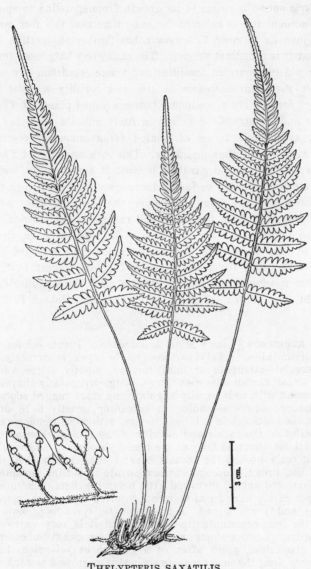

3 cm.

THELYPTERIS SAXATILIS

are curiously like the characters of a juvenile stage through which *Thelypteris normalis* passes in its growth from sporeling to sporophyte. On this account it was believed for some time that this fern was a precocious juvenile form of *T. normalis*, but further observation has indicated that it is a distinct species. The characters have been found constant in widely separated localities and where conditions are unusually favorable the plant increases in size and fertility without material change of form. The resemblance between young plants of *Thelypteris normalis* and *T. saxatilis* does not in itself indicate that they are not distinct, as juvenile forms of related ferns commonly resemble one another more closely than do adults. This rock associate of *Thelypteris normalis* has been called *saxatilis* because it has thus far been found only in crevices of rocks or in soil thoroughly filled with rock particles. It has been collected from cliffs along the Suwanee River near Ellaville, Florida, and from lime-sinks and ravines in central pen. Florida. It is here described for the first time. The type specimen, in the herbarium of The New York Botanical Garden, was collected on rocks along the Suwanee River at Ellaville, Florida, Robert P. St. John, 86. Other specimens are Falling Waters near Chipley, Florida, Small & Knight, Dec. 5 and 6, 1934; Goulds, Florida, Robert P. St. John, 1613.

9. **T. augescens** (Link) Munz & Johnston.. Plants colonized: rootstock horizontal or nearly so, woody, the apex moderately clothed with lanceolate-attenuate or linear-tortuous stoutly setose and ciliate scales: scales castaneous with large, long, irregularly-shaped translucent lumina with ends usually angular, and stout rugged septa opaque when mature: leaves ascending or spreading, mostly 6–18 dm. long, borne on the rootstock in a bilineal series, with more slender and translucent scales on the rachis and midribs of the leaflets than on the rootstock; petioles about as long as the blades, brownish, moderately stout, somewhat scaly toward the arcuate base; blades usually 4–10 dm. long and 2–5 dm. broad, lanceolate or lance-ovate in outline, acuminate, abruptly narrowed above, narrowed little below; leaflets numerous, sessile (the upper rarely have basal segments inserted on rachis), mostly 6–24 cm. long and 1 cm. broad, linear-attenuate, spreading, more or less curved, the long-acuminate tip serrate until it is very narrow thence finally entire, glabrous above except midribs, somewhat pubescent below but not glandulose, green often of a grayish or yellowish shade, the texture very firm, the lower leaflets somewhat narrowed toward the base and little reduced, the segments separate usually about two-thirds toward the midrib, subfalcate often revolute, the basal segments somewhat elongate: veins simple, prominent, in 5–10 pairs, the basal ones entering the apex of the acute sinus separated by a short callous mem-

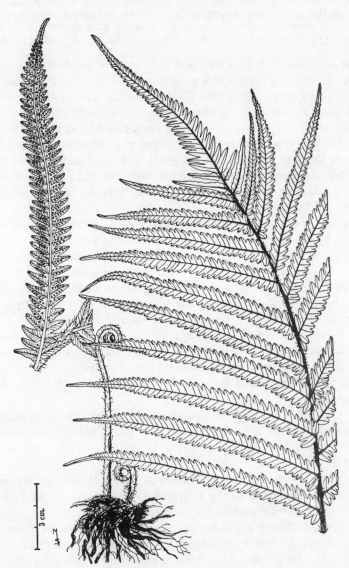

3 cm.

THELYPTERIS AUGESCENS

brane or the distal basal vein reaching the margin slightly above the apex of the sinus: sori supramedial: indusia persistent brown, setose: sporangia dark-brown.—Hammocks, rockpits, and stony bluffs, Everglade Keys to central pen. Fla.—(*W. I., Mex., C. A.*)—Fig. reduced.

The characters of *Thelypteris augescens* have not been well understood. Link's description was so broad that it apparently included *T. normalis* and other forms that have since been distinguished. Kunze wrote a very clear definite description[1] of the species but later when Christensen distinguished *T. normalis* from allied ferns his emphasis on intergrading forms that could be referred to *T. augescens* caused many students to place with the latter a great variety of material that might have been assigned elsewhere. Consequently one will get very little aid toward obtaining a clear conception of the type by turning the sheets in most herbaria.

Typical *Thelypteris augescens* differs from *T. normalis* by the firmer texture, by the more prominent veins, by the long scales on the rootstock with rugged setae, by persistent small scales underneath the rachis and costae, by the narrower leaflets with slender approximate subfalcate segments, by a more extensive adnation of the basal segments of the upper leaflets to the rachis, by the blade's narrowing abruptly into a pinnatifid apex, and by a preference for sunnier dryer locations.

It differs from typical *T. Serra* by the latter's having a conform terminal leaflet, by *T. Serra's* still firmer texture, slenderer leaflets more narrowed toward the rachis, more prominent veins, more veins connivent to the sinus, and by its different rootstock and habit of producing leaves.

In spite of *Thelypteris augescens* being a well-defined species, the student in the field is likely to find many plants that grade between it and *T. normalis* or toward *T. Serra* before he sees one that is truly typical.

This fern was first found in Florida in 1915. It is at its best on the floor of the hammocks in the Everglades, where leaves eight feet long with slender narrow leaflets hardly more than half an inch wide and over a foot in length are not unusual. A tangled mass of these large plants covering from a square rod to a quarter of an acre of a rocky glade in the jungle is a remarkable sight. One would think that such a fern would, like some of the aspleniums, wait a generation or more before appearing where improvements had exposed bed rock. Such is not the case. In the northern part of its range *Thelypteris augescens*

[1] See Gustav Kunze, Die Farrnkräuter, 134, *pl. 59.*

in one of its forms is found most frequently on the sides of lime-sinks and abandoned phosphate mines. Where excavations have been made most ferns must wait until the growth of trees has brought shade, but *T. augescens* is one of the first to establish itself in such artificial locations. When it grows in full sun, it not only fruits more freely but it clings closer to type and its texture becomes more leathery and its leaflets narrower and more twisted. The type specimens came from Cuba and were named in 1841. Originally the type locality, in error, was recorded as Caracas, Venezuela.

9a. T. augescens Lindheimeri (A.Br.) R. St. John. Christensen in discussing the forms that lie between *Thelypteris normalis* and *T. augescens* says: ''The form from Texas called *Dryopteris normalis* var. *Lindheimeri* seems to show that we have only one very variable species, which should be named *D. augescens,* but on the other hand it is unnatural to unite in a single species the typical forms of *D. normalis* and *D. augescens.*'' He placed subspecies *Lindheimeri* under *D. normalis* and described it as below.[1] This subspecies is here placed with *T. augescens* not only because of its close structural relationship but also because it shows a preference for drier sunnier locations than are favored by *Thelypteris normalis* and thus is often associated with *T. augescens* or with forms closely resembling it. It is not a very distinct variety, for specimens are seldom found that conform to all characters of the type. It is best recognized by its distant and often opposite leaflets which commonly produce a long blade of unique appearance. Ferns of this aspect, but evidently allied in other respects more or less closely to *Thelypteris augescens,* *T. normalis,* *T. ovata,* and *T. ovata Harperi,* are common throughout the area adjacent to the northern coast of the Gulf of Mexico.

10. T. Serra (Sw.) R. St. John. Plants colonized: rootstock moderately stout, woody, creeping, the apex and bases of petioles clothed with linear castaneous scales: scales with translucent lumina usually fusiform in outline, 4–10 times as long as broad, opaque, narrow septa and few spreading crooked setae and cilia; hair-like scales, with only 2 or 3 rows of lumina nearly as wide as long frequently on veinlets, margins, and indusia: leaves scattered and more or less distant on rootstock, erect, 7–20 dm. long; petioles about as long as the blades, shortly

---

[1] *Dryopteris normalis Lindheimeri* A. Br. "pro specie sub *Aspidio,* ms. Intermediate between typical *D. normalis* and *D. augescens,* and some specimens could as well be referred to the latter. It differs from *D. normalis* type by the firmer texture, the more distant and often opposite pinnae, the lower ones scarcely reduced but distinctly narrowed towards their base as in the preceding variety [*Harperi*] and in *D. augescens;* segments acute, often subfalcate; veins generally somewhat prominent beneath, the two lower ones meeting at sinus: sori near to the edge; in some specimens some few small scales are found on the costae beneath, quite as in *D. augescens,* from which species it differs by its broader pinnae, and by its lamina not being so abruptly narrowed upwards."—C. Chr. Vidensk. Selsk. Skr. VII **10**: 182. 1913.

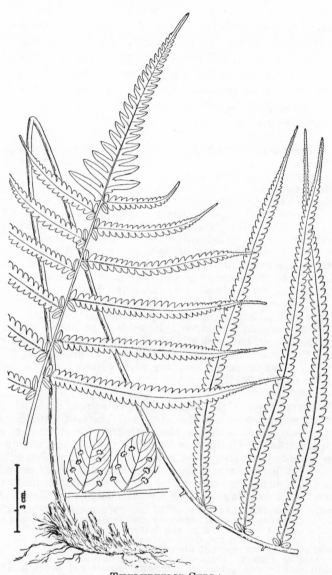

THELYPTERIS SERRA

arcuate at base, deeply sulcate anteriorly, stramineous or brown, glabrous above when mature; blade 1-pinnate, oblong, 3–10 dm. long, excepting terminal leaflet, little narrowed above and still less narrowed below, light-green to olive-green, coriaceous or stiffly leathery, glabrous above except rachis and costae which have few hairy scales and are puberulous by short hairs often furcate at top, densely woolly-pubescent beneath; leaflets sessile, spaced, oblique or spreading, narrowly linear-attenuate, of uniform width in the typical form except those of the lower third of the blade which are narrowed toward their bases, often only 6–8 mm. wide and 6–25 cm. long, with elongate attenuate tip serrate with diminishing segments to the end, more or less twisted, the lowest leaflets narrowed like adjacent leaflets toward base and scarcely reduced in length, the terminal leaflet conform or broader having at base unequal entire lobes often asymmetrically elongate on one side the rachis with branched veins, the segments oblong-triangular, acute and usually revolute, separate at the middle of the leaflet about half-way to the costa but less deeply cut toward the ends of the leaflet, the basal segments conform with adjacent segments except on the upper leaflets where distal basal segments are inserted on the costa distant 2–3 mm. from the rachis while proximal basal segments are adnate to the rachis or are inserted on the rachis 2–3 mm. below the costa (in atypical forms basal segments are often slightly enlarged): veins 5–10 pairs, simple, slightly arcuate, the basal veins very arcuate, 2–4 connivent to the apex of the sinus—frequently two proximate reach the apex of the sinus but the second distal enters the side of the sinus slightly above the apex; sinus patent, the callous membrane translucent (often deeply keeled when foliage is revolute): sori large, medial, with sporangia dark-brown or black when mature: indusia changing from blue-gray to stramineous to reddish-brown, persistent, pubescent with hair-like scales and simple long white hairs with no glands. [*Polypodium Serra* Sw. *Dryopteris Serra* Kuntze.]—(PARCHMENT FERN.)—Dry or moist rocky banks often in sun. Southern pen. Florida.—(*W. I.*) —Fig. reduced.

This fern was named in 1788 from specimens brought from the West Indies where it is fairly common on moist rocky banks. It was first found in Florida by Gertrude Peterson in 1934 growing with *T. augescens* in full sun on the sides of a rock-pit in the outskirts of Miami and was thought to be an extreme form of *T. augescens*. The basal segments of the Florida plants are not so much reduced nor is the terminal leaflet so strictly conform as is usual among West Indian specimens. Ferns that lie between *T. Serra* and *T. augescens* have been collected in several sections of southern Florida but none close to type have been reported elsewhere than at the original station.

11. **T. patens** (Sw.) Small. Rootstock stout, erect or very nearly so, the apex and bases of petioles clothed with large ovate scales:

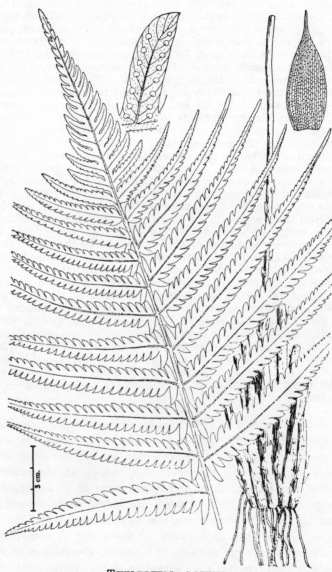

THELYPTERIS PATENS

scales light-brown, entire, and glabrous, having frequently 40 or more nearly opaque, slender, fairly continuous longitudinal septa and small nearly transparent lumina rectangular or varying in form: leaves fasciculate, erect or usually arching, 1.5 m. long or less; petioles stout, arising straight from the rootstock, stramineous, quadrangular when dried, scaly at base, deciduously hairy, often a little shorter than the blade; blades oblong to lanceolate in outline, abruptly short-acuminate, slightly narrowed below, more or less softly pubescent and glandular beneath, dark-green, firmly membranous: leaflets numerous, spreading, or the lower ones somewhat shortened and deflexed, the blades linear-attenuate, all broadest at base, the tips acuminate with gradually diminishing segments or somewhat repand near the end; the segments linear to linear-oblong, long-falcate or long-subfalcate, acutish, often revolute, separate about two-thirds toward midrib, the basal segments of the lower leaflets considerably enlarged, parallel to the rachis or turned from it at a slight angle, the anterior often auricle-like, sometimes incised: veins simple, 8–15 pairs, the basal ones decidedly arcuate, entering the apex of the sinus separated by a cartilaginous membrane: sori medial or supramedial: indusia persistent, light-brown, deciduously pubescent. [*Polypodium patens* Sw. *Aspidium patens* Sw. *Aspidium stipulare* Willd. *Dryopteris stipularis* Maxon.]—On limestone, Ross Hammock, Everglade Keys, Fla.—(*W. I., Mex., C. A., S. A.,*)—Fig. reduced.

In spite of the fact that the West Indian *Thelypteris patens*, through indefinite taxonomy and misidentification, has been considered a widely distributed fern in the Gulf States, it is a very rare plant even in Florida. Its occurrence in our area is based on a single plant collected from a limestone crevice in Ross Hammock near Silver Palm Schoolhouse [near Naranja P.O.], Florida.[1] Careful search throughout the state and especially south of Miami has failed to rediscover it. This is not to be wondered at since a leaf of the Eaton collection seems to duplicate in many characters leaves of *T. unca* and some forms of *Thelypteris normalis*. The Florida specimen without rootstock could scarcely be identified were it not for the scales which cling to the base of the petiole. An examination of the rootstock, were it available, would also show at a glance that the plant was *T. patens* and not *T. normalis*. The leaves of the latter arise more or less arcuately from a horizontal rootstock while those of *T. patens* grow in a crown straight up from an erect rootstock. The scales of *T. patens* differ from those of *T. unca* and *T. normalis* in lacking cilia and setae, in being much broader, and in having finer and more uniform reticulations. In the West Indies *Thelypteris patens* grows frequently

[1] First collected in Florida by A. A. Eaton, February 1905.

in moist thinly shaded situations in company with *T. panamensis*. The original specimens were collected in Jamaica, W. I., and named in 1788.

12. **T. unca** R. St. John.[1] Rootstock decumbent or frequently horizontal, with fibrous rootlets, the apex covered with large lance-ovate scales. Scales light-brown, stoutly setose, ciliate, having broad, long, irregular translucent lumina and 15–25 longitudinal translucent septa: leaves 7–10 dm. long, clustered or arising irregularly along the rootstock, but not distichous, erect or arching; petiole not longer than the blade, terete, deciduously pubescent; blade lanceolate or lance-oblong in outline, acuminate, slightly narrowed below, usually broadest at the third leaflet from the base, minutely glandulose and whitish-pilosulous beneath, very dark-green, the texture firmly membranous, with rachis and midribs light-yellow, prominulous, pubescent above and below: leaflets sessile, somewhat approximate, ascending or falcate, except the lower ones, all except the basal ones broadest at base, with distinct and entire or undulate tip, the basal ones broadest at the middle, little reduced in length and slightly reflexed, the segments separate about two-thirds toward midrib, very oblique, ciliate, falcate, acute, revolute, the basal ones falcate and elongate, usually having branched veins: veins simple, except in basal segments, 6–9 pairs, the basal ones arcuate entering the sinus slightly separated but with little or no callous membrane: sori medial, small, numerous: indusia persistent, ferruginous pilose.— Hammocks, lime-sinks, and thickets, southern and central pen. Fla. —Fig. reduced.

This fern, like *Thelypteris ovata*, is more likely to dot roadsides and hammocks with individual plants than to grow in masses. Its dark-green foliage, clustered leaves, yellow rachis and costae, broad-based, entire-tipped, curving leaflets and falcate segments, help to distinguish it from *T. normalis*. Typical plants of the two species are quite different in appearance, but there are intergrading forms. From *T. patens* it is distinguished by the latter's erect rootstock and finely reticulate scales. When drought turns its edges revolute the long, basal segments take on needle points and curve like scimitars, and the entire plant takes on a skeleton-like appearance. This fern grows in hammocks and on rocky borders in the Everglade Keys south of Miami and it has also been collected as far north as central peninsular Florida. It is described here for the first time. The type specimen, consisting of two sheets, in the herbarium of the New York Botanical Garden, was collected on Costello Hammock, Dade County, Florida, March 28, 1934, by Robert P. St. John, 172.

[1] *Thelypteris* **unca** R. St. John, sp. nov., rhizoma repens, foliis dispersis: laminae acuminatae, ad basem paulo reductae: stipites rachides costaeque straminei: pinnae adscendentes, falcatae, ad basem latissimae, apicibus integris: segmenta falcata, infima longissime: sori inter costam et marginem medii.—Costello Hammock, Dade County, Florida, Martio 28, 1934, R. P. St. John, typus in herb. Hort. Bot. Noveboracensis.

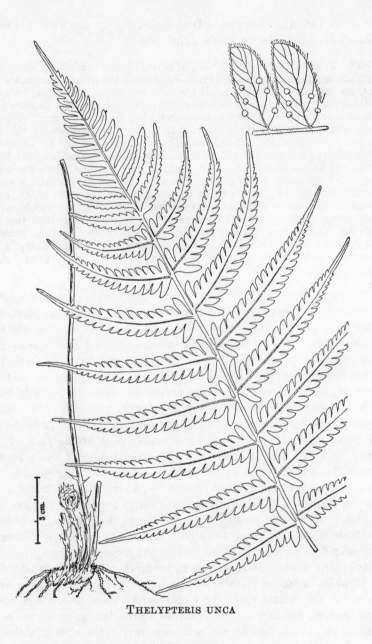

THELYPTERIS UNCA

St. John, 346, A, and B, and at Deep Lake, Big Cypress Swamp, Florida, March 27, 1934, Robert P. St. John, 164.

13. T. gongylodes (Schkuhr) Kuntze. Rootstock widely creeping or horizontal, branching, cord-like, black except the green tip: scales lacking on rootstock; but on rachis and costae minute scales stoutly setose, with broad, loosely-stranded irregular septa, and elliptic or hexagonal, translucent lumina: leaves not clustered but in colonies, erect or reclining, 2 m. long or less; petioles pale-brown, or purplish at the base, naked or nearly so; blades lanceolate often narrowly so to oblong-lanceolate, dark-green, 1-pinnate: leaflets 3 dm. long or less, the blades linear to linear-lanceolate, thick, more or less lustrous, often coriaceous, on short minutely scaly stalks, coarsely crenate or pinnatifid usually separated less than half way to the midrib, the segments ovate, or triangular by the revolute margins: veins 7–17 pairs, the basal ones of adjoining segments united, the resulting vein running into the apex of the sinus: sori copious, medial or nearly so: indusia glabrous. [*Nephrodium unitum* R. Br.]—Low hammocks, marshes, damp woods, swamps, and cypress swamps, pen. Fla.—(*W. I., Mex., C. A., S. A., O. W.*)—Fig. reduced.

There is great latitude in the robust and feeble growth among our ferns. Some species growing in wet soil rich in humus are remarkably vigorous; others with only a crevice of a cliff to exist in are often quite feeble. The present species belongs to the former class. From the extensive tropical plant reservoir this fern may have reached the Floridian tropical area in two invasions and later spread far and wide into all the plant regions of the peninsula. Most of our shield-ferns are high-hammock plants, but the present one grows in marshes, swamps, low praries, and everglade hammocks. It thrives luxuriantly in partly open swamps where water stands most of the year. It will grow in either sun or shade and prefers a tangle of many sorts of vegetation where it can support itself on the underlying growth. The slender widely-creeping black rootstocks, only twice as broad as the strong petioles, will follow ditches into outlying territory and like other marsh ferns of this group gain a footing in dryer ground. Although variable in size, according to habitat, it holds its characters well except young plants growing in shade, which often resemble young plants of *Thelypteris dentata* so closely as to be practically indistinguishable—a fact which indicates close relationship and perhaps a common origin in a not too remote past. Like *Thelypteris augescens* it has narrow firm leaflets, but may be distinguished by its triangular segments and joined basal veins and by the coalescent sori which, a little within the margin, form a line so continuous and uniform as to suggest the stitch-

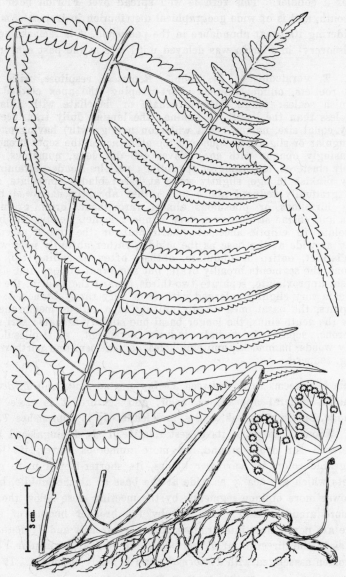

THELYPTERIS GONGYLODES

ing of a cobbler. This fern is well spread over Florida both north and south, and is of wide geographical distribution in tropical America. Considering its great abundance in the peninsula, it is remarkable that its discovery[1] in Florida was delayed until late in the past century.

14. T. versicolor R. St. John.[2] Rootstock cespitose, with many small rootlets, obliquely erect, short-creeping, the apex clothed with brownish scales: scales linear-attenuate or flagellate with cilia and setae less than the length of lumina; the lumina dully translucent of nearly equal size, narrow, (but wider on new growth) having one end rectangular or slightly oblique and the other acute, the septa broad and increasingly opaque with age: leaves 4–8 dm. long, numerous, often densely clustered, ascending or spreading; petioles slender, stramineous, rarely pinkish in age, slightly scaly at base; blades lanceolate, somewhat gradually reduced above and rather abruptly narrowed below, thinly hirtellous or pilosulous almost throughout, bright-green, the rachis and costae stramineous, very slender: leaflets sessile, the blades lanceolate to elliptic-lanceolate, horizontal or the upper ascending, nearly as wide at the base as the middle, rather abruptly narrowed to the distinct, entire or undulate, obtuse, often ascending tip, membranous, the segments broadly ovate, but somewhat oblique and slightly acutish, approximate, separate two-thirds toward the midrib, the basal segments very slightly enlarged with veins very rarely branched: veins 4–6 pairs, the basal ones usually uniting in a callous membrane just below the acute sinus, the longer basal one slightly arcuate: sori small, numerous, separated, medial: indusia persistent, short-pilosulous.— Rocky woods, hammocks, and sink-holes, central pen. and northern Fla. —Fig. reduced.

This fern seems to lie between *Thelypteris normalis* and *T. dentata*. In habit, general appearance, color, and texture it is close to *T. normalis*, but in rootstock, scales, and leaflet-tip it approaches *T. dentata*. From *T. dentata*, its closest relative, it is distinguished by its preference for drier ground, its more numerous leaves, its lighter changeable color, its narrower blades, its shorter-tipped more obtuse leaflets which are nearly as wide at the base as at the middle, by the narrower more oblique segments, by the meeting close below the sinus of more arcuate basal veins, and by the broader lumina of scales. There are neverthless intergrading forms between it and *T. dentata* as well as in the direction of *T. normalis*. In central peninsular Florida it is often associated with *T. normalis* and is fairly abundant. It seems

[1] First collected in Florida by C. E. Faxon in 1873.
[2] *Thelypteris* **versicolor** R. St. John, sp. nov., rhizoma breviter repens: folia multa dense caespitosa: laminae angustae, pallide virides vel flavae: stipites straminei: pinnae lanceolatae vel elliptico-lanceolatae: venae infimae infra sinum in proximas anastomosantes.—Brooksville, Florida, Decembri 17, 1934, R. P. St. John, typus in herb. Hort. Bot. Noveboracensis.

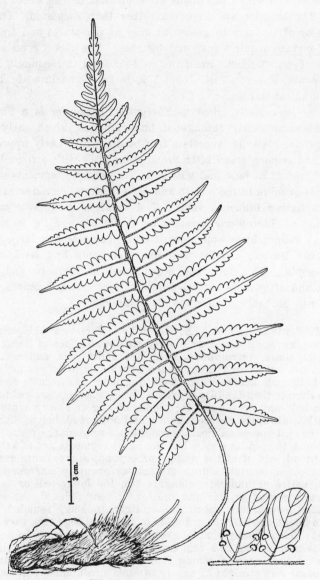

3 cm.

THELYPTERIS VERSICOLOR

to thrive as well where the woods are somewhat dry as where they are moist. The colonies are dispersed rather than congested. Its light-green color often turns to golden or gray as it matures and frequently the leaf-surface acquires rusty-red blotches. The rachis remains light-colored. Type specimens are from well-shaded rich hammock, Brooks-ville, Florida, Robert P. St. John, 109, in the herbarium of The New York Botanical Garden.

More or less closely allied to *Thelypteris versicolor* is a dimorphic fern, pubescent nearly throughout but glandless, which early in the season produces sterile lanceolate leaf-blades with closely approximate leaflets and segments and later broad sporophyls with sori medial and leaflets broadest at base and with long very oblique segments separate two-thirds or more to the midrib and with elongate incised-serrate basal segments having branched veins. The venation irregularly resembles either that of *Thelypteris normalis* or *T. dentata* and the large scales, somewhat unique, have long crooked cilia and setae and large unequal transparent lumina, usually with one end acute and bordered with rugged septa. This fern has been found in northern and central Florida, and after more extensive observation, unless it proves to be a hybrid, will probably require specific standing.

15. T. dentata (Forsk.) E. St. John. Rootstock obliquely erect, short-creeping, stout, the apex clothed with scales; scales linear-attenu-ate or flagellate, ferruginous, with few short cilia and setae, with dully translucent lumina rarely twice as wide as the septa and usually having both ends acute: leaves 6–12 dm. long, fasciculate, ascending; petioles shorter than the blade, scaly at base, when mature reddish from the base half-way up the rachis; blades oblong or oblong-ovate in out-line, rather abruptly reduced above and narrowed below, thinly hir-tellous or pilosulous almost throughout, very dark-green; leaflets chartaceous, the blades sessile but the basal segments not adnate to the rachis, broad, widest at the middle or beyond, approximate except the lower ones, horizontal, elliptic-lanceolate, abruptly narrowed to the distinct, entire or undulate, elongate tip, the lower one or two pairs somewhat resduced in size and the lowest pair reflexed, the segments very close, sometimes imbricate, straight, oblong, rounded, ciliate, separate about one-half toward midrib, the basal segments very slightly enlarged: veins usually simple, except in basal segments, in 6–9 pairs, the basal ones uniting in a vein excurrent to the acute, linear sinus, but which may end before reaching it or the short callous membrane, the longer basal vein straight or nearly so: sori small, numerous, separated, medial: indusia persistent, short-pilosulous. [*Polypodium dentatum* Forsk. *Polypodium molle* Jacq, *Dryopteris parasitica* Kuntze.]—Rocky, moist woods, hammocks, and ditches. Fla. to Ala., and La.—(*W. I., Mex., C. A., S. A., E. I., China, Japan, and Hawaii.*)—Fig. reduced.

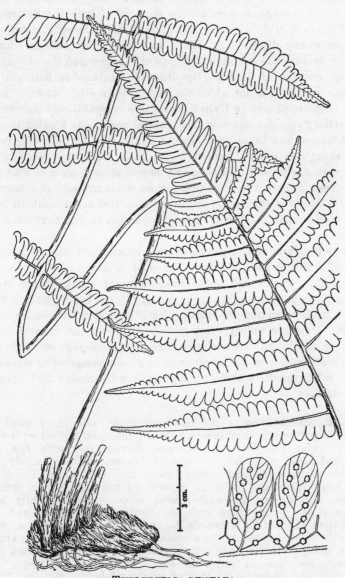

THELYPTERIS DENTATA

Thelypteris dentata, or a species of fern closely resembling it, has been found throughout considerable portions of both the Eastern and the Western World. Scarcely any other fern of the southeastern flora is more widely distributed. While specimens from foreign countries vary in details, they maintain the typical venation and the very characteristic contour of leaflet. Despite the considerable habitatal and climatic variation under which the fern lives in other lands, it is confined in the southeastern United States to a comparatively narrow strip of territory that extends only from central peninsular Florida to southern Alabama and Louisiana. In this range it seems to prefer reasonably moist rich soil adjacent to rock. It is found frequently in company with *Thelypteris tetragona* around well shaded edges of lime-sinks. Sometimes it chooses to grow in a row on the shady side of a large log. It takes kindly to cultivation and is often planted about southern homes. This species was named in 1775 from specimens said to have come from Arabia.

There is a form of *Thelypteris dentata* which has much of the appearance of a hybrid with *T. unca.* The color is dark yellowish-green and texture thin; rachis and costae stramineous or yellow; blade broadly lanceolate in outline, slightly or not at all reduced below; leaflets broadest at base, ascending or falcate; leaflet-tips elongate, entire or undulate; segments oblong, very obliquely-tipped, the basal segments elongate and broad: veins simple except in basal segments, the basal veins indifferently united at sinus or in a vein excurrent to sinus: sori small, submarginal: scales with slightly broader lumina that are usual in *T. dentata.*

16. **T. reducta** Small.[1] Rootstock cespitose, with many small rootlets, obliquely erect, short-creeping, stout, the apex clothed with scales. Scales linear-lanceolate or flagellate, ferruginous, with few short cilia and setae, with dully translucent lumina which are rarely twice as wide as the septa and usually having both ends acute: leaves 7–15 dm. long, fasiculate, erect or ascending; petioles shorter than the blades, dark-stramineous and reddish when mature, slightly scaly: blades slightly dimorphic with the fertile blades taller and more erect than the sterile, lanceolate to ovate-lanceolate in outline, rather abruptly reduced above to the acuminate apex, and gradually narrowed below, thinly hirtellous or pilosulous almost throughout, very dark-green,

[1] *Thelypteris* **reducta** small, sp. nov., folia caespitosa, fertilia quam sterilia majora et erectiora : laminae sensim ad basem reductae : stipites roseatis laminis breviores : pinnae inferae distantes auriculatae : venae infimae anastomosantes in venam ad sinum excurrentem.—Inter Bowling Green et Fort Green, Florida, Decembri 11, 1934, E. P. St. John, R. P. St. John, Wm. A. Knight, J. K. Small, typus in herb. Hort. Bot. Novebora-censis.

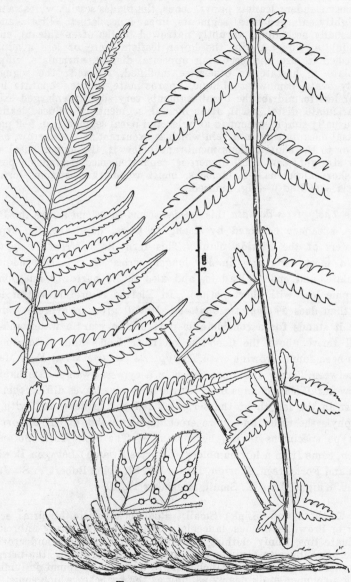

THELYPTERIS REDUCTA

the rachis pinkish when mature, except at the tip, the costae stramineous, very slender; leaflets papyraceous, the blades sessile, widest across the slightly enlarged basal segments, linear-lanceolate to elliptic-lanceolate, usually ascending, abruptly narrowed to the often falcate, entire or undulate, elongate tip, the lower leaflets more or less gradually diminished in size and becoming opposite, distant, auriculate, elliptic-lanceolate to hastate or otherwise modified, reflexed; the segments broadly ovate, somewhat oblique, approximate, ciliate, separate halfway or less to midrib, the basal segments very slightly enlarged except the auriculate, distal, basal, often incised, segments of reduced leaflets; veins usually simple, except in auricles and basal segments, in 5–9 pairs, the basal ones uniting in a vein which is excurrent to the narrow, acute sinus or to the short callous membrane below it, the longer basal vein nearly straight; sori small numerous, separated, medial: indusia persistent, short-pilosulous.—Hammocks, moist woods, and swamps, central pen. Fla.—(*China.*)—Fig. reduced.

Like *Thelypteris dentata* this species seems to extend across the Pacific. A specimen collected by Tsang in China duplicates the typical characters of the Florida plant. This fern differs from *Thelypteris dentata* most strikingly in its longer series of reduced, modified, auriculate, and spaced leaflets, and also in its narrower and longer dimorphic leaf with short petiole. In Florida it prefers wetter locations than does *Thelypteris dentata*. It will grow in cypress swamps where it stands for a considerable part of the year in water and yet it will thrive above the flood-line on river banks and in hammocks. It has been found growing with *Thelypteris panamensis* at Fort Meade and between Torrey and Fort Green in a cypress swamp. Its habit is to grow in tall close clumps in which the numerous leaves differ from one another in the length of the series of reduced leaflets, and with the sporophyls the taller and more erect, being to this extent dimorphic. The type specimens in the herbarium of The New York Botanical Garden, came from a low hammock (Cypress Swamp) between Bowling Green and Fort Green, Florida, Edward P. St. John, Robert P. St. John, Wm. A. Knight, John K. Small, December 11, 1934.

17. T. tetragona (Link) Small. Rootstock horizontal, firm: scales amber or brown, caducous, lanceolate with long (but rarely unbroken) acuminate tips, thinly clothing the apex of the rootstock and croziers, and occasionally also found on the petiole and the rachis, the margins ciliate with dendroid, 3–5 branched hairs (rarely also found on lumina) having a common stalk nearly as long as the branches which sometimes are again branched; the small translucent lumina vary in size but are usually 2–4 times as wide as the heavy opaque septa and are rarely more than 2–3 times as long as wide, with ends usually oblique: leaves

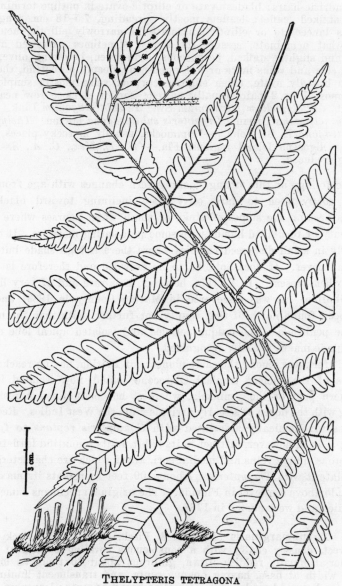

THELYPTERIS TETRAGONA

few, erect, 4–9 dm. tall; petioles quadrangular, hirtellous with stellate or dendritic hairs; blades ovate or elliptic-ovate in outline terminating in a stalked leaflet: leaflets mostly spreading, 7.5–18 cm. long, the blades lanceolate or elliptic-lanceolate to narrowly elliptic, acute or somewhat acuminate, sessile, the lowest sometimes narrowed at the base and slightly stalked, herbaceous, livid-green, becoming olive, with the rachis and veins more or less pubescent, deeply pinnatifid, the segments broadly ovate, often slightly curved: veins mostly simple, the lowermost 1 or 2 pairs usually united: sori in a close row near the midrib. [*Polypodium tetragonum* Sw. *P. subtetragonum* Link. *Dryopteris tetragona* Urban. *Dryopteris subtetragona* Maxon. *Thelypteris subtetragona* E. St. John.]—Hammocks, usually in rocky places, limesinks, Oligocene Island regions, Fla.—(*W. I., Mex., C. A., S. A.*)— —Fig. reduced.

The foliage of this strange-looking fern changes with age from pellucid soapy-green to dark olive-green inclining toward black. It grows best on the slopes of sinks or small water courses where there is plenty of rock-filled humus with some percolating moisture. It occurs usually in small dispersed colonies where there is high shade but little ground cover. It does not like to be crowded and therefore is easily seen when present. In Florida, however, it is rare and of very limited distribution. It was discovered in Marion County in 1883[1] and has not been found north of that county nor further south than the middle of the peninsula. The unique petioled and isolated apical lobe of the leaf-blade makes it easily recognized.

This fern was among the early pioneers of Florida, having reached the shores of the ancient tropical Oligocene Island, now isolated in the northern part of the peninsula, where it has maintained a residence along with the dozen or so early arrivals from the West Indies. Recently it was taxonomically associated with *Goniopteris reptans* to form a group. It is, however, distinct in its habit, in its pinnatifid leaflets with numerous simple veins and medial sori, all of which are characters that associate it with *Thelypteris*. About 100 feet represents its maximum altitude above sea-level in Florida. The original specimens came from Jamaica and were named in 1788.

18. **T. submarginalis** (Langsd. & Fisch.) Small. Rootstock stout, suberect, densely chaffy with a conspicuous covering of scales: scales slender-attenuate, reddish-brown, glabrous about 30 times as long as their width at base, having opaque septa, and translucent lumina 3–6 times as long as broad and 3–6 times as broad as septa: leaves up to 1.5 m. long, erect or arching, clustered or in colonies; petioles rather stout,

[1] First collected in Florida by Mary C. Reynolds, April 1883.

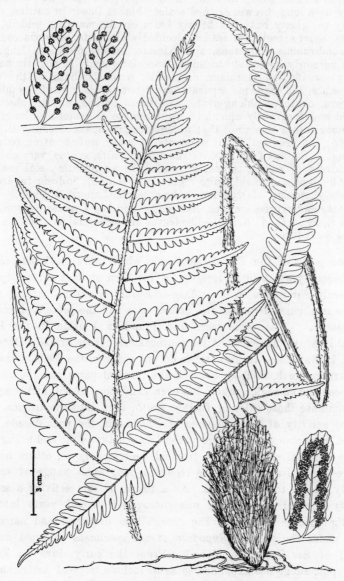

THELYPTERIS SUBMARGINALIS

somewhat stramineous above the straight purplish base, like the rachis shaggy with long, brown, crisped scales; blades linear in outline, often broadly so, glossy but with bristly hairs on the margins, midrib, and veinlets, short-acuminate: leaflets decidedly alternate, subcoriaceous, or firm membranous, numerous, approximate, mostly 6–11 cm. long, the blades narrowly lanceolate to linear-lanceolate, acute or slightly acuminate, pinnatifid, short-stalked or sessile, with the base of the stalk brown-scaly, the segments separate about two-thirds toward the midrib, numerous, ovate to oblong-ovate, sometimes curved, obtuse, obscurely toothed and frequently apiculate, approximate or sometimes longitudinally imbricate with a sinus that widens near its apex, becoming slightly revolute; the proximal basal segments of lower leaflets often reduced, wanting, or distant from rachis: veins 6–12 pairs, simple, very oblique, the midvein of segments usually ending in an apicula; sori median, mostly 9–25 on a segment, quite regularly developed: indusia fugaceous, minutely glandular. [*Dryopteris submarginalis* Langsd. & Fisch.]—Wet hammocks and cypress swamps, Everglades and Big Cypress Swamp, Fla. —(*W. I., Mex., C. A., S. A.*)—The leaves are somewhat fragrant in drying.—Fig. reduced.

Those parts of the Florida peninsula which were most inaccessible until recent years held in reserve for the fern student several species apparently not native in other long-accessible localities. Among these may be mentioned *Dennstaedtia adiantoides* and the present species of *Thelypteris*. These ferns were first found in Florida in the Everglades[1] in a wild hammock at the southeastern corner of Lake Okeechobee in 1926. These tropical types do not occur in the Florida tropics, but further north, midway between the tropical parts and the ancient Oligocene Island region, where however, conditions of soil and temperature simulate those existing further south, even into the tropics. Increased activity of fern students in Florida in the past decade augmented our previous knowledge of the ferns of that state and brought to light additional species—some tropical American types, others new to science—and also enlarged the recorded geographic range of species already known to occur there. As a result of this activity a second locality for this shield-fern was discovered several years later in the Big Cypress Swamp.[2] The species was described and named in 1810, under the genus *Polypodium*, from specimens collected on the Island of St. Catharine, Brazil. From the early days its known geographic range has expanded so as to include tropical American and contiguous regions from Florida and Mexico to Uruguay.

[1] First collected in Florida by J. K. Small and C. A. Mosier, May 14, 1926.
[2] First found in the Big Cypress Swamp by W. M. Buswell, May, 1933.

34. DRYOPTERIS Adans.

Coarse or delicate typically terrestrial wood, frequently humus, plants. Leaves erect, spreading, or drooping, usually clustered on the rootstock, often somewhat dimorphic, mostly evergreen: petioles not jointed to the rootstock: blades narrow or broad, 1–3-pinnate or dissected, the leaflets subcoriaceous or firm-herbaceous, the segments usually toothed, lobed, or pinnatifid. Veins simple or forked, usually free, the tips running to the margin either toward a tooth or a notch but remote from the sinus. Sori nearly or quite orbicular, borne on the back of the unmodified leaf-blade or its divisions, on the veins or rarely at their tips. Indusium orbicular-reniform, attached at the center or at or near the sinus. [*Aspidium* Sw. in part.]—SHIELD-FERNS. WOOD-FERNS.—About two hundred species, of wide geographic distribution.—The genus is based on *Polypodium Filix-mas* L.—The name is Greek, meaning oak-fern.—Spores mature, for the most part from spring–fall. —Our species of *Dryopteris* are predominantly northern ferns.—For notes on varieties and forms, see Am. Fern Jour. 26: 60–69. 1936.

Leaf-blades 1-pinnate or if 2-pinnate the segments toothed.
   Sori submarginal or marginal: indusium thick, tumid.

                                                  I. MARGINALES.

   Sori medial or toward the midrib or toward the
      margin: indusium thin, flat.   II. CRISTATAE.
Leaf-blades 3-pinnate, or if 2-pinnate the segments
   pinnatifid.
   Leaf-segments spinulose-toothed.   III. SPINULOSAE.
   Leaf-segments crenate or crenately lobed.
      Leaf-rachis with many brown or reddish scales:
         leaflet-segments separated: veins and vein-
         lets minutely scaly.   IV. AMPLAE.
      Leaf-rachis glabrous or with few slender white
         hairs: leaflet-segments contiguous or over-
         lapping at the base: veins and veinlets with
         long spreading whitish hairs.   V. SETIGERAE.

I. MARGINALES

Leaves evergreen, the rachis pale, the leaflets coriaceous, pale beneath: scales at the base of the
   petiole long-attenuate.   1. *D. marginalis.*

II. CRISTATAE

Leaf-blades 1-pinnate.
   Sporophyls with the dimorphism between sterile
      and fertile portions slight and gradual
      at maturity.
      Leaf-blades elongate, of a linear or lanceo-
         late type, in outline, the sides parallel
         or bowed.
      Leaf-blades broadly linear to linear-lan-
         ceolate in outline, the sides usually
         nearly parallel: leaflets acute or only
         slightly acuminate.   2. *D. cristata.*

Leaf-blades narrowly or broadly lanceolate in outline, the sides bowed :
leaflets more or less acuminate.

Teeth of the segments more or less
flaring, thus giving the leaflets a
spinulose aspect.   3. *D. Boottii:*

Teeth of the segments directed forward, appressed, or incurved.

Leaflets of the lower pair with
ovate   or   triangular-ovate
blades, those of the upper
ones   lanceolate :   veins   of
the fertile segments usually
branched twice or thrice.   4. *D. Clintoniana.*

Leaflets with blades of a lanceolate type throughout : veins
of the fertile segments usually
branched once.[1]   5. *D. celsa.*

Leaf-blades short and broad, ovate to triangular in outline.

Leaf-blades triangular in outline, broadest at base : veins of the fertile seg-
ments once branched.   6. *D. atropalustris.*

Leaf-blades ovate to obovate in outline,
broadest near middle or thereabouts :
veins of the fertile segments twice
branched.   7. *D. Goldiana.*

Sporophyls with the dimorphism between sterile
and fertile portions abrupt and conspicuous at maturity.

Lower pairs of leaflets slightly reduced in
size : teeth of the leaflets with short hard
spine-tips.   8. *D. australis.*

Lower pairs of leaflets much reduced in size :
teeth of the leaflets obtuse or acute, her-
baceous.   9. *D. ludoviciana.*

Leaf-blades 2-pinnate.   10. *D. separabilis.*

III. Spinulosae

Indusium glandular : leaflets usually at right
angles to the rachis, the lowest pair inequilaterally lanceolate-triangular or ovate-lanceolate,
conspicuously narrowed basally.   11. *D. intermedia.*

Indusium glabrous or nearly so : leaflets oblique
to the rachis, the lowest pair inequilaterally
broadly deltoid, conspicuously widest at
base.

Sori terminal on the veinlets : indusium glabrous : leaflets flat, decurrent : leaf-blade
ovate-lanceolate.   12. *D. spinulosa.*

Sori subterminal on the veinlets : indusium glabrous or with a few glands : leaflets concave,
some of them not decurrent : leaf-blade del-
toid-ovate.   13. *D. campyloptera.*

IV. Amplae

Pale-green fern, the aerial part of the rootstock
erect, densely clothed with bright-red scales. 14. *D. ampla.*

V. Setigerae

Dark-green fern, the aerial part of the rootstock
horizontal or ascending, clothed with dark-brown
scales.   15. *D. setigera.*

[1] An aberrant form of *D. celsa,* with twice branched veins occurs in the
Dismal Swamp.

1. D. marginalis (L.) A. Gray. Rootstocks stout, woody, ascending: scales[1] large, lanceolate, with attenuate tips, shining, chestnut-brown, sometimes slightly darkened at base, glabrous, abundant on apex of rootstock, lower petiole, and croziers, less numerous and smaller on upper petiole, rachis, and leaflet-veins, with slender clearly defined septa of uniform width almost as translucent as the lumina, the latter nearly transparent, usually 3–7 times as broad as the septa and 12–35 times as long as the lumina are broad, having ends commonly rectangular, often shortly and acutely pointed, or rarely rounded or bent: leaves in a crown, up to 1 m. long, evergreen; petioles stout, chaffy and with a dense mass of scales below; blades ovate-oblong or ovate-lanceolate, 1- or 2-pinnate, acuminate, slightly narrowed at the base: leaflets coriaceous, numerous, nearly sessile, glabrous, the blades 5–15 cm. long, the lower unequally triangular-lanceolate, those above lanceolate to oblong-lanceolate; all pinnatifid, with the sinuses reaching nearly or quite to the midrib, the segments oblong or lanceolate, falcate, subentire, crenate, or pinnately lobed, partially adnate or the lowest sessile: sori few to several, distant, 1.5–2 mm. in diameter, borne on the distal branch of a vein far above the fork and thus close to the margin: indusia relatively large, firm, glabrous. [*Polypodium marginale* L.]—(Evergreen Wood-fern. Marginal Shield-fern.)— Rocky woods, hammocks in swamps, and talus-slopes, various provinces, Ga. to Ark., B. C., Ont., and N. S.—Spores mature in summer and fall. —Fig. reduced

This rather elegant fern is frequently an associate of the common polypody (*Polypodium virginianum*), a favorite among fern-students. Consequently it is one of the larger evergreen ferns that the beginner in plant studies is likely to become acquainted with in the field. It may be collected in the winter as well as in the summer. Rocky woods are to its liking. It grows equally well in the rich deep soil of the forest or in accumulations of soil on rock or in crevices of rocks or cliffs. Like its taxonomic associates, *Dryopteris Goldiana, D. cristata, D. Clintoniana,* and *D. ludoviciana,* it is an outstanding fern, both in pattern and in port. The deep-green upper side of the leaf-blade, the pale under side, and mass of bright-buff scales on the lower part of the petiole make the leaf very conspicuous and attractive. This species has a greater south and north distribution than any of its associates, running from the mountains of Georgia into Canada where the original specimens were collected. It was named in 1753.

2. D. cristata (L.) A. Gray. Rootstock stout, creeping: foliage devoid of trichomes, except scales: scales large, ovate below, lanceolate and smaller on the upper part of the plant, dull pale-brown and slightly

[1] Description of scales in the first ten species of *Dryopteris* are by Robert P. St. John.

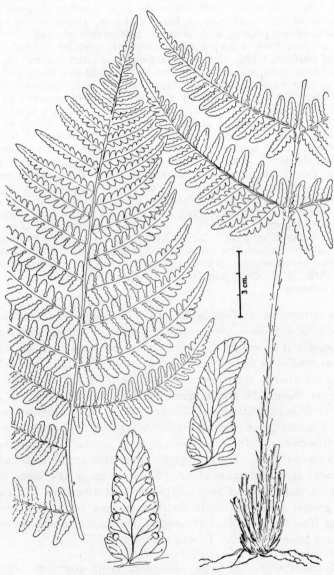

DRYOPTERIS MARGINALIS

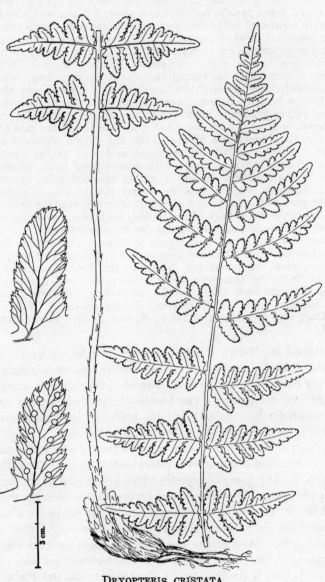

3 cm.

DRYOPTERIS CRISTATA

browner at base, glabrous, imbricate, abundant on apex of rootstock, croziers, and lower petiole, numerous on upper petiole, rachis and leaflet veins, with somewhat indistinct, flat, translucent septa, with translucent lumina, irregular in shape, usually 2–5 times as wide as the septa and 10–30 times as long as the lumina are broad, having ends often rounded, rarely rectangular or acute, sometimes crooked, hooked, forked, or knobbed: leaves erect or spreading, up to 12 dm. long, evergreen; petioles one-third to one-half the length of leaf, stramineous above the base; blades broadly linear, linear-oblong or linear-lanceolate, 20–90 cm. long, rather gradually narrowed to the tip, also gradually narrowed to the base: sporophyl with the greater part fertile in the case of vigorous leaves, the dimorphism of the sterile and fertile segments not conspicuous, the latter relatively as broad and long as the former, the margins of both sharply serrate with spine-tipped teeth, especially at the tips of the segments, the teeth, rather inconspicuous, appressed or directed forward: leaflets opposite nearly throughout, or opposite on the lower part of the blade and alternate above, spreading or ascending especially on the upper part of the rachis, the blades coriaceous, various, those of the lower ones triangular or triangular-ovate, 2.5–5.5 cm. long, those of the upper ones ovate to lanceolate, 6–9 cm. long, all obtuse or acute, broadest at the base by the lengthening of the proximal and distal basal segments: sori borne on the distal branch of a vein above the fork, the two rows about midway between the midrib and margin. [*Polypodium cristatum* L. *Aspidium cristatum* Sw.]—Low woods, swamps, and boggy thickets, various provinces, N.C. to Ark., Sask., Ont., and Newf.—(*Eurasia.*)—Spores mature in summer.—Fig. reduced.

The crested shield-fern stands out from its relatives by the narrow elongate leaf-blade; the leaflets too are smaller, and usually with broad, less deeply cut blades than in related species, the segments being broad and short and not spaced. The blades of the lower leaflets are very broad, sometimes as wide as long; the blades of each succeeding pair of leaflets is reduced in width up to the tip of the leaf.

The plants of this genus in coming down from the primitive ancestral form have travelled along several rather definite lines. These lines are now represented by groups of species which are helpful in the taxonomic study of the genus. These groups are further indicated in the main divisions of the key to the species. The *cristata* group of species with leaves of rather thick or subcoriaceous texture is represented over a wide geographic area. Most of the species prefer more northern regions or the highlands. Only one, *Dryopteris ludoviciana*, not only prefers the lowlands, but is confined to the southeastern Coastal Plain. Curiously enough there is a very close relationship between the species under consideration and *D. ludoviciana*. In fact, although the geographic ranges of the two may meet in the Coastal Plain of North Carolina, specimens from widely separated points, sterile specimens, for example, from Florida (*D. ludoviciana*) and from Ohio (*D. cristata*), are difficult to separate by habit alone, although the Coastal Plain species is much more scaly. The questions suggested are: Did *Dryopteris cristata* and *D. ludoviciana* have a common ancestor? Or is one an offshoot from the other? *Dryopteris cristata* was named in 1753, the name being based on European specimens. The altitudinal range is rather extensive. It can be found in the higher parts of the Blue Ridge and thence out into the Coastal Plain. The crested fern has the narrowest leaf-blade of the *cristata* group.

3. D. Boottii (Tuckerm.) Underw. Rootstock stout, horizontal and ascending at tip: foliage devoid of trichomes, except scales: scales glabrous, thin, ovate-deltoid or broadly lanceolate with short acute tip, imbricate, the larger and longer ones with narrower scales adnate to the base, pale-brown, numerous on apex of rootstock, croziers, and lower petiole, decreasing in number above, smaller scattered scales on rachis and leaflet-veins, the septa of medium width somewhat translucent, the lamina translucent, broad, varying much in shape in different parts of the scale, usually 4–8 times as wide as the septa and 7–18 times as long as the lumina are broad, the sides rarely straight, the ends often knobbed, or rectangular, or obtuse, lapped by irregularly curved ends: leaves erect; petioles one-third to nearly one-half as long as the leaf; blades of sporophyls lanceolate, sometimes narrowly so, to oblanceolate, 40–75 cm. long, acute or acuminate, gradually narrowed to the base, or sometimes scarcely narrowed: sporophyl the upper half usually fertile, abruptly passing into the lower sterile part, with the dimorphism of the sterile and fertile segments not conspicuous, sharply serrate with more or less flaring teeth, the larger teeth often lobe-like with two or more secondary teeth with the tips of spines flaring: leaflets opposite nearly throughout the rachis or sometimes alternate even from the lowest ones, spreading or ascending, the blades slightly coriaceous, various, those of the lower ones inequilaterally triangular-lanceolate, 3–9 cm. long, those of the upper ones lanceolate, sometimes broadly so, up to 13 cm. long, all acute or acuminate, broadest at the base: sori borne on the distal branch of a vein above the fork, medial or supramedial: indusium glandular. [*Aspidium Boottii* Tuckerm.]—(BOOTT'S SHIELD-FERN.)—Low woods, swamps, and moist hillsides, various provinces, N. C. to Ohio, Vt., and N. H.—Spores mature in summer and fall.—Fig. reduced.

Some ferns have had a quiet existence in literature, others like the present one have stirred up controversy. The main disputed points are as to whether or not it is of hybrid origin and its presumable parents. The leaf is intermediate, in many respects, between *Dryopteris cristata* and *D. intermedia*. It stands between the two in shape, texture, and

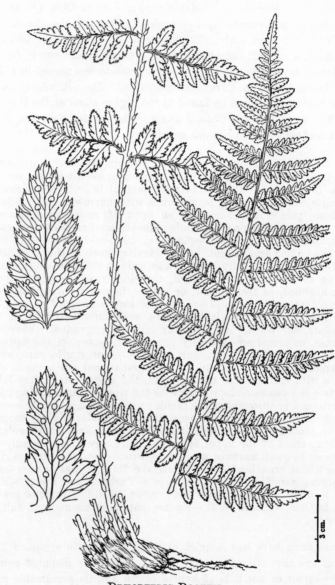

3 cm.

DRYOPTERIS BOOTTII

cutting of the margins. Moreover, these two supposed parents are often associated in the field, at the very place where *Dryopteris Boottii* is found. However, sorus-positionally considered, *Dryopteris Clintoniana* would be a more likely parent than *D. cristata*. This fern was discovered before the middle of the past century and was named in 1843. Later it was made a variety of *Dryopteris spinulosa*, and also considered a hybrid, several alleged parents being involved. At any rate it is an elegant fern with the leaf combining the laciness of the *spinulosa* group and the regular clean-cut form of the *cristata* group, irrespective of its hybrid or non-hybrid origin. Plants referable to *Dryopteris Boottii* have quite regular leaves in regard to the pinnate blades and the cutting of the ultimate leaflets or segments. If a hybrid, it does not show the more or less erratic leaf-forms of other hybrid ferns. A list of described hybrids between species is given at the end of this generic treatment.

4. **D. Clintoniana** (D. C. Eaton) Dowell. Rootstock stout, creeping: foliage devoid of trichomes, except scales and some scurf on the leaflets: scales large, moderately imbricate, broadly lanceolate on the lower part of plant, lanceolate above, dull light-brown, usually darker at base and center, abundant on apex of rootstock, croziers, and lower petiole, less numerous, smaller, and more slender on upper petiole, rachis, and leaflet-veins, with somewhat indistinct flat translucent septa, with rather broad translucent lumina fairly regular in shape, 3–7 times as wide as the septa and 8–35 times as long as the lumina are broad, having ends commonly rounded or obtuse, sometimes rectangular and sometimes linear-attenuate, at the base of the scale frequently crooked, hooked, forked, or knobbed: leaves erect or ascending; petiole one-third to one-half the length of the leaf; blades of sporophyls elliptic to elliptic-lanceolate or elliptic-oblanceolate in outline, 25–80 cm. long, rather abruptly narrowed at the tip, gradually narrowed to the base: sporophyl fertile throughout or in less vigorous leaves only on the upper leaflets, the dimorphism of the sterile and fertile leaflets not conspicuous, the margins of both serrate with appressed somewhat spine-tipped teeth directed forward: leaflets alternate or several of the lower pairs opposite or subopposite, spreading or ascending, blades various, slightly coriaceous, those of the lower ones triangular-ovate, mostly 6–11 cm. long, more or less oblique at the base by the reduction or elimination of the lower proximal segment, those of the upper ones lanceolate, sometimes broadly so, up to 15 cm. long, all acute or acuminate, broadest at the base: sori borne on the distal branch of a vein above the fork, the two rows nearer the midrib than the margin, sometimes with additional irregularly placed ones near the midvein. [*Aspidium cristatum Clintonianum* D. C. Eaton.]—Swamps, low woods, and bogs, various provinces, except the Coastal Plain, N. C. to Wis., Ont., and Me.—Spores mature in summer.—Fig. reduced.

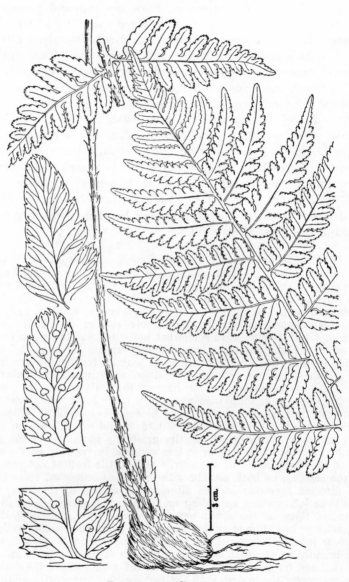

DRYOPTERIS CLINTONIANA

In a general way the habit of the Clinton-fern resembles the crested-fern, but the leaf-blade is wider, the lower leaflets less reduced and thus less different from the upper ones, and the blades of all the leaflets are more decidedly pinnatifid as well as acuminate. Thus it is a step nearer the Goldie-fern.

Accompanying the original description, a note records that this is "A showy fern, unlike any European form of A[spidium]. cristatum, and often mistaken for A. Goldianum." Wood ferns growing in abundance in our higher altitudes and latitudes are, perhaps through former hybridization, liable to present taxonomic difficulties until thoroughly and carefully studied. The plants of this species often grow in company with Dryopteris Goldiana and D. cristata. If these were its associates ages ago, one would be justified in considering the present species to be of hybrid origin. Of the two it more resembles D. Goldiana, but the narrower leaf-blade, the usually horizontal leaflets which are broadest at the base and the scarcely falcate segments easily separate it from that species. The petiole too is less scaly. The plants are typically larger than those of D. cristata. The leaf-blade is broader, the leaflets more coriaceous and slender-pointed, and the petiole more scaly. A diagnostic character is the less medial position of the sori. This plant was described, as a subspecies of Dryopteris cristata, in 1867. At that time its range was given as New England to New Jersey, New York and westward. All of these plants produce fine leafage. When one has seen well developed specimens of each it is difficult to decide which has the more elegant leaves.

5. **D. celsa** (W. Palmer) Knowlton, Palmer, & Pollard. Roostock loosely rooted, horizontal and ascending, stout, woody: foliage without trichomes, except scales and more or less scurf: scales glabrous, large, centrally dark-brown, lustrous, numerous on apex of rootstock, croziers, and lower petiole, those on upper petiole, rachis, and leaflet-veins fewer, smaller, narrower, and more translucent, with root-like or horn-like marginal branches and a tip ending in a flat jointed hair, the septa of both forms of scales somewhat heavy and opaque, the lumina becoming slightly opaque, nearly uniform in width, 4–8 times as wide as the septa and 7–18 times as long as the lumina are broad, the sides straight, except where bent when lapping, the ends broadly obtuse, very rarely angular: leaves few, erect; petioles abundantly scaly at the enlarged base, stramineous, the scales extending up the rachis; blades of sporophyls broadest about the middle, relatively narrower than in D. atropalustris and D. Goldiana, very slightly reduced at the base, rather abruptly acuminate at the apex but more gradually so than in D. Goldiana, with the dimorphism between sterile and fertile portions gradual, not conspicuous: leaflets olive-green above, somewhat lighter beneath;

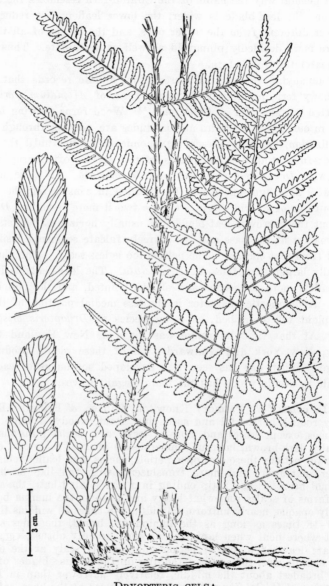

DRYOPTERIS CELSA

blades coriaceous, those of the sterile leaflets widest about the lower
third, slightly inequilateral, acute or acuminate at the tip, with the
distal first segment often reduced and vertical, the proximate basal
segment often wanting; the segments of the sterile leaflets oblong or
ovate-oblong, obtuse, moderately approximate but slightly closer
than in the fertile and slightly broader, those of fertile leaflets
lanceolate, with segments moderately approximate and relatively narrower and less prominently toothed than in *D. Clintoniana*, triangular-
ovate or ovate, somewhat separated, the teeth small, tipped with slender
vertical or spreading, (seldom introrse) hard, polished spines: venation
not very evident, the veins of the sterile segments sometimes branched
more than once, those of the fertile segments, except near the tip and
the base, branched once with the distal branch ending in a spine on the
margin: sori near the midrib, borne on the fork or on the back of the
distal vein slightly above the fork, but nearer the midrib than the
margin.—[*Dryopteris Goldiana celsa* W. Palmer.]—(LOG-FERN.)—On
rotted logs and at bases of large trees where humus has collected,
Coastal Plain and adj. Piedmont, Great Dismal Swamp region, N. C.
and Va. to Del. and Md.—Spores mature in summer and fall.—Fig.
reduced.

Although most of the close relatives of the log-fern are common
species, *Dryopteris celsa* itself, as far as general knowledge went, remained hidden in the almost inaccessible confines of the Great Dismal
Swamp of Virginia and North Carolina for forty years. The log-fern
was first found near the head of the Washington ditch near Lake
Drummond and was mistaken for *Dryopteris Clintoniana* and was later
associated with *D. Goldiana*. About three years later it was found
growing abundantly about eight miles east of the former locality and
then was recognized as distinct from its relatives.

The name *celsa* was suggested by its preferred habitat in the Dismal
Swamp on logs or on waste material at the foot of large gum trees,
and thus above the ground. Like its closer relatives it produces sporophyls with somewhat dimorphic leaflets and requires a moist situation.
But unlike the other species of the *cristata* group, it is largely satisfied
in the Dismal Swamp with moist air, not growing below the normal
flood line nor having roots that penetrate humus deeply seeking percolating water.

To our great surprise, recent studies disclose the fact that this fern
is not confined to secluded swamps. Specimens were collected along
the Patapsco River, about ten miles west of Baltimore, Maryland, the
year (1890) after it was discovered in the Dismal Swamp. This Maryland locality lies in the Piedmont province. This fern has also been
collected in moist areas adjacent to cultivated fields northeast of the

Dismal Swamp. Here the form is slightly different from that which occurs near Lake Drummond. The veins of fertile segments frequently branch twice and basal segments are often present in normal form. It had also been collected still earlier in Delaware. The discovery of a locality in the Piedmont materially weakened the idea that the log-fern was a product of the Great Dismal Swamp and on the other hand suggested that its occurrence in the swamp represents the main remnant of a one-time much wider geographic distribution. The next discovery of a locality outside the Coastal Plain made the situation clear. In 1931 specimens were found in the Blue Ridge of Tennessee near Hot Springs, North Carolina. Thus, in the light of existing collections the Great Dismal Swamp must be considered as the last refuge of a once-flourishing fern. Unlike the next following species, this log-fern seems not to have spread into the Mississippi Valley. However, there is a somewhat closely related fern on the other side of the Mississippi River in Arkansas. From *Dryopteris ludoviciana* which may yet be found growing with it, it is distinguished by its fertile leaflets extending further down the blade, its less dimorphic leaflets, its less distant fertile segments, and by sori nearer the midvein. From *D. Goldiana*, of which it was originally made a subspecies, it is separated by its more erect habit, narrower, more acuminate leaf-blades, firmer texture, more ascending leaflets with broader and less elongate fertile segments which bear sori somewhat further from the midvein: in addition, the leaflets are broadest somewhat nearer the base, and the scales on the leaflet-veins are small and less numerous.

6. **D. atropalustris** Small.[1] Rootstock horizontal: foliage without trichomes except scales: scales glabrous, deltoid or broadly lanceolate, dull light-brown to medium brown with a slightly darker stripe in center, numerous on apex of rootstock, croziers, and lower petiole, less numerous and more slender, lighter colored, tortuous scales with short horn-like or root-like marginal projections on the upper plant, the septa broad, never straight, somewhat opaque, the lumina moderately translucent, 1–5 times as wide as septa and 10–30 times as long as the lumina are broad, the sides very irregular, the ends often rounded or knobbed, sometimes diagonal, sometimes acute: leaves erect: petioles copiously scaly at the base, stramineous or purplish; blades of sporophyls triangular, widest at the base, narrowed abruptly at the apex, relatively wider than those of *D. celsa* and also of *D. Goldiana*, the

[1] *Dryopteris* **atropalustris** Small sp. nov. *Dryopteridem Goldianam* atque *D. celsam* referente, a quibus dignoscitur lamina brevi lataque, facie triangulari: foliolis paucis, distalibus rare fertilibus: venis segmentorum fertilium semel dichotomis: soris medianis vel extramedianis. Great Dismal Swamp, ad Lake Drummond, Octobri 2, 1921, E. Jerome Grimes, typus in herb. Hort. Bot. Noveboracensis.

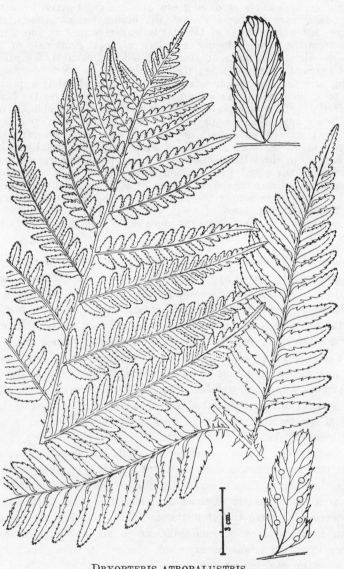

DRYOPTERIS ATROPALUSTRIS

dimorphism very little, the graduation from the sterile to the fertile
portion even: leaflets medium-green above, lighter-green beneath, the
lower ones more or less alternate, the blades thin-coriaceous, slightly
oblique, spreading, those of the sterile leaflets widest at the third seg
ment from the base, decidedly inequilateral, short acuminate at the tip,
with the distal first segment often reduced and vertical, the proximate
basal segment often wanting; the segments of the sterile leaflets long-
oblong or nearly so, oblique or slightly falcate, moderately approximate,
with teeth more conspicuous than in the fertile segments; the blades of
the fertile leaflets lanceolate or linear-lanceolate, with oblique, oblong,
moderately approximate segments, the teeth of both primary and secondary long curved spreading or forward-bent hard spines: venation
rather evident, the veins of the lower sterile segments usually with veins
forking two or three times, those of the middle fertile segments usually
once-forked, the distal fork ccntinued to a tooth on the margin: sori
borne on the distal branch of a vein at a varying distance above the
fork, the two rows nearer the margin than the midrib.—In humus or
rich soil about the bases of trees, Coastal Plain, S. C. to Del.; also
Central Lowland, Ohio.—Spores mature in summer and fall—Fig.
reduced.

Whatever may have been the source of the ancestors of the log-ferns,
the descendents have, apparently developed two different lines of
variation. The one is represented by the first described log-fern (*Dryopteris celsa*) in which the sporophyl is fertile nearly or quite to the base
and the sori placed nearer the midvein, as they are in its relatives *Dryopteris Clintoniana* and *D. Goldiana*. On another branch lies the fern
under consideration, with distally fertile sporophyls and sori nearer the
margin than the midrib as in its somewhat distant relatives *Dryopteris
ludoviciana* and *D. australis*. This is an interesting case showing
how isolated and circumscribed areas should be suspected of holding
unusual species that may have originated there. Typical specimens
were generally known only from the Great Dismal Swamp, Virginia,
for many years. However, a recent study of herbarium specimens
shows that this fern was collected about a century ago far to the south
along the Santee Canal, South Carolina. During exploration of a
swamp in Kent County, Delaware, during the years 1935 and 1936,
specimens also were collected there. This extension of the former
known geographic range was sufficient to arouse the suspicion that
further extension might be expected. Indeed, a recent study of herbarium material discloses a specimen collected in rich woods in Lorain
County, Ohio, in 1892. Our fern growth is becoming extinct, if not
through natural causes, certainly through the inroads of civilization.
The present disjointed distribution of this species indicates a former

more complete representation within a geographic area. However, additional collections are to be expected in the lowlands throughout the East. *Dryopteris atropalustris* seems to have become extinct in the highlands whence the ancestors of the present occupants of the lowlands were derived. It is easily distinguished from ferns that resemble it by its relatively short blade being broadest at the base.

7. **D. Goldiana** (Hook.) A. Gray. Rootstock stout, woody, horizontal and ascending: foliage devoid of trichomes, except scales: scales glabrous, moderately imbricate, ligulate or lanceolate with tips often attenuate, lustrous, dark-brown with translucent margins, numerous on apex of rootstock, croziers, and lower petiole, and sparsely scattered, smaller, and light-brown on upper petiole, rachis, and leaflet-veins, both forms of scales having broad septa which are prominent and more or less opaque, and narrow lumina becoming opaque, usually 1–5 times as wide as the septa and 10–30 times as long as the lumina are broad, with ends frequently obtuse lapping a similar end for 2 or 3 times the width of a lumen: leaves erect or ascending; petioles stramineous, one-half as long as the leaf, or somewhat shorter; blades broadest about the middle or two-thirds from the base, thus oval or obovate in outline, very abruptly acuminate from the broad tip, nearly as broad at the base as at the middle, the dimorphism between sterile and fertile portions very slight: leaflets alternate or opposite in part or throughout; blades of the basal or lower ones widest about the middle, acute or short-acuminate at the tip, with the distal basal segments slightly reduced, the proximate basal segment often wanting, those of the middle leaflets broadest at middle or one-third from the base, acute or short-acuminate, relatively wider than in *D. celsa*, but all leaflets sometimes conspicuously subparallel sided, the segments of the sterile leaflets oblong or oblong-lanceolate, often acute, moderately approximate and rather closer together than in *D. celsa*, those on the upper side shortened: blades of the fertile leaflets more gradually narrowed to an acuminate tip, thus lanceolate; the segments of the fertile leaflets more obtuse than those of the sterile: teeth spinulose, the spines sharp, polished, curved, directed forward or introrse: venation clear, the veins of the sterile segments usually branched twice, and occasionally anastomosing, those of the fertile segments also branched twice, the distal first branch continuing to a tooth, but frequently failing to reach the margin it anastomoses with another vein: sori very near the midrib, rather nearer than in *D. celsa*, usually borne at the first fork or on the distal vein slightly above the fork. [*Aspidium Goldianum* Hook.]— (GOLDIE'S-FERN.)—Rich woods, swamps, and mossy mountain slopes, on the edge of the Coastal Plain only southward, N. C. and Tenn. to Minn. and N. B.—Spores mature in summer.—Fig. reduced.

The Goldie-fern has relatively the broadest leaf-blade of the species of the *cristata* group. The leaflets are unusually uniform, the main difference being in the narrowing of the blades by the reduction of the

DRYOPTERIS GOLDIANA

basal segments. The quite uniform crenations loose their spine-tips early. The sori are placed closer to the midvein than in any of the other species. They are also close together in a vertical line. The leaves of our group of *Dryopteris* vary greatly in the proportion of the width to the length of the blade. In some species the leaf-blades are narrow, in others broad. Indeed, the outline of the leaf-blades of each species is distinctive. In the case of the present one the leaf may be characterized as large, very broad, and abruptly short-acuminate; the leaflets are also broad and are separated at the rachis, from which they stand out, resembling so many spreading feathers. The lower pair or several pairs of leaflets are not reduced in size or only slightly so, and are not spore-bearing. This, with one exception, is a fern of the higher provinces, reaching more than 6600 feet in the Blue Ridge. Curiously enough it occurs in the outer Piedmont region from eastern North Carolina to Pennsylvania, and apparently crosses into the inner Coastal Plain in aberrant forms. *Dryopteris Goldiana* was named in 1822, the specimens having been collected at Montreal, Canada.

8. D. australis (Wherry) Small. Rootstock horizontal: foliage without trichomes except scurf and scales: scales glabrous, variable in shape but usually broadly lanceolate, light-brown becoming darker in center, often with translucent margin, irregularly imbricate, numerous on apex of rootstock, croziers, and lower petiole, fewer lighter-colored and more translucent, with horn-like marginal projections on upper petiole, rachis, and leaflet-veins, the septa heavy and somewhat opaque,[1] the lumina narrow, often elongate, moderately translucent, 1–6 times as wide as septa and 15–30 times as long as lumina are broad, the ends usually diagonal or acute: leaves erect; petioles with numerous scales, especially at the enlarged base, the scales also extending along the rachis; blades of sporophyls relatively broader than those of *D. ludoviciana*, broadest slightly above the middle, moderately reduced at the base, rather abruptly acute or acuminate at the apex, the dimorphism between sterile and fertile portions abrupt and conspicuous: leaflets coriaceous, deep-green above, somewhat lighter-green beneath, alternate except the lower spreading pairs, which are more distant than in *D. ludoviciana*, the blades of the basal and lower ones widest at the second segments, slightly inequilateral, nearly as long as those of the middle leaflets, with the proximate basal segment little reduced: the middle leaflets broadest near the base tapering gradually to the acute or acuminate tip; the segments of the sterile leaflets decidedly obtuse, moderately separated, those on the upper side of the midrib somewhat the shorter: the segments of the fertile leaflets broader at the base, slightly less distant than in *D. ludoviciana*, conspicuously shorter in the upper part of the

[1] Specimen 733113 Acad. Nat. Sci. Phila., Wherry, July 15, 1932, Forney, Ala., has very short lumina; specimen 733112 of the same locality and date has long lumina.

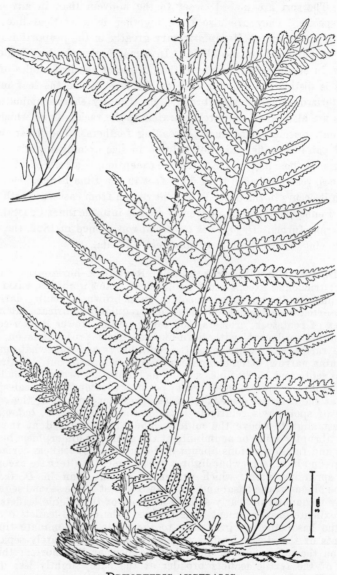

DRYOPTERIS AUSTRALIS

blade and so somewhat deltoid and approximate, but in the lower fertile leaflets resembling those of the sterile leaflets (fertile leaflets narrower and more distant than in *D. celsa*): teeth small spinulose, appressed or directed forward, with rarely any sign of secondary teeth, the spines variable usually of moderate length, herbaceous or sometimes hard and polished: venation clear, that of the sterile segments once branched or rarely twice-branched, that at the middle of the fertile segments branched once with the distal branch running to a tooth: sori borne on the distal fork nearer the midrib than in *D. ludoviciana*, further from the midrib than in *D. celsa*, the two rows about midway between the midrib and the margin.—[*D. Clintoniana australis* Wherry.] —Woods, sometimes in rocky places, various provinces, Ga. to La., Ark. and N. C.—Spores mature in summer.—Fig. reduced.

As in the case of *Dryopteris ludoviciana*, which follows, the sporophyls of this species are dimorphic. The earlier (1896) collections in Alabama seem to have been only or mainly of the foliage leaves. These were referred without exception to *Dryopteris floridana*, the name under which *D. ludoviciana* was then known, the leaves of which, however, they resemble only slightly, the main dissimilarities being slightly reduced lower leaflets and the more deeply pinnatifid leaflet-blades. The general port of the sporophyl resembles that of *Dryopteris ludoviciana*, but the blade is relatively broader and the dimorphism less marked and the fertile segments less widely separated from one another. The species was discovered in 1896, and named and described in 1937. It is suspected further exploration in Alabama will show a wider geographic distribution than is now known in that state. Although long known only from Alabama this fern has a wider distribution. In 1928 specimens very close to this species were found near Shirley, Arkansas. Exploration in the swamps of Louisiana in the summer of 1936 discovered this fern in that state. It is also suspected as occurring in Georgia.

9. **D. ludoviciana** (Kunze) Small. Rootstock horizontal, often elongate, woody: foliage without trichomes except scales and scurf: scales glabrous, imbricate, broadly lanceolate with attenuate tips, medium brown with darker base, abundant on apex of rootstock, croziers and lower petiole, and numerous and more variable in size on upper petiole, rachis, and leaflet-veins, the septa broad and usually opaque, the lumina moderately translucent and often bent at ends, 4–7 times as wide as septa and 8–30 times as long as the lumina are broad; the ends obtusely short-pointed, or less commonly rectangular or oblique: leaves erect; petioles about one-third to one-half the length of the blades; blade broadest slightly above the middle, or in fertile leaves where the sterile and fertile leaflets meet, the dimorphism of sterile

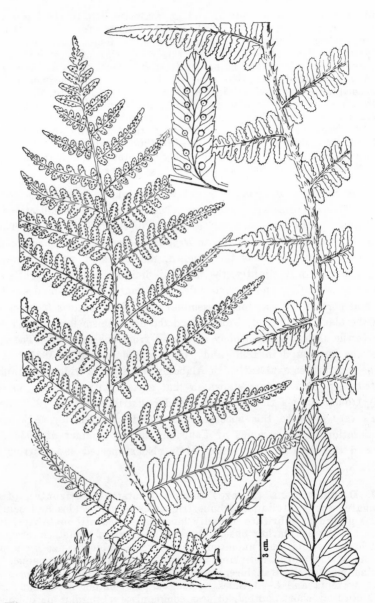

DRYOPTERIS LUDOVICIANA

and fertile leaflets being abrupt and conspicuous, more or less abruptly acuminate at the apex, much reduced below, by several pairs of leaflets conspicuously shorter than those above them: leaflets numerous, coriaceous, olive-green above, much lighter beneath, alternate, except the lower two or three pairs, the lower ones nearly horizontal, the upper fertile leaflets sharply ascending, those at the middle of the blade with the longer petiolules, those at the base of the blade nearly sessile, those of the basal pair inequilaterally triangular, obtuse, with basal segments longest or the two basal pairs about equal in length, those of the middle of the leaf slightly inequilateral with the longest segments below, acute, and those of the upper leaflets acuminate: the segments of the sterile leaflets broadly oblong and more or less falcate; the segments of the fertile leaflets triangular and separated above, more distant and oblong below: teeth very short, more nearly apiculate than spinulose, often introrse: venation fairly clear: veins in the middle of fertile segments branched once, or rarely twice, the distal vein continuing more often to a sinus than to a tooth, the venation of the middle of the sterile segments similar to that of the fertile: sori on distal branches of veins, each the space of about one sorus above the fork, the two rows about midway between the midrib and the margin. [*Aspidium ludovicianum* Kunze. *Aspidium floridanum* Hook. *Dryopteris floridana* Kuntze.] —(FLORIDA SHIELD-FERN.)—Low or wet hammocks, cypress swamps, rocky woods, lime-sinks, and grottoes, Coastal Plain, Fla. to La. and N. C.—Spores mature in spring to fall.—Fig. reduced.

The genus *Dryopteris* is well represented throughout the entire length of the Atlantic seaboard, except the Florida Keys. No one species occurs throughout the whole length, the ranges of some, however, overlap in the middle ground. This wood-fern ranges through the southeastern Atlantic and Gulf Coastal Plains. For a long time, in fact almost up to the present, the Florida shield-fern was the only representative of the *cristata* group recognized in the southeastern Coastal Plain, south of North Carolina, where the typically northern species range southward. Although known in the Gulf Coastal Plain for many years from Louisiana to Florida (and reported from eastern Texas), it was not until 1931 that it was collected as far north as North Carolina. The species was discovered in Louisiana about the beginning of the past century and in Florida in 1842. Considering the rather extended range and the variety of habitats this fern holds its technical and habital characters very well. It grows on rock ledges, on cliffs, and in grottoes as well as in permanently wet, mucky swamps. The foliage leaves and sporophyls are strikingly different. In the former the leaflets are uniformly reduced to the apex of the leaf, while in the latter the spore-bearing leaflets are abruptly different from those below them. The leaves vary much in size, and although it will grow on rock where a little humus has collected, its best development is reached when its rootstock and roots are embedded in rich humus laden soil in a semi-aquatic habitat. In the hammock swamps of the eastern coast of Florida great clumps of this fern, up to a meter and a half wide, grow nearly head-high associated with massed clumps of the large needle-palm (*Rhapidophyllum Hystrix*) and the blue-stem (*Sabal minor*) and all these in the dense shade of the cabbage-tree (*Sabal Palmetto*). Curiously enough it has the same palm associates where it occurs in the dry rocky fern grottoes of Florida, where, however, the fern itself and its associates are decidedly stunted. It is difficult to tell whether the climax of the career of this fern has not been reached or if it is past. Along the Gulf its range is narrow, but northeastward it enters the coastal region of North Carolina where it approaches the outlying stations of some of its northern relatives.

10. **D. separabilis** Small, sp. nov.[1] Rootstock stout, horizontal, densely chaffy with dark-brown scales: scales broadly lanceolate, with jointed filiform tips and broad bases which clasp a small point of attachment, or are perfoliate about it, with horn-like projections on the margins, glabrous, dull medium-brown with somewhat darker stripe in center, the septa moderately translucent, the lumina translucent, elongate, fusiform or linear, varying considerably in width, usually 1–4 times as broad as septa, 12 to 36 times as long as broad, the sides more or less curved, the ends obtuse or diagonal, rarely acute or rectangular, the undersized angle-filling lumina rare; the scales of the upper petiole somewhat smaller, narrower, and more translucent with lumina of more uniform width: leaves erect or arching; petiole and rachis with fairly abundant long and slender scales, light-stramineous; blades of sporophyls broadest about the middle, short-acuminate at the tip, moderately reduced at the base; the dimorphism between sterile and fertile parts slight and the change gradual: leaflets membranous, medium-green above and lighter-green beneath, alternate, except the lower two or three pairs, usually opposite below and above, all moderately ascending, blades of the lower leaflets somewhat inequilateral, those of the middle leaflets decidedly acuminate, broadest one-third to one-half from the base; the segments of the sterile leaflets moderately distant, acute, broader at the base, more deeply toothed than the fertile ones, with no wings on midrib of the primary leaflet; the fertile segments distant, acute, connected by slight wings on the midrib: primary and secondary teeth spinulose, the spines very short, slightly spreading or directed forward: venation clear, the veins in middle of fertile segments branched

[1] *Dryopteris* **separabilis** Small sp. nov. ingenti, ex affinitate *Dryopteridis cristatae, D. Goldianae, D. ludovicianae*, a quibus differt foliis amplis bipinnatis: foliolis numerosis magis minusve inter se distantibus: soris ad costam. Great Dismal Swamp, Virginia, Carolinae Septentrionalis fines, in oriente Lake Drummond, Novembri 22, 1935, Arthur N. Leeds, typus in herb. Acad. Nat. Sci., Philadelphia, Pa.

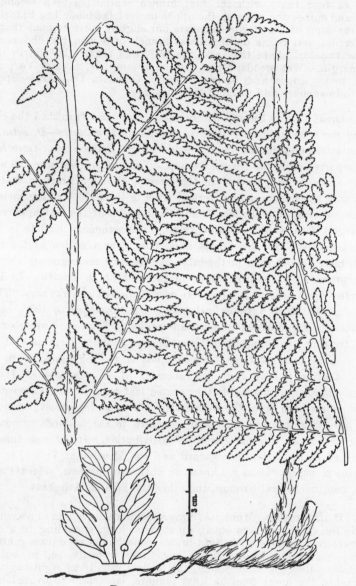

3 cm.

DRYOPTERIS SEPARABILIS

three or four times with the first branch continuous to a secondary tooth and spine; the veins on the upper part of the blade less branched, the branching of the sterile segments but slightly more copious than in the fertile: sori borne on the distal branch of a vein the distance of one or two sori above the fork, the two rows nearer the midrib than the margin.—Wet woods, Great Dismal Swamp, N. C. and Va.; also moist rocky woods and bases of bluffs, Ouachita Co., Ark.—Spores mature in summer and fall.—Fig. reduced.

The Great Dismal Swamp within this century has furnished the clues to and the type specimens of three species of *Dryopteris—D. celsa, D. atropalustris,* and the one under consideration. Sixteen other ferns have been reported from the Dismal Swamp. The new species were the more recent kinds to be gathered in the swamp, although growing in company with the more common ferns. This is the most striking member and considering both the length and the breadth of the leaf apparently the largest fern of the *cristata* group. The secondary leaflets in well developed leaves are exceedingly numerous. The venation of the leaflets is more forked than in the other species, and the segments also are more prominently toothed except in the case of *D. Boottii.* In 1928 imperfect specimens of a large fern were collected in Arkansas. These were distributed to various herbaria. On November 3, 1935, better specimens were collected in the same region. Then on November 22, 1935, the fern was found in the Great Dismal Swamp, Virginia.[1] There is a peculiar form of *Dryopteris Goldiana* in the highlands, south and north, that may have been the ancestor of *D. separabilis.* It has coarsely toothed and somewhat separated leaf-segments. *D. separabilis* is not now known from the highlands. However, in primeval times it may have migrated eastward and westward to the lowlands, gradually dying out in its original center of distribution. If, at one time, it flourished in the Atlantic seaboard and the Mississippi Valley, it now remains to us, as far as we know, in only two outposts, retreats as it were, one the Dismal Swamp, the other the hills of Aranksas.

11. D. intermedia (Muhl.) A. Gray. Rootstock creeping or ascending at the tip, chaffy; leaves equal, up to 1 m. long, spreading in a complete crown; petioles with light-brown concolorous or darker-centered scales; blades mostly lanceolate, sometimes broadly so, in outline, glandular-pubescent when young, the leaflets usually at right-angles to the rachis, the lower ones at least pinnate, lanceolate to ovate-lanceo-

[1] The type specimens of *Dryopteris separabilis* collected in wet woods east of Lake Drummond, Dismal Swamp, Virginia by Arthur N. Leeds, November 22, 1935, number 3583, are in the Herbarium of the Academy of Natural Sciences, Philadelphia.

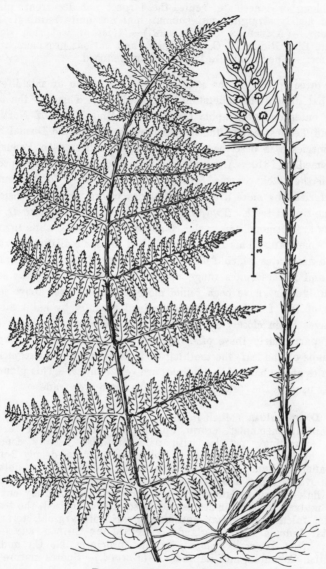

3 cm.

DRYOPTERIS INTERMEDIA

late, the upper ones lanceolate to oblong, acuminate, the segments convex, oblong or lanceolate, acute, the largest not decurrent, pinnately
divided nearly straight: sori submarginal not quite terminal: indusia
glandular.—(AMERICAN SHIELD-FERN.)—Moist or wet rich woods or
swamps, Blue Ridge, N. C., and Tenn., and various provinces, to Wisc.
and Newf.—Spores mature in fall.—Fig. reduced.

The three species of the so-called *spinulosa* group of shield-ferns are
somewhat difficult to understand taxonomically. This and the two following enter our geographic range in the Blue Ridge of North Carolina and Tennessee, and the next following also in the Dismal Swamp.
This species was described from specimens collected in Pennsylvania
and named in 1810. Although this fern and the following species belong to the thicker-tissued group, collectively they form a subgroup
characterized by more divided leaf-blades whose ultimate divisions end
in spine-tipped teeth. Two of the species, *D. spinulosa* and *D. campyloptera,* are cosmopolitan in the Northern Hemisphere, while the present
one is American. This fern probably has the same altitudinal range as
its two associates which follow. In the New England mountains this
plant and its associates range up to 5000 feet, while in the southern
Blue Ridge they have been found more than 6500 feet above sea-level.
Plants of this fern cannot be determined casually by habit alone, for
the leaves often closely simulate those of members of a very distinct
genus, particularly those of *Athyrium asplenioides* and *A. angustum.*
The shape of the leaf, the toothing or incising of the leaf-segments and
the scales at the base of the petioles are very similar.—This plant is frequently used as the ''fancy-fern'' of the cut-flower trade.

12. **D. spinulosa** (Muell.) Nutt. Rootstock stout, creeping, chaffy:
leaves in an incomplete crown, up to 1 m. long, the taller erect, the
others spreading; petioles with pale brownish usually concolorous
scales; blades ovate-lanceolate to oblong, acuminate, deeply 2-pinnate;
the leaflets oblique, the lower ones unequally triangular, deltoid, or
deltoid-ovate, those above lanceolate to oblong, acuminate; the segments flat, oblong to lanceolate, acute, decurrent, pinnately cut almost
to the midveins, the ultimate segments somewhat incised, the teeth mucronate, falcate, somewhat appressed; sori submarginal, terminal on
veinlets: indusia without glands.—(SPINULOSE SHIELD-FERN.)—Moist
woods, often in rocky places, various provinces N. C., and Tenn.
to British Columbia, and Labrador.—(*Europe.*)—Spores mature in fall.
—Fig. reduced.

As the groups of *Dryopteris* are divided for taxonomic study, the
present and following species form another subgroup of two species

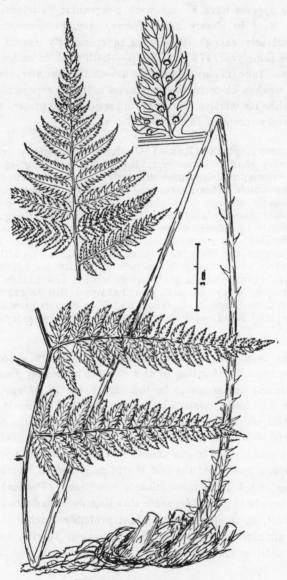

DRYOPTERIS SPINULOSA

of the same value as the preceding species, *Dryopteris intermedia*. Two of the species have a very wide geographic distribution, which extends, at least in closely allied forms, around the northern hemisphere. Curiously enough, they were independently named and published in the same year, 1795, in Europe—both of them under the genus *Polypodium*. Like its close taxonomic associate, *Dryopteris intermedia*, this plant reaches close to the maximum altitude represented in our range. Unlike its relative, the preceding species, the present one occurs in the lowland swamps of the Coastal Plain.

13. **D. campyloptera** (Kunze) Clarkson. Rootstock creeping or ascending, very chaffy: leaves equal, up to 1.5 mm. long, spreading in a complete crown; petioles copiously scaly, especially toward the base, with dark brownish, often darker-centered, scales; blades triangular to ovate or broadly oblong, acuminate, 2- to 3-pinnate, the leaflets variable, the lower ones broadly and unequally ovate or triangular, those above lanceolate to oblong, acute or acuminate, the lowermost, at least pinnately divided, the segments convex, broadly oblong to lanceolate, acute, the largest not decurrent, pinnately divided; the ultimate segments pinnately lobed, the teeth mucronate, usually not appressed; sori mostly submarginal: indusia glabrous or with a few glands. [*Dryopteris dilatata* A. Gray, in part.]—(SPREADING SHIELD-FERN.)—Moist rocky woods, Blue Ridge, N. C., Tenn. and Va.; various provinces, Pa. to Minn., Alas., and Newf.—(*Greenland, O. W.*)—Spores mature in fall.—Fig. reduced.

There has been and is much difference of opinion concerning the specific or subspecific standing of this and the preceding plants. However, the present one seems to be thoroughly worthy of specific standing. From its closest relative in eastern North America it differs in the horizontal rootstock, the less-evergreen leaves, and the very broad basal leaflets with their more or less diminutive odd-leaflet near the rachis. For many years it was almost universally confused with *Dryopteris dilatata*, a species of the Old World and western North America. Then it was called *Dryopteris dilatata americana* (Fischer) Fernald; and two attempts to give it separate standing were made, but were slow in taking root, so to speak. This plant probably reaches the limit of the higher altitudes in our range. Its altitudinal distribution increases southward until an elevation of fully 6000 feet is achieved in the Blue Ridge.

14. **D. ampla** (Humb. & Bonp.) Kuntze. Rootstock erect, at least at the tip, 0.5 m. tall or less, densely red-scaly: leaves arching, 2 m.

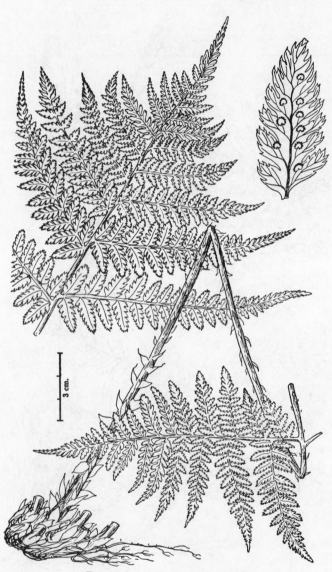

DRYOPTERIS CAMPYLOPTERA

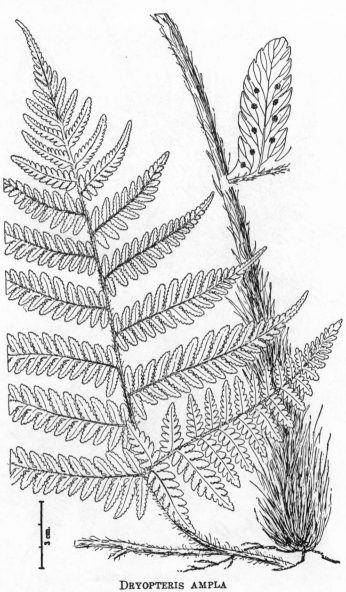

DRYOPTERIS AMPLA

long or less; petioles stout, very densely clothed with long bright-red, hair-like scales at the base, sparingly short-scaly above; blades bright-green, deltoid or ovate-deltoid, about as long as the petioles, the primary divisions 1-pinnate, the lower leaflets inequilaterally deltoid to lanceolate-deltoid, larger than those above, on short scaly stalks, the pinnules lanceolate to elliptic-lanceolate, much larger on the lower side of the rachis than on the upper, the segments crenate or crenately incised: veins simple or forked: sori several to many to each segment, medial: indusia minute, fugacious.—Rocky hammocks, Everglade Keys, and Big Cypress Swamps, S. pen. Fla.—(*W. I., Mex., C. A., S. A.*)—Spores mature all year.—Fig. reduced.

After this fern came north of the Gulf Stream from the West Indies, it evidently found few places suited to its peculiar demands for growth. It is far from hardy even in Florida and has selected a few tropical hammocks on the Everglade Keys and among the royal-palms in the Big Cypress Swamp, where the air is continuously moist and more or less stagnant and the soil mostly humus. Even the protected hammocks of the Lake Okeechobee Region lack it, and much less is it to be expected in the ancient Oligocene Island tropical area in the northern part of the peninsula. It grows in small lime-sinks or on the hammock floor. This is our largest native wood-fern. It was discovered in Florida in 1903[1] but previously had been known from continental and insular tropical America. The erect rootstock is commonly raised above the surface of the ground a foot or a foot and a half, thus forming a trunk which supports a crown of beautiful arching leaves with a spread of twelve feet. In habit it is thus a tree-fern. The leaves separate readily from the rootstock and in parting retain a large dense tuft of brilliant red scales at the base of the petiole. The original specimens came from tropical America and were named in 1810.

15. **D. setigera** (Blume) Kuntze. Rootstock stout, horizontal and ascending, clothed with long ciliate dark-brown scales: leaves several together, arching, sometimes 8-10, often up to 2 m. long; petioles stout, clothed with brown scales at the base; rachis and branches glabrous; blades dark-green, deltoid-ovate to deltoid-lanceolate, mostly longer than the petioles, the primary divisions lanceolate to elliptic-lanceolate, 1-pinnate, acute, acuminate, or caudate, the leaflets broadly lanceolate to narrowly-elliptic, on almost glabrous stalks (but the midrib and leaf-surfaces with long white hairs), pinnatifid, the segments rounded or obtuse, sparsely toothed: veins simple or forked: sori few, 1–3 to each segment, medial: indusia very delicate, fugacious.—Swamps, wet hammocks, springy slopes, cypress heads, and marshes, middle peninsular Fla.—Spores mature all year.—Fig. reduced.

[1] First collected in Florida by J. K. Small, J. J. Carter, and A. A. Eaton. in November, 1903.

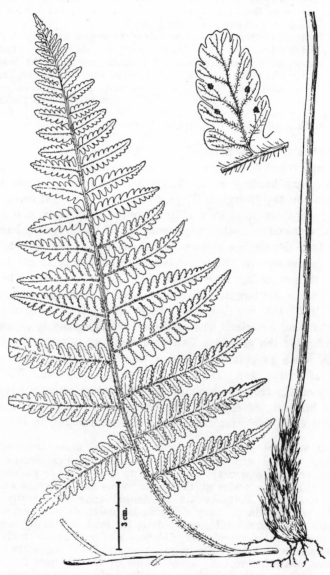

3 cm.

DRYOPTERIS SETIGERA

''Is *Dryopteris setigera* native in Florida or is it naturalized from the Old World?'' This is a very frequent query, especially since the fern is appearing spontaneously in many remote localities and in great abundance. In fact, during the past few years it has spread like wild-fire. If not native, it is one of the few of our introduced and natural-ized ferns. It is known to be native in Asia and the adjacent islands, and is widely cultivated. This fern was first found in Florida near Oviedo,[1] in Seminole County. Although a naturalized plant there seems to be no indication as to how it got a foothold in the several localities where it first came to the attention of students, for it often grows in dense cypress swamps remote from roads. The original specimens came from the mountains of Java and were named in 1828. The ranges of this and the preceding fern, which rival each other in size, in Florida do not meet. They are easily distinguished as the leaf-trichomes of *Dryopteris ampla* are scales and of *D. setigera*, hairs. The maximum altitude recorded for this species in Florida, is about 100 feet above sea-level.

LIST OF DESCRIBED HYBRIDS

Dryopteris Clintoniana × *intermedia* Dowell, Bull. Torrey Club **35**: 136. 1908.

Dryopteris Clintoniana × *marginalis* Slosson, Bull. Torrey Club **37**: 202. 1910.

Dryopteris Clintoniana × *spinulosa* Benedict, Bull. Torrey Club **36**: 45. 1909.

Dryopteris cristata × *Goldiana* Benedict, Bull. Torrey Club **36**: 47. 1909.

Dryopteris cristata × *marginalis* Davenp. Bot. Gaz. **19**: 497. 1894, as syn.

   Aspidium cristatum × *marginale* Davenp. Bot. Gaz. **19**: 494. 1894.

Dryopteris cristata × *spinulosa* (Milde) C. Chr. Ind. Fil. 259. 1905.

   Aspidium cristatum × *spinulosum* Milde, Nov. Act. Acad. Leop.—Carol. **26**: 533. 1856.

Dryopteris Goldiana × *intermedia* Dowell, Bull. Torrey Club **35**: 138. 1908.

Dryopteris Goldiana × *marginalis* Dowell, Bull. Torrey Club **35**: 138. 1908.

Dryopteris Goldiana × *spinulosa* Benedict, Bull. Torrey Club **36**: 47. 1909.

Dryopteris intermedia × *marginalis* Benedict, Bull. Torrey Club **36**: 48. 1909.

Dryopteris marginalis × *spinulosa* Slosson, Fern Bull. **16**: 99. 1908.

   Dryopteris pittsfordensis Slosson, Rhodora **6**: 75. 1904.

[1] First collected in Florida by T. L. Mead about 1906.

Nephrodium pittsfordense Davenp. Rhodora 6: 76. 1904, as syn.
Aspidium spinulosum × *marginale* Eggl. Rhodora 6: 138. 1904.

35. POLYSTICHUM Roth.

Tufted, coarse, and usually rigid terrestrial plants, with chaffy short, erect or horizontal rootstocks, often with chaffy foliage. Leaves clustered, mostly evergreen: petioles firm, not jointed to the rootstock: blades 1–3-pinnatifid or pinnate, the foliage leaves and the sporophyls usually somewhat similar, but the sporophyls and the spore-bearing leaflets relatively narrower than the foliage ones, the leaflets with toothed or pinnatifid blades. Veins once-to-several-times forked, free. Sori orbicular, usually borne on the back of the veins. Indusium superior, centrally peltate, orbicular, without a sinus, opening all around.— Approximately one hundred species widely distributed, but most abundant in temperate regions.—The genus is founded on *Polypodium Lonchitis* L. The name is Greek, alluding to the many rows of sori, in some species.

1. **P. acrostichoides** (Michx.) Schott. Rootstocks stout, often short, densely chaffy. Leaves evergreen, several or many together, 2.5–8 dm. tall; petioles stout, rusty, often copiously chaffy; blades lanceolate in outline, or sometimes in the case of sterile ones elliptic-lanceolate, 1-pinnate; leaflets somewhat coriaceous, linear-lanceolate to lanceolate or elliptic-lanceolate, and half-hastate, 2.5–7 cm. long, more or less falcate, with appressed or oblique bristly teeth; sporophyls somewhat contracted above, the reduced leaflets forming a conspicuous narrow tapering apex to the leaf bearing many mostly contiguous sori, which sometimes nearly cover the lower surface; veins in the sterile leaflets twice to five times forked, in the sori-bearing leaflets simpler: sori about 1 mm. in diameter, confluent in age; indusium glabrous, entire. [*Aspidium acrostichoides* Sw. *Dryopteris acrostichoides* Kuntze.]— (CHRISTMAS-FERN. DAGGER-FERN.)—Rocky, shady or rich soil, ravines and stream-banks, hillsides, in bogs, and in woods, various provinces, Fla. to Tex., Wis., Ont., and N. S.—The form with deeply toothed, incised, or pinnatifid leaflets has been described as *P. acrostichoides Schweinitzii*.—Spores mature from spring to fall.—Fig. reduced. For notes on varieties and forms, see Am. Fern Jour. 26: 97, 98. 1936.

The Christmas-fern is generally distributed in eastern North America. It is a frequent associate of its distant relative, the marginal shield-fern (*Dryopteris marginalis*) and like it, it is in season the year round, the leaves of both being evergreen. The Christmas-fern is a northern type, but curiously enough, the plants growing at the Gulf of Mexico and those growing in Canada are identical in habit and in the ever-

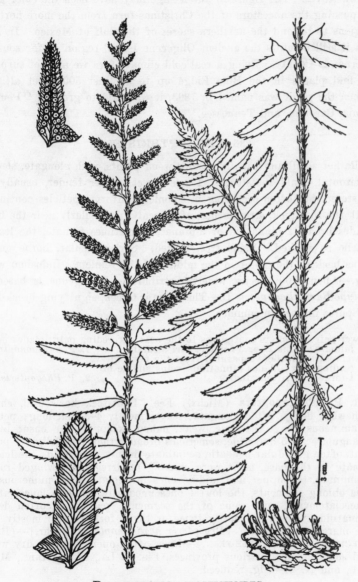

POLYSTICHUM ACROSTICHOIDES

green leaves. The rigors of the ice-age may have been the chief agent
in pushing the ancestors of the Christmas-fern from the more northern
regions to beyond the northern shores of the Gulf of Mexico. In Florida it still inhabits the ancient Oligocene Island region as far south as
Hernando County. Being a real cold climate fern we are not surprised
to find plants in the Blue Ridge up to at least 5000 feet altitude.
When the plant was named in 1803, it was said to grow in ''Pennsylvania, Carolina, and Tennessee.''

36. **PHEGOPTERIS** Fée.

Rather small and usually slender wood plants, with elongate, slender,
horizontal, scaly rootstocks. Leaves erect, rather tender, usually not
clustered, but often occurring in colonies, uniform: petioles continuous
with the rootstock, stramineous, often scaly, particularly near the base:
blades broad, 2-pinnatifid or 2-pinnate, sometimes ternate, the leaflets
sessile or stalked. Veins free, forked. Sori orbicular, borne on the
veins back of the tip or in the middle of the veinlets. Indusium wanting.—About 100 species widely distributed.—The genus is based on
Polypodium Phegopteris L.—The name is Greek, signifying beech-fern.
—Spores mature in summer.

Lower pair of leaflets contiguous to the next succeeding pair ; blades nearly
    pinnate ; veins 2- or 3-forked : sori medial.   1. *P. hexagonoptera.*
Lower pair of leaflets separated from the next suc-
    ceeding pair ; blades pinnatifid : veins simple or
    1-forked : sori marginal.   2. *P. Phegopteris.*

1. **P. hexagonoptera** (Michx.) Fée. Rootstock horizontal, chaffy,
somewhat fleshy, often elongate; leaves mostly 4–8 dm. long; petioles
stramineous above the base, weak, naked except at the base; blades
triangular, 2–3.5 dm. wide, sometimes broader than long, slightly pubescent, often glandular beneath, acuminate deeply pinnatifid; the leaflets
adnate at the base, as it were, making an irregularly winged rachis,
acuminate, the upper and middle ones lanceolate, with numerous obtuse oblong segments, the lowest ones unequally ovate to lanceolate or
lanceolate-ovate, with some of the segments spaced and often deeply
pinnatifid: veins few, mostly twice or thrice-forked: sori mostly near
the margin, separated. [*Dryopteris hexagonoptera* C. Chr.]—(BROAD
BEECH-FERN. TRIANGLE-FERN.)—Rich, often open rocky or dry woods
and shaded banks, various provinces, Fla. to La., Okla., Kans., Minn.,
Ont., and N. S.—Fig. reduced.

There are four species of *Phegopteris* in eastern North America.
Three of them are also natives of the Old World. The present species

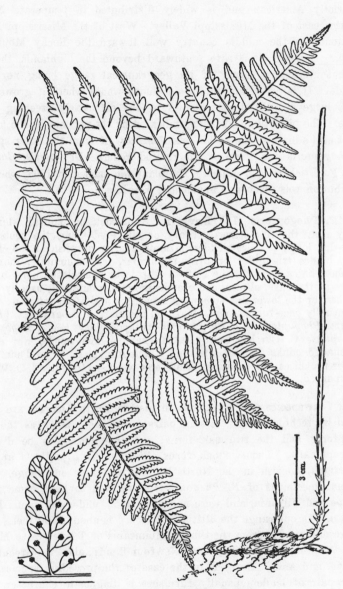

PHEGOPTERIS HEXAGONOPTERA

is strictly American and is widely distributed in temperate North America east of the Mississippi Valley. West of the Mississippi River it extends in the middle country well toward the Rocky Mountain region. However, it is rare southward beyond the highlands, the extreme southeastern corner of its geographical range being northern Florida. It is an inhabitant of deciduous woods where it grows and forms large but not dense colonies by the extensively creeping rootstocks. The pinnatifid leaf-blade, indicated by the portions of the lowest leaflet still adnate to the rachis sets this fern off from the other species of *Phegopteris* and those of the related genera—*Dryopteris, Goniopteris, Polystichum,* and others. The plant was named in 1803, when its distribution was given as Canada and Virginia.

2. **P. Phegopteris** (L.) Keyserl. Rootstock horizontal, slender, chaffy near the tip: leaves solitary or clustered along the rootstock, 2.5–6 dm. long; petioles slender, stramineous, or purplish at the chaffy base: blades triangular or ovate-triangular, long-acuminate, more or less short-hairy beneath, the leaflets elliptic to lanceolate, more or less adnate at the base, obtuse, acute or acuminate, pinnatifid, usually close together, or the lower one somewhat separated and often reflexed: veins few, usually once-forked: sori almost on the margin, separated. [*Polypodium Phegopteris* L. *Phegopteris polypodioides* Fée. *Dryopteris Phegopteris* C. Chr.]—(LONG BEECH-FERN.)—Low woods, wet cliffs, and shaded banks, Smoky Mts. and Black Range, N. C. to Tenn. and various provinces, Va. to Wash., Alas., and Newf.—(*Greenland*, O. W.)—Fig. reduced.

The four species of *Phegopteris* in eastern North America are associated by technical characters in pairs, sometimes known as the two beech-ferns and the two oak ferns; yet they may also be divided geographically. The two oak ferns, *Phegopteris Dryopteris* and *P. Robertiana*, flourish in the North but do not enter our range. The original specimens of *P. Phegopteris* were said to have come from Europe and Virginia, and were named in 1753, under the genus *Polypodium*. In our range the altitudinal record is about 5500 feet. The geographic area is from the Smoky Mountains of Tennessee to Michigan, Washington, Alaska, and Newfoundland; also in Greenland, Europe, and Asia. Here, as in the case of the preceding species, the lower pair of leaflets usually furnishes a diagnostic character. As compared with the preceding species, the blades of the lower pair of leaflets are often shorter and scarcely if any, wider than those of the contiguous pair.

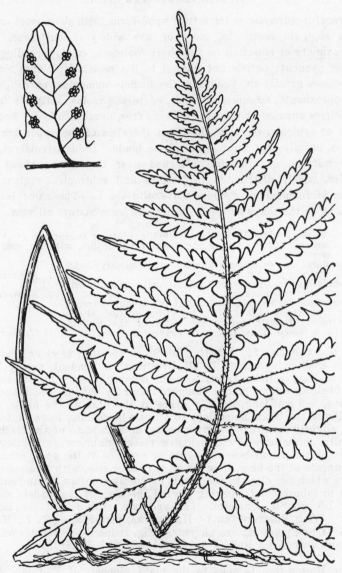

PHEGOPTERIS PHEGOPTERIS

37. NEPHROLEPIS Schott.

Graceful epiphytic or terrestrial wood-ferns, with short erect or somewhat elongate rootstocks, more or less widely stoloniferous. Leaves approximate or clustered on the short rootstock, erect, spreading, arching or pendent; petiole not jointed to the rootstock; blades elongate, sometimes greatly so, 1-pinnate, the leaflets numerous, narrow, spaced or approximate, conspicuously jointed to the rachis, entire or toothed, sometimes auricled at the base. Veins free, usually forked. Sori reniform or orbicular-reniform, borne at the apex of the upper branch of a vein, usually near the margin of the blade. Indusia reniform, orbicular-reniform, or orbicular, attached near the sinus.—About thirty species, widely distributed in tropical and subtropical regions.—The genus is founded on *Polypodium exaltatum* L.—The name is Greek, alluding to the shape of the indusium.—Spores mature all year.

Blades of the leaflets distinctly auricled, cordate or subcordate at the base, sessile: indusia facing the apex of the leaflet, with an open sinus, persistent.
  Leaflets not callous-margined: veins mostly twice forked: plant not tuber-bearing.   1. *N. exaltata*.
  Leaflets callous-margined: veins mostly once forked: plants tuber-bearing.   2. *N. cordifolia*.
Blades of the leaflets not auricled at the broadly cuneate or truncate base, but often somewhat angled, short-petioled: indusia facing the sides of the leaflets, with a closed sinus, fragile or fugaceous.   3. *N. biserrata*.

1. **N. exaltata** (L.) Schott. Rootstock stoutish, erect or nearly so: leaves erect or spreading in all directions, or pendent, mostly 2.5 m. long or less; petioles rather slender, shining, mostly brown, more or less fibrillose-scaly; blades elongate-linear in outline, the leaflets numerous, 3–6 cm. long, broadly ovate at the base of the blade, at the middle of the blade lanceolate to elliptic-lanceolate, more or less falcate, slightly serrate or singly crenate, or with some of the teeth occasionally accompanied with smaller teeth, glabrous or coarsely and sparingly pubescent beneath, acute or rounded at the apex, subcordate to truncate at the base, rounded on the lower side, with a broad auricle above which lies close to the rachis or partly overlaps it: indusia reniform to suborbicular, opening toward the apex of the leaflet: sori less than 1.5 mm. in diameter. [*Polypodium exaltatum* L.]—(BOSTON-FERN. WILD BOSTON-FERN.)—Hammocks, pen. Fla.—(*W. I., Mex., C. A., S. A.*)—Spores mature all year.—Fig. reduced.—For notes on varieties and forms, see Bull. Torrey Club **43**: 207–234. 1916.

The Boston-fern belongs to the plant pioneers of Florida. Apparently it came north of the Gulf Stream and established itself on the ancient tropical area in the northern part of the peninsula where it still persists. After the second tropical area, the Everglade Keys, were

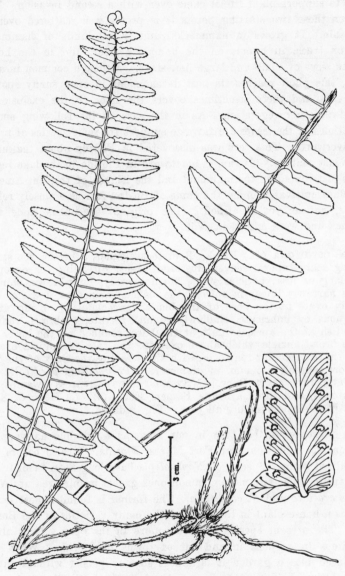

NEPHROLEPIS EXALTATA

ready to support plant life it came over with a second invasion. Now, between these two starting points it is pretty well scattered over the peninsula. It grows in hammocks, and in all kinds of hammocks, both on trees, in humus on the hammock floor, and in the honey-combed sides of small and large lime-sinks. Although common in dense shade, this plant reaches its best development in open sunny spots in hammocks and there sometimes covers the floor to the exclusion of nearly all other vegetation. As in the case of the following species, the petioles of the leaves are favorite support for some species of mosses and liverworts. This fern was discovered in Florida about the middle of the last century.[1] It ranges northward in Florida to the lake region, and is distributed on the mainland and the islands of tropical America. The plant cultivated under the name of Boston-fern is a closely related species, not as yet identified.   The original specimens came from Jamaica and were named in 1759.

2. **N. cordifolia** (L.) Presl. Rootstock slender, suberect, the stolons bearing scaly tubers: leaves clustered, erect, spreading, or drooping, 1 m. long or less; petioles stout, fibrillose-scaly, light-brown, shining; blades narrowly linear in outline, the leaflets numerous, 1–3 cm. long, broadly ovate at the base of the blade, lanceolate, to oblong above, contiguous or imbricate, shallowly crenate-serrate, glabrous, rounded or acutish at the apex, cordate at the base, rounded on the lower side of the broad auricle which above overlaps the rachis: indusia broadly reniform to orbicular-reniform, with sinus facing the apex of the leaf-let: sori scarcely 1.5 mm. in diameter. [*Polypodium cordifolium* L. *Aspidium tuberosum* Bory.]—(SWORD-FERN.)—Cypress swamps, old homesteads, and rubbish heaps, S. pen. Fla.—(*W. I., Mex., C. A., S. A., O. W.*)—Spores mature all year.—Fig. reduced.

The presence of this fern in our area, as a possible native plant, rests on one collection near Fort Myers, Florida. It also occurs as a naturalized plant. Species of *Nephrolepis* have long been favorites for cultivating. The two more common ones grown in our area are *Nephrolepis exaltata* and *N. cordifolia*. The former is found almost univer-sally as a house plant in the form of the many varieties of the Boston-fern. The present species is grown more in the open. It is almost ubiquitous in gardens in and out of towns in Florida. When once introduced into a garden it is almost sure to persist without further care. Although it is naturally a petrophyte, in cultivation it becomes a rampant epiphyte, especially seeking out the crowns and boots of palm trees. The plants have much the same habit as those of *Neph-*

[1] First collected by Florida by J. G. Cooper in 1859.

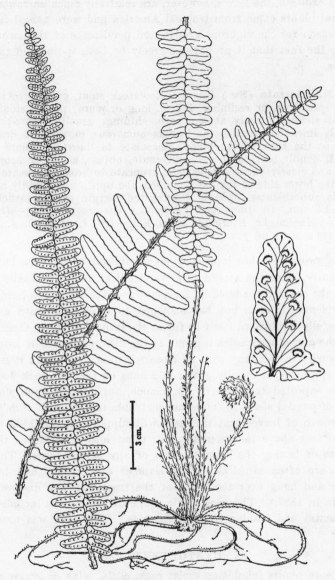

NEPHROLEPIS CORDIFOLIA

rolepis exaltata, the leaves, however, are relatively much narrower. The original plants came from tropical America and were named in 1753. The reason for the vigorous growth and persistence of this sword-fern lies in the fact that it propagates freely by both spores and tuberous stolons.

3. **N. biserrata** (Sw.) Schott. Rootstock stout, often erect: leaves erect, spreading, or reclining, 1–5 m. long or more; petiole stout, more or less slenderly scaly at the base, shining, usually brown; blades broadly linear in outline, the leaflets numerous, mostly 1–2 dm. long, ovate at the base of the blade, lanceolate to linear-lanceolate above, spaced, doubly serrate or doubly crenate, obtuse, acute, or acuminate, finely and closely pubescent beneath, truncate to broadly cuneate at the base, the lower side of the base rounded, the upper side slightly angled: indusia suborbicular, opening toward the margin of the leaflet: sori fully 1.5 mm. in diameter. [*Aspidium biserratum* Sw.]—(SWORD-FERN.)—Hammocks, Everglade Keys, Fla.—(*W. I., Mex., C. A., S. A.*)—Spores mature all year.—Fig. reduced.

This sword-fern has long been an inhabitant of Florida, but only, apparently, since the second primeval tropical area was finally raised above the sea and rendered fit for plant growth. It is less hardy than *Nephrolepis exaltata*, but has managed to creep northward and has successfully established itself as far as the latitude of Lake Okeechobee. Like the preceding species it grows in the different kinds of hammocks and usually in company with its close relatives. Although it is sometimes epiphytic, it usually grows in humus on the hammock floor. It may be expected anywhere in a hammock, but often in open places or areas of partial shade it forms impenetrable tangles with such a copious growth of leaves that the mass will support men walking over it several feet above the ground. This plant must be granted the distinction of having the longest leaves of any of our ferns. The long leaves are often vine-like. They clamber over shrubs and up tree trunks and hang over the limbs of the trees. It was discovered in Florida in 1887.[1] The geographic range of the species includes both continental and insular tropical America. This fern was named in 1801.

38. CYSTOPTERIS Bernh.

Delicate plants inhabiting moist rock, cliffs, talus or grassy places, with short branching rootstocks. Leaves erect or pendent, often several together or clustered, sometimes bulblet-bearing, not evergreen:

[1] First collected in Florida by Ralph M. Munroe in 1887.

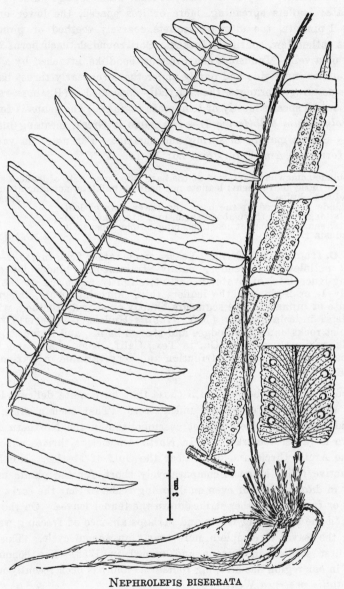

NEPHROLEPIS BISERRATA

petioles slender, scaly at the base, at least when young: blades 1- or 2-pinnate; leaflets spreading, more or less spaced, the lower ones at least 1-pinnate, the ultimate leaflets coarsely toothed or pinnatifid. Veins rather few, sparingly forked. Sori roundish, each borne on the back of a vein. Indusium membranous, hoodlike, attached by a broad base on its inner side and partly under the sorus, early thrust back by the expanding sporanges, thus partially concealed.—(BLADDER-FERNS.) —About 10 species mostly of temperate regions.—The genus is founded on *Polypodium bulbiferum* L.—The name is Greek, meaning bladder-fern.—Spores mature in spring and summer.—For notes on varieties and forms see Am. Fern. Jour. 26: 12–14. 1936.

Leaf-blade somewhat narrowed at the base, the lower pair of leaflets shorter than those above them: leaflets not bearing bulblets, not long-attenuate: indusia obtuse. 1. *C. fragilis.*
Leaf-blade broadened at the base, the lower pair of leaf-lets longer than those above them, long-attenuate: leaf-lets, some of them at least, bearing bulblets beneath: indusia truncate. 2. *C. bulbifera.*

1. **C. fragilis** (L.) Bernh. Leaves erect, rather firm, tufted, 1–4 dm. long; petioles very slender, mainly stramineous; blades lanceolate, oblong-lanceolate, or ovate in outline, slightly narrowed at the base, mostly 1- or 2-pinnate, the leaflets thin, lanceolate-ovate, irregularly pinnate or pinnatifid, the segments bluntly or sharply toothed, without bulblets: indusia obtuse. [*Filix fragilis* Underw.]—(BRITTLE-FERN.) —Moist rocks and cliffs, ledges and stream-banks, and in moist grassy woods, various provinces, Ga. to Tex., Calif., Alas., Lab., and Newf. Almost cosmopolitan in distribution and very variable in leaf-pattern. —Fig. reduced.

The brittle-fern belongs with those that have quite delicate leaves, both with regard to texture and pattern. That such a frail plant should have made itself almost cosmopolitan in the Northern Hemisphere is rather remarkable. In North America it thrives almost up at the Arctic Circle and down near the Gulf of Mexico. Northward the active foliar stage is comparatively short, for the plants usually grow in damp places or even on dripping rocks so that the early heavy frost or freezing weather strikes down the tender leaves. On the other hand in the south mild frosts and perhaps absence of freezing weather allow the leaves to complete more nearly an annual cycle. This fern was first studied in Europe and named in 1753.—The commonest form in our region has creeping rootstocks and has been recently named *C. fragilis protrusa* Weatherby.

2. **C. bulbifera** (L.) Bernh. Leaves weak, often tufted, decumbent, prostrate or pendent, up to 1 m. long or more; petioles slender, mainly

CYSTOPTERIS FRAGILIS

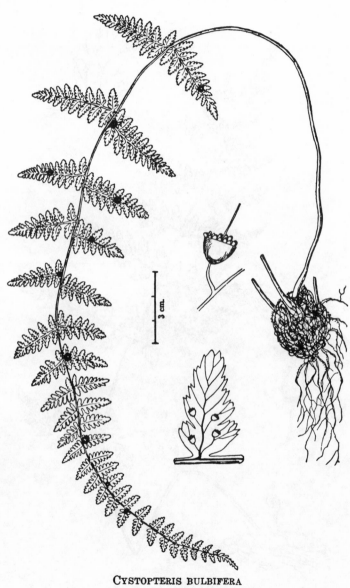

CYSTOPTERIS BULBIFERA

stramineous; blades lanceolate, sometimes elongate-lanceolate, from a broad base and frequently long-attenuate, 1- or 2-pinnate, the leaflets coarsely toothed or pinnatifid, commonly bearing underneath, in the axils of the leaflets and segments, fleshy bulblets, these early deciduous and giving rise to new plants, the segments toothed or incised: indusia truncate. [*Filix bulbifera* Underw.]—(BLADDER-FERN.)—Moist rocks, wet ledges, mossy cliffs, talus, shaded stream-banks, often on limestone, various provinces, Ga. to Arizona, Okla., Man., Ont., and Newf.—Fig. reduced.

The preceding species of *Cystopteris* reproduces by spores only, and is very widely distributed as already recorded. On the other hand the bladder-fern, reproducing by spores and also by bulblets which are borne on the backs of the leaflets, has a relatively restricted area of distribution within North America. The original specimens were collected in Canada and were named in 1753.

39. WOODSIA R. Br.

Small or medium-sized plants inhabiting exposed rocky places and cliffs, with branching but usually congested and thus tufted rootstocks. Leaves often evergreen, erect, clustered: petioles often jointed above the base and finally separating: blades 1- or 2-pinnate, rather narrow, the leaflets pinnatifid or pinnate. Veins few, mostly once forked. Sori round, borne on the simply forked free veins. Indusia inferior, either roundish and soon cleft into irregular lobes, or deeply stellate, the broad or filiform divisions partially concealed or inflexed over the sporanges.—About 25 species mainly of cold and temperate regions.— The genus is based on *Polypodium ilvense* L.—The generic name is in honor of Joseph Woods, an English architect and botanist.—Spores mature late spring–summer.—For notes on varieties and forms, see Am. Fern Jour. 26: 11. 1936.

Indusium small and inconspicuous, the ultimate lobes very narrow, filiform or nearly so.
    Lobes of the indusia more or less inflexed over the
        sporangia: petiole jointed near the base.   1. *W. ilvensis.*
    Lobes of the indusia mostly concealed beneath the
        sporangia: petiole not jointed.   2. *W. scopulina.*
Indusium ample and conspicuous, the lobes broad, jagged
    and more or less spreading.   3. *W. obtusa.*

1. W. ilvensis (L.) R. Br. Leaves tufted, often copiously and densely so, 1–4 dm. long; petioles stramineous or purplish, often scaly, jointed near the base; blades lanceolate in outline, glabrous or nearly so above, more or less covered with rusty chaff beneath, the leaflets approximate or crowded, sessile, pinnatifid or pinnately parted, the crowded segments oblong to ovate, obscurely crenate: sori near the

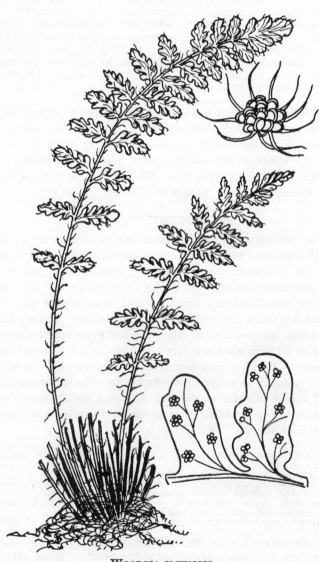

WOODSIA ILVENSIS

margins, confluent with age: indusium minute, largely concealed beneath the sorus, its filiform segments inflexed over the sporanges.— (RUSTY CLIFF-FERN.)—Exposed rocks, cliffs, talus, various provinces, N. C. to Minn., Alas., Ont., and Lab.—(*Greenland, Eurasia.*)

The woodsias are among the smaller ferns. Taxonomically they are situated close to the genus *Cystopteris*. The plants too, are often quite similar in habit, except that the woodsias are generally more copiously and densely tufted. The leaf-tissues of the plants of the two genera, however are quite distinctive. In the case of *Cystopteris* the leaf is quite delicate, the petiole and the rachis slender, and the blade thin, but in drying these parts are not particularly fragile; while in *Woodsia*, although the leaf is of firmer tissues, when dry the various parts are quite fragile and tend to crack and separate at almost any point. The present species is very widely distributed in North Temperate regions. Being partial to cold climates, it reaches our range only in the mountainous regions where, in the Blue Ridge, specimens have been found at an altitude of 4000 feet. The plants on which the name was based, in 1753, came from Europe.

2. **W. scopulina** D. C. Eaton. Leaves tufted, often copiously and densely so, 1–4 dm. long; petioles chestnut-colored, tawny, or coppery near the base, paler above, often finely scaly, not jointed; blades lanceolate, often finely glandular-puberulent and villous-hispidulous, the leaflets several to numerous, lanceolate, triangular, or ovate, pinnatifid or pinnate, the segments coarsely toothed or incised: sori near the margin, somewhat confluent: indusia mostly concealed, the very narrow lobes spreading.—(ROCK-WOODSIA.)—Crevices of rocks, cliffs, ledges, and talus, various provinces, N. C. to Calif., B. C., Ont., and Que.—Fig. reduced.

The outlying limits of the geographical areas of some well-known species are slow in coming to light. The present species is a conspicuous example. The plant was named and described in 1865 from specimens collected in the Rocky Mountains. As late as 1908 the geographic range was given as Quebec; South Dakota; Rocky Mountains.[1] In 1913 the range was considerably extended and was recorded as "Quebec to Ontario, British Columbia, Michigan, south in the Rocky Mountains to Arizona and in the Sierra Nevada to California."[2] The history of this species in our range starts about the beginning of this century. The discovery in our area is claimed for White Oak Mountain, North Carolina, in 1897. Four years later, in 1901, a discovery

[1] Gray's New Manual of Botany, 44.   1908.
[2] Illustrated Flora, ed. 2.   1 : 13.   1913.

3 cm.

WOODSIA SCOPULINA

was claimed for Great Craggy Mountain, North Carolina. Up to the present time the occurrence at the second of the localities in North Carolina has not been authenticated. However, quite recently the plant has been found in abundance near Erwin, Tennessee, near where the Blue Ridge and the Appalachian Valley meet. In recent years it has also been found at a number of localities in the mountains of Virginia and West Virginia.

In the latter location it grows with *W. obtusa,* from which it is easily distinguished by *W. scopulina's* more finely cut leaves, the more slender, redder, and more erect petioles, the numerous flattened hairs (instead of scales) on petioles, the numerous long-stalked (instead of nearly sessile) glands, the rootstock-scales which are narrow and have a deep-red longitudinal stripe (instead of the broader filiform-tipped scales of *W. obtusa,* which are a uniform light-brown or at most are merely splotched with red). In some of these characters the south-eastern form of *W. scopulina* differs quite materially from the type found in the west.

3. W. obtusa (Spreng.) Torr. Leaves clustered, 1–4 dm. long: petioles stramineous in drying, or purplish, often scaly, not jointed; blades broadly lanceolate or elliptic in outline, minutely glandular-pubescent, 1- or 2-pinnate at least below, the leaflets spaced, ovate, triangular-ovate or broadly lanceolate, pinnately parted or pinnatifid, the segments obtuse crenate-dentate: sori nearer the ·margin than the midvein: indusia conspicuous, splitting into several broad jagged lobes. (CLIFF-FERN.)—Rocks, cliffs, sandy banks and stone walls, various provinces, N. Fla. to Tex., Wis., B. C., Alas., and Me.—Fig. reduced.

As in the case of the two common species of *Cystopteris, C. fragilis* and *C. bulbifera,* there is considerable difference in the geographic distribution of our two more common eastern species of *Woodsia.* There is a certain similarity in the distribution of these pairs of representatives of the two genera. The preceding species, *W. scopulina* ranges far north in North America. On the other hand, the present species, like *Cystopteris bulbifera,* ranges less into boreal regions, but somewhat further south in eastern North America. Furthermore, as in the case of *Cystopteris bulbifera,* it is not native in the Old World. Instead of stopping in the mountains of North Carolina and Tennessee, this fern ranges southward to the highlands of Georgia and through the higher parts of the Gulf States, and was first collected in Florida by E. P. St. John and Herman Kurz, November 28, 1936. The original specimens came from a geographically intermediate point on

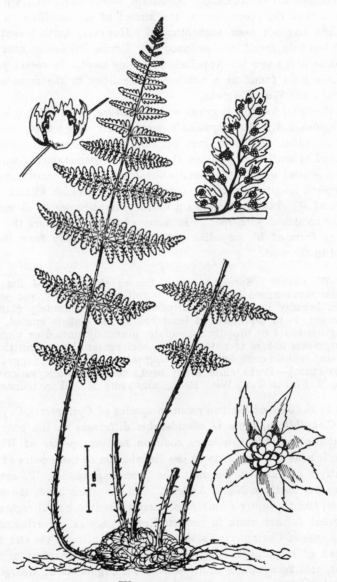

WOODSIA OBTUSA

the Atlantic seaboard, namely Pennsylvania, and were named in 1804. The highest altitude recorded for this woodsia is 4700 feet in the Blue Ridge.

40. **SPHENOMERIS** Maxon

Delicate terrestrial rock-plants with slender, scaly rootstocks. Leaves single or clustered on the creeping rootstock, ascending or drooping: petiole not jointed to the rootstock: blades obliquely 3–4-pinnate or 3–4-pinnatifid, the leaflets or ultimate segments narrow, separated, dilated upward, with apical teeth or incisions. Veins free, simple or sparingly forked. Sori dilated, borne at or near the apices of the leaf-segments on the top of a vein, single or several joined together. Indusia pocket-like, attached at the base and the sides, opening toward the tip of the leaf-segment.—Consists of the following species of the American tropics.—The genus is based on *Adiantum clavatum* L.—The name is Greek, alluding to the cuneate leaf-segments.

1. **S. clavata** (L.) Maxon.   Rootstock slender: leaves usually close together, 1–5 dm. long; petioles slender, purple or purplish at the base, yellowish above; blades deltoid-ovate to oblong in outline, as long as the petiole or shorter, bright-green, the rachises zigzag, the ultimate segments linear-cuneate, often narrowly so, 1–2 cm. long: veins running towards or into the sinuses of the toothed apex of the leaf-segments: indusia single at the clavate tips of the veins, or if joined borne on a translucent veinlet connecting the veins. [*Adiantum clavatum* L.   *Odontosoria clavata* J. Smith.]—Lime-sinks and honey-combed limestone pinelands, S. pen. Fla., particularly on the Everglade Keys and rarely in hammocks, Cape Sable region.—(*W. I.*)—Spores mature all year.—Fig. reduced.

The leaves of this plant are as little suggestive of a fern in pattern as any thing could be. They are more like a parsley than a fern. The West Indies form the center of the geographic distribution of this fern. From that reservoir plants evidently entered Florida in ancient times, but not with the earlier invasion. It maintains a mere foothold in the vicinity of the Gulf Stream.

Unlike the great majority of our ferns, which are strictly hammock-loving species, the present one is usually an inhabitant of the pinelands. It is confined mostly to a few lime-sinks in the Biscayne pineland and in the Long Key pineland. At these few localities it grows plentifully, usually lining the walls of the sinks. It was most plentiful on a large rocky island lying east of Naranja. This island is fully three miles long and averages over a mile in width. In 1907

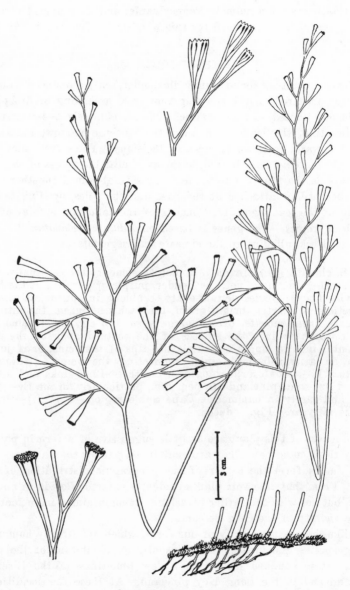

SPHENOMERIS CLAVATA

the rough rock surface was carpeted with this delicate fern. It may rarely be found in the hammocks of the Lossman's River limestone. It was discovered in Florida in 1903,[1] having been previously known only from the West Indies. This fern was named in 1753.

41. DENNSTAEDTIA Bernh.

Medium-sized or large terrestrial wood or hammock plants with wide-creeping scaly rootstocks. Leaves more or less clustered or colonized, but somewhat distant on the horizontal rootstock, erect, or arching: petiole glabrous, not jointed to the rootstock: blade ample, broad, 2–4-pinnate, the leaflets or ultimate segments generously toothed or lobed, giving the leaf a lacy appearance. Veins free, simple or pinnately branched. Sori marginal, solitary, terminal on the free veinlets. Indusium cup-like or pouch-like, formed in part of a more or less modified recurved segment of the leaf-margin.—Consists of about seventy-five species, mostly of tropical regions.—The genus is based on *Dennstaedtia flaccida* Bernh.—The name is in honor of August Wilhelm Dennstaedt, a Swedish botanist.

Leaflets with membranous blades : indusia pouchlike.   1. *D. punctilobula.*
Leaflets with subcoriaceous blades : indusia urceolate.   2. *D. adiantoides.*

1. **D. punctilobula** (Michx.) Moore. Rootstock very slender, rather extensively creeping, finely scaly, sometimes much-branched: leaves clustered or in colonies, up to 1 m. long; petioles slender, except at the base when young, dull, chaffless, pale-green; blades lanceolate to deltoid-lanceolate, acute to long-attenuate, 2-pinnate, the leaflets thin and delicate, numerous, lanceolate, the ultimate leaflets very numerous, elliptic to ovate, finely toothed or pinnatifid, the teeth or lobes oblique; rachis and under leaf-surface minutely glandular and pubescent: veins forked, very fine: sori minute, each on or at the base of a recurved toothlet, usually one at the upper margin of each lobe: indusium pouch-like, as long as wide. [*Dicksonia punctilobula* A. Gray.]— (HAY-SCENTED FERN. BOULDER-FERN. FINE-HAIRED FERN. PASTURE-FERN.)—On open hillsides, poor and often acid soil in coniferous or deciduous woods, and rocky bluffs, various provinces, Ga. to Ark., Minn., Ont., Que., and N. S.—Spores mature in summer.—Fig. reduced. —For notes on varieties and forms, see Am. Fern Jour. 26: 99. 1936.

Ferns may rarely be detected by the sense of smell. Of course, many of them have a slight amount of the peculiarly "ferny" odor, especially when bruised or in drying; but few species give off naturally the amount of fragrance characteristic of the hay-scented fern. In addition to its fragrance, an outstanding characteristic of this fern

[1] First collected in Florida by C. T. Simpson in 1903.

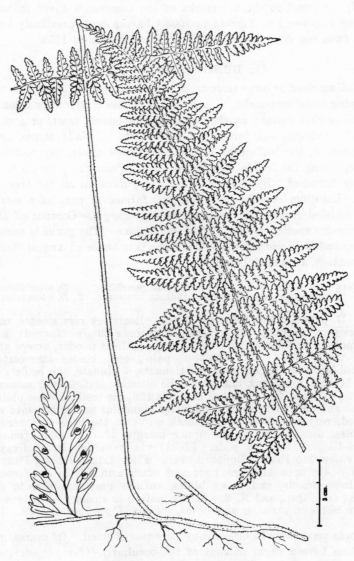

DENNSTAEDTIA PUNCTILOBULA

is the rather delicate and lacy appearance of the leaf-blade as a result of the numerous and finely cut leaf-segments. Although widely distributed, this fern prefers the more northern and higher plant-provinces. Stony hillsides and pastures and edges of woods are its favorite haunts. It occurs high up in the Blue Ridge, approximately 6000 feet altitude. The original specimens came from Canada and were named in 1803.

2. **D. adiantoides** (Humb. & Bonpl.) Moore. Rootstock stout as compared with that of the preceding species, scaly: leaves clustered, 1.5–2.5 m. long; petiole stout, brown, often scaly at the base when young, shining; blade ovate, usually broadly ovate in outline, as long as the petiole or longer, 2–3-pinnate, bright-green, the leaflets very numerous, subcoriaceous, the ultimate leaflets mostly ovate in outline, inequilaterally cuneate at the base, somewhat lobed or incised-toothed and crenate or dentate at the broad apex: veins pinnately branched, running nearly or quite to the margins of the segments: sori urceolate, about 1 mm. long, vertical. [*Dicksonia adiantoides* Humb. & Bonpl.] —Hammocks along Lake Okeechobee, Fla.—Spores mature all year.— Fig. reduced.

The ferns comprising this genus are confined, for the most part, to the tropics. There they vary greatly in size and pattern of the leaf, but they frequently are large. As in the case of several other tropical American ferns, this species now occurs rather remote from the typically West Indian parts of southern Florida. It may have been more widely scattered over the southern part of the peninsula at an earlier period. If it was, fires and ''freezes'' may be held responsible for its now shrunken range. Today it is hidden in the dense jungle about Lake Okeechobee where fires and freezing weather have until a recent date been rare occurrences. It was first found in Florida in 1926.[1] This fern furnishes a case where a plant may be very unlike a relative in habit, as on first sight this and the preceding species show little in common, yet in technical characters there is no doubt of their relationship. The original specimens came from Tropical America and were named in 1810.

42. ONOCLEA L.

Succulent, tender plants with widely creeping black scaleless rootstocks. Leaves dimorphic, erect, borne singly or several together upon the rootstocks: foliage leaves conspicuous, the blades broad, pinnatifid into few, undulate, toothed, or lobed segments. Veins forming numerous areolae, which are larger toward the midrib and smaller

[1] First collected in Florida by J. K. Small and C. A. Mosier, May 14, 1926.

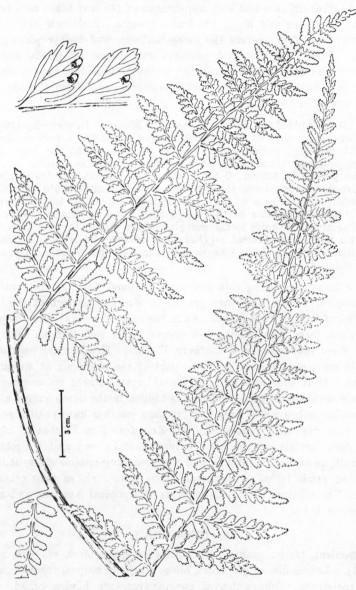

3 cm.

DENNSTAEDTIA ADIANTOIDES

towards the margin. Sporophyls less conspicuous than the foliage leaves, rigidly erect, the leaf-segments tightly contracted and bipinnatifid, the ultimate divisions round, berry-like, completely concealing the sori, finally dehiscent, but persistent. Sori roundish, on elevated receptacles, partially covered by delicate hood-shaped indusia fixed at the base.—The genus consists of only the following species.—The name is Greek, and was not originally associated with this plant.

1. O. sensibilis L. Rootstocks widely spreading, thus forming colonies of leaves: foliage leaves 3–13 dm. high; blades triangular to ovate, deeply pinnatifid, the segments few, irregularly lanceolate-elliptic, lanceolate, broadly linear or ovate, entire, undulate, or sinuate-pinnatifid, the teeth or lobes obtuse or rounded: sporophyls rigid, 3–7 dm. high, the contracted divisions separated, borne in a narrow panicle and resembling elongate berries, or a cluster of long berries, ascending or appressed to the rachis. Intermediate forms between foliage leaves and sporophyls occur.—(BEAD-FERN. SENSITIVE-FERN.)—Moist soil in woods, stream-banks, river-bottoms, meadows, hillsides, fence-rows, and bogs, various provinces, N. Fla. to Tex., Minn., Ont., and Newf.—Spores mature in fall.—Fig. reduced.—For notes on varieties and forms, see Am. Fern Jour. 26: 15, 16. 1936.

The reason for the dimorphic habit of this ancient type of fern is a mystery. This peculiarity is not of recent origin, but dates back to the Cretaceous period among the fossils of which a related plant appears. A somewhat similar case is that of the chain-fern, *Lorinseria areolata,* but in the present case the modification of the sporophyl is carried to a greater degree, the sporangia being wrapped up in separate little globular bundles and arranged in strings. When sporophyls are not available the sterile leaves of these two species may be distinguished by noting the opposite leaflets of this fern as compared with the alternate leaflets of the chain-fern. A cool climate is most favorable, if not necessary, for the best growth of the sensitive-fern. The ice-age may have been responsible for extending the range of the ancestors of this fern southward even as far as Florida. The leaves are not evergreen like those of some of the northern ferns, in fact they are very sensitive to frost, but the rootstocks or underground stems are perfectly immune even to the extreme cold of Canada. The sensitive-fern grows rather sparingly in the southern part of our range. It is more abundant in many of the other states east of the Rocky Mountains, where it ranges from sea-level to moderately high altitudes. It was first found in Virginia and named in 1753. The maximum altitude in the Blue Ridge seems to be about 3300 feet.

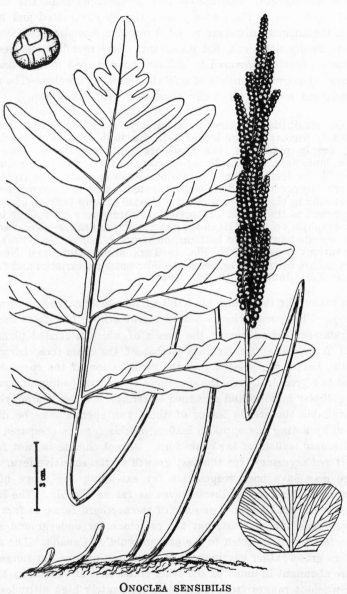

ONOCLEA SENSIBILIS

Family 3. **CERATOPTERIDACEAE**

Floating-fern Family

Aquatic or amphibious succulent plants, floating, or anchored in mud, with a short horizontal fleshy stem. Leaves of two kinds, often viviparous, the foliage leaves floating or emergent, pinnatifid or 1–several pinnate, the sporophyls erect, several times pinnately divided, the ultimate segments narrow, often linear, the margins revolute, but without included veinlets. Sporangia scattered in 1 or 2 longitudinal lines, on the elongate areolae, nearly sessile, globose, thin-walled, with a complete or vestigial ring.— Comprises the following genus:

1. **CERATOPTERIS** Brongn.

Plants soft-succulent, often growing and floating in wide mats. Leaves tender: petioles stout, with large air-cavities: blades broad, the margins uneven. Sporophyls usually more divided than the foliage leaves.—(Floating-ferns.)—Few species, estimated at 4, widely distributed in tropical and subtropical regions.—The name is Greek, referring to the antler-like sporophyls.—Spores mature all year, unless the plants are frozen.

Mature sterile leaves floating; blades pentagonal in outline, 20 cm. long or less, 2–4-pinnatifid : annulus few-celled, the lip-cells wanting : spores 32 in each sporangium.   1. *C. pteridoides.*
Mature sterile leaves emergent ; blades broadly deltoid in outline, 25–50 cm. long, 2-pinnate : annulus and lip-cells well-developed : spores 16 in each sporangium.   2. *C. deltoidea.*

1. C. pteridoides (Hook.) Hieron. Plants floating or partly submerged: larger floating leaves 25 cm. long or less; petioles expanded, bulbous; blades pentagonal, 6–20 cm. long and broad, 1–3 times pinnatifid, the ultimate segments broadly ovate or deltoid, or in succeeding leaves 2–4 times divided, with narrowly oblong segments; leaves of emersed plants similar, but the petioles not expanded, the areolae relatively large, rather abruptly diminishing towards the margins from quite large and long cells within: sporophyls 40 cm. long or less, the segments linear or linear-lanceolate; annulus 4–10-celled.—(Floating-fern.)—Still or slow-flowing water, Fla.—(*W. I., S. A.*)—Fig. reduced.

Ferns in general, like other plants, have developed a wide range of resistance to heat and cold. The floating ferns came into Florida during the first primeval plant invasion from the tropics. The plants still maintain their old-time sensitiveness to cold. The foliage cannot long

3 cm.

CERATOPTERIS PTERIDOIDES

survive freezing temperatures, at least not directly. They have always remained tropical types of ferns. However, their experience with freezing weather has developed a method of self-preservation. When the foliage leaves are frozen buoyancy is lost and the entire plant sinks to the bottom where it is protected against cold. Buds are formed which in due time sprout and rise to the surface to continue growth, as does also the old plant after a period of rest. Other plants, old or young, are stranded beneath protecting vegetation at the beginning of the winter dry season. When warmer days come again they resume growth and root in the soft mud awaiting the summer floods. Their aquatic habitat and fragile tissues lend them ready distribution by water-birds. After the pioneers of our two species were brought across the Gulf Stream, the water-birds doubtless were responsible for spreading both species northward in Florida and along the Gulf Coast. *Ceratopteris pteridoides* is apparently the more abundant of our two species of floating-fern in Florida, and grows further north in the peninsula than the following. It was discovered in our range in 1879,[1] a year later than *Ceratopteris deltoidea*. It has been found growing abundantly in the headwaters of the St. John's River on the eastern side of the peninsula and in the upper waters of the Withlacoochee River on the western side. Outside of Florida this fern is known from Cuba and from northern South America. The species was discovered in British Guiana and described in 1825.

2. **C. deltoidea** Benedict. Plants partly submerged: larger mature leaves 25–50 cm. long; petioles not bulbous, 10–20 cm. long; blades deltoid, 20–35 cm. long, 15–25 cm. broad, acute, 2-pinnate or pinnatifid, with 5–8 pairs of pinnae, the lowest pinnae broadly deltoid, 3–4 cm. long, acute or acutish, the areolae rather small and numerous, gradually diminishing towards the margins from longer ones within: sporophyls 40–65 cm. long, the petioles flattened, the blades deltoid, 40 cm. long or less, 4 times pinnately divided, the ultimate segments narrowly linear; annulus 40–50-celled.—(FLOATING-FERN.)—Still, or slowly moving water, Fla. to La.—(*W. I., S. A.*)—Fig. reduced.

Both of our floating-ferns seem to have reached primeval Florida during the earlier invasion of tropical plants. A certain difference of experience with climatic conditions has been registered in the greater resistance to cold weather in the case of the present species. It has migrated slightly further north than the preceding species. Although only lately described, this was the first of our two species to be found

[1] First collected in Florida by A. H. Curtiss in the St. Johns River, in 1879.

CERATOPTERIS DELTOIDEA

in Florida. It was collected in 1878 in Prairie Creek northeast of Charlotte Harbor. Outside of our range it is known from some of the West Indian islands and northern South America. The original specimens were collected on the Orange Bay River, Jamaica, W. I., and the species was described in 1909.

FAMILY 4. GLEICHENIACEAE

NET-FERN FAMILY

Xerophilous erect or straggling plants, the rootstock elongate. Leaves not jointed to the rootstock, the petiole usually passing into an indeterminate rachis with one or several pairs of opposite branches which are 1- or 2-pinnate and determinate or 1–several times dichotomous. Sori borne on the veins, without indusia. Sporangia subsessile, pyriform, 2–6 radial in one row on a low receptacle or rarely more numerous and in several ranks.—Comprises three genera and about one hundred and fifty species.

1. DICRANOPTERIS Bernh.

Rootstock long-creeping, often branched. Leaves rather wiry and firm: leaflets pectinate, deeply pinnatifid or pinnate. Veins free, 1–several times forked—in our species.—About one hundred and ten species, mostly tropical.—The name is Greek, referring to the forking of the veins of the leaves.

1. **D. flexuosa** (Schrad.) Underw. Rootstock coarse, wiry, ultimately more or less muricate: petioles terminated by a ternate rachis, the branches repeatedly forking, the nodes with a pair of small stipule-like pinnae at the sides; leaflets linear, lanceolate, or oblong-lanceolate, 9–25 cm. long, deeply pinnatifid, the segments linear or nearly so, notched at the apex: veins 2–4-forked: sori borne on one or two veins in each group. [*Mertensia flexuosa* Schrad. *Gleichenia flexuosa* Mett.]—(NET-FERN.)—S. Ala.—(*W. I., Mex., C. A., S. A.*)— Spores mature in summer and fall.—Fig. reduced.

No representative of this fern family was known to be native in North America, north of Mexico, prior to 1913. Its occurrence in Alabama evidently is the result of spores carried by the wind from southern Mexico or the West Indies. The Alabama locality is Mon Louis Island. The habitat is pine barren country. The geological formation is a clay, evidently part of the delta of the Mobile River.

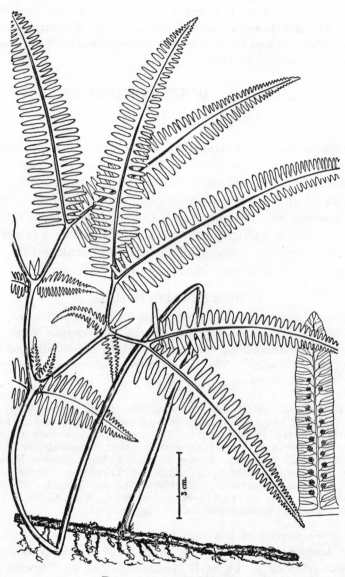

3 cm.

DICRANOPTERIS FLEXUOSA

This fern was originally described from Brazil in 1824, under the
generic name *Mertensia*. It is now known to range from southern
Mexico to Brazil, and occurs in the West Indies. The species was
discovered in our area in 1913.

FAMILY 5. **SCHIZAEACEAE**

CURLY-GRASS FAMILY

Erect and rigid or climbing (twining), mainly terrestrial plants,
sometimes tufted. Leaves with simple pinnate or dichotomous
and palmate-lobed blades. Sporophyls borne on the ordinary
leaves or on specialized leaves. Sporangia borne in double rows
on narrow specialized leaf-lobes or leaf-segments, ovoid, sessile,
naked or indusiate, provided with a transverse apical ring, opening vertically by a longitudinal slit. Prothallia green.—Comprises six genera or more. Besides the following another genus,
Schizaea, is represented in New Jersey, Nova Scotia, and Newfoundland. The curly-grass family is very sparingly represented
in eastern North America.

Plant erect: leaves not twining.
    Sporophyls borne on specialized leaves: leaves with narrow simple,
       terete or flattish blades.   1. ACTINOSTACHYS.
    Sporophyls borne on the elongate pinnae of
      ordinary leaves: leaves with pinnately com-
      pound blades.   2. ANEMIA.
Plant climbing: leaves twining.   3. LYGODIUM.

1. **ACTINOSTACHYS** Wall.

Epiphytic, low, sometimes tufted, often humus plants, often grass-
like. Leaves erect: blades simple, linear, often narrowly so, triquetrous or flattish, 1-veined. Sporophyls erect: segments (sporangio-
phores), terminal in a penicillate tuft, spuriously digitate. Sporangia borne in 2 rows, sometimes apparently in 4 rows by the crowding together. Indusium continuous, formed of the narrowly reflexed
margin of the segments.—Four species, tropical and subtropical.—The
name is Greek, referring to the form of the sporophyl.—Represented
in the United States by the following species:

1. A. Germani Feé. Leaves rigidly erect, one or several from a
bristly tuber which is usually buried in rotten wood, borne upon a
slender chestnut-brown rootstock, 5–15 cm. long, about 1 mm. in diameter, triangular or flattish in drying: spore-bearing segments (sporan-

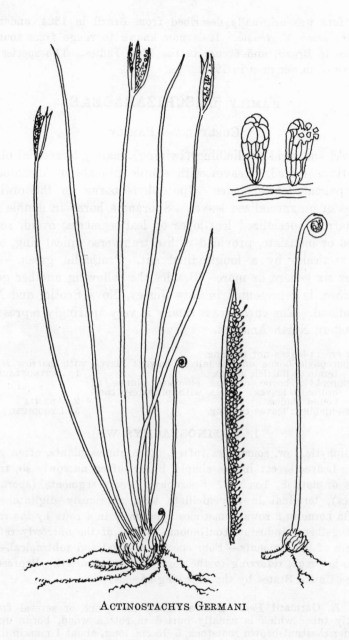

ACTINOSTACHYS GERMANI

giophores) linear, 1–4 pairs, 8–15 mm. long, the sporangia in 2 rows, often appearing in 4's from crowding, the midvein pilose.—Low hammocks, Everglade Keys.—(*W. I.*)—Spores mature all year.

The word fern to the botanist is inclusive. To the non-botanist it may rather be exclusive. What is known to be a true fern to the botanist, may seem nothing more than a stem of a grass or sedge to the non-botanist. The present plant has little to recommend it as a fern to the popular mind. Considering the paucity of spores in the case of this fuzzy fern as compared with the prodigious number of spores produced by some of its associates, it is difficult to realize how it migrated from the West Indies to Florida. It appears to reproduce itself in a very limited number of individuals. This relative of the northern curly-grass has been found but twice in Florida. It was discovered in low hammocks about the headwaters of the Miami River in 1904,[1] and over a decade later in Royal Palm Hammock. It was always found growing in decaying wood, sometimes in stumps over a meter from the ground. The maximum altitude at which it occurs is only a few feet above sea-level in Florida. The original specimens were collected in Guadeloupe, West Indies. The species was described in 1866. In the north *Schizaea pusilla,* generically a close relative of *Actinostachys,* occurs in New Jersey, Nova Scotia, and Newfoundland.

2. ANEMIA Sw.

Terrestrial erect plants, with creeping or ascending rootstocks. Leaves clustered or distichously placed on the rootstock (in our species) with the lowermost pair of leaflets (sporophyls) of some of the blades greatly elongate, often overtopping the rest of the blade, and bearing numerous panicles of sporangia in 2 rows on the back of very narrow divisions, the sporophyls thus erect, contracted, long-stalked. Foliage part of the leaf-blade pinnatifid, pinnate, or pinnately decompound, the lobes or leaflets with forking free veins.—A tropical genus of several dozen species; besides the following another occurs in western and southern Texas.—The name is Greek, referring to the exposed sporophyl.

1. **A. adiantifolia** (L.) Sw. Plants 1 m. tall or less, with creeping, stoutish, brown-scaly rootstocks: leaf-blades triangular-ovate to deltoid in outline, 12–30 cm. long, on usually elongate, wiry, slightly pubescent petioles, which are dark at the base and paler above, pinnately decompound; ultimate segments obovate or cuneate, or rarely almost linear,

[1] First collected in Florida by A. A. Eaton in 1904.

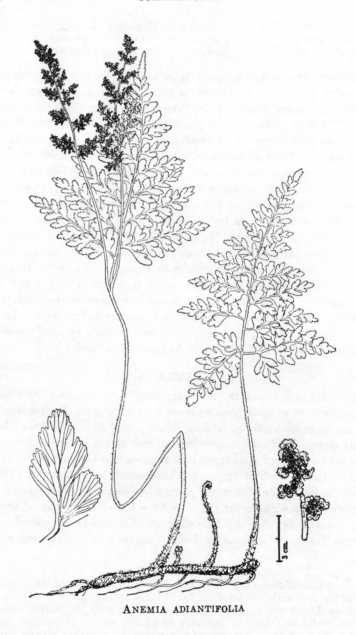

ANEMIA ADIANTIFOLIA

shallowly toothed or lobed, striate above with numerous flabellate veins: panicle of the sporophyl ascending or erect, slender-stalked, tan or brown, fuzzy on the back, continuous and dense or slightly interrupted and open. [*Osmunda adiantifolia* L.]—(PINE-FERN.)—Dry rocky pinelands and hammocks, Everglade Keys and vicinity, Fla. and lower Florida Keys; also rocky outcrops, cliffs and ledges, Oligocene Island region.—(*W. I., Mex., C. A., S. A.*)—Spores mature all year southward.—Fig. reduced.

Two species of *Anemia* have reached the continental United States. One is in the Texano-Mexican region; the other in Florida. This fern long ago spread over insular and continental tropical America, and northward of the Gulf Stream passed beyond the technical boundary of the tropics. However, after it became established in Florida its migrations ceased, and in historic times, at least, it has been best known as a fern of the oolitic limestone regions of the southern end of the peninsula and the Keys. Recently (1934) it has been found in an isolated region further north, indicating that it came into what is now Florida with the first migration from the tropics. Though more common and evenly distributed in the pinelands than in the hammocks, this fern usually grows two or three times as large in hammocks as in pinelands. A form with very finely divided foliage leaf-blades is found occasionally. In the northern locality just referred to the plants are in more circumscribed stations. Citrus County seems to be its center of distribution in the upper part of the peninsula. There it occurs on rocky hammock floors, rock outcrops, cliffs, and the walls of limesinks. It seems to have been first collected in Florida in the early part of the last century either on Key West or on Big Pine Key.[1] The maximum altitude at which it occurs in Florida is about 100 feet above sea-level in the Oligocene Island region where plants only an inch or two in height sometimes reach full maturity. The original specimens were collected on Dominica, West Indies. The species was named in 1753, under the genus *Osmunda*.

3. LYGODIUM Sw.

Vines with elongate climbing or twining leaves, the rachis wiry and more or less flexuous. Leaves consisting of stalked lobed, pinnate, or pinnately compound secondary divisions arising in pairs from alternate slender or short naked stalks, the primary petiolules; leaflets mostly lobed. Veins several times forked, mostly free, the midvein mostly zigzag. Sporophyl-leaflets usually narrower. Sporangia obovoid, borne

[1] First collected in Florida by J. L. Blodgett about 1838.

in a double row upon the contracted and more or less revolute segments. Indusia scale-like or clamshell-like, hooded, fixed by their broad
bases to short oblique veinlets, opening antrorsely.—Comprises nearly
thirty species which are most abundant in the tropics.—The name is
Greek, alluding to the pliable rachis.

Foliage leaflets simple; blades palmately lobed, orbicular or broadly reniform in outline, the lobes slightly unequal: sporophyl-leaflets much
contracted, scarcely any leaf-surface showing be-
tween the indusia.   1. *L. palmatum.*
Foliage leaflets compound; blades 1–3-pinnate, the
segments linear, linear-lanceolate, lanceolate, or
ovate, the terminal much larger and longer than
the others: sporophyl-leaflets somewhat contracted,
much leaf-surface showing between the indusia.   2. *L. japonicum.*

1. **L. palmatum** (Bernh.) Sw. Rootstock slender, wide-creeping:
leaves 5–15 dm. long, narrow, vine-like; foliage leaflets simple, orbicular to broadly reniform in outline, 2.5–6 cm. long, 3–8 cm. broad,
pedatifid one-half to one-third the distance to the cordate base into 4–8
spreading unequal lobes, thus subpalmate, the outer lobes small,
rounded or emarginate at the apex, the main ones elliptic to lanceolate,
obtuse or obtusish: sporophyl-leaflets usually terminal, 3- or 4-pinnate,
the divisions narrowly linear or linear-lanceolate, covered beneath with
the scale-like indusia, somewhat revolute: indusia 0.6–0.7 mm. wide, the
free edge uneven.—(Climbing-fern.)—Low woods, shaded banks,
meadows, and pastures, various provinces, N. Fla. to Tenn., Ohio,
N. H., and Mass.—Spores mature in summer and fall.—Fig. reduced.

To the uninitiated popular mind a fern masquerading as a vine is
almost incredible. However there are native ferns in our range that
climb, some by their stems, others by their leaves. There are also
recliners. Whatever its remote history may have been, this fern is now
localized in the eastern United States. Thus it is a temperate region
plant. Its distribution in latitude is not as great as many of our ferns.
In the North it does not reach Canada. It apparently reached Florida
from the north—its ancestors, perhaps, driven southward during the
progress of the ice-age. It is somewhat local in its general area of
distribution, but occurs as far north as New Hampshire and out to
the western parts of Kentucky and Tennessee. It is most abundant
in the last-named state. High soil-acidity is most favorable to it. The
original specimens were collected in Pennsylvania, and the species was
described in 1801. However, in the latter part of the eighteenth century William Bartram observed this fern in North Carolina, recording
that he "Observed near Cambleton a very curious scandent fern
(*Pteris scandens*) rambling over low bushes, in humid situations; the
lower larger fronds were digitated, or rather radiated, but towards the

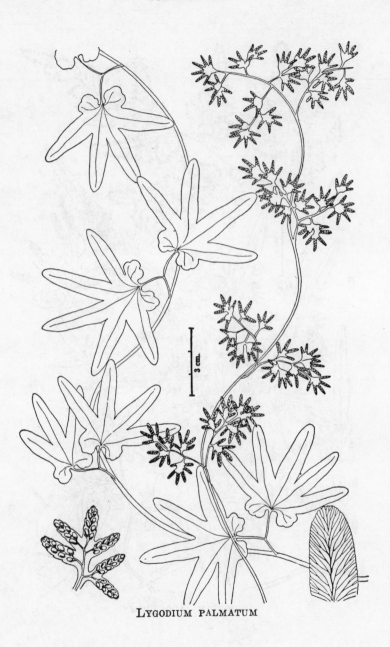

LYGODIUM PALMATUM

LYGODIUM JAPONICUM

tops of extremities of the branches they became trifid, hastated, and lastly lanceolate: it is a delicate plant, of a yellowish lively green, and would be an ornament in a garden.'' Its maximum altitude, in North Carolina, is between 3000 and 4000 feet; thence it ranges to sea-level. Besides climbing-fern, it is known as creeping-fern, Hartford-fern, and Windsor-fern.

2. **L. japonicum** (Thunb.) Sw. Rootstock slender, often much-branched: leaves elongate, up to 5 meters long, relatively broad, vine-like; foliage leaflets ample, pinnate, petiolate, ovate-deltoid in outline, 10–20 cm. long, 9–12 cm. broad, with 2–5 pairs of more or less elongate linear-lanceolate, lanceolate, or ovate segments, these gradually smaller toward the apex and often confluent, the lower ones pinnately incised or lobed, with the terminal lobes elongate; sporophyls similarly divided but with the divisions 1–3-pinnate, usually more deeply incised, the ultimate segments subrhombic, flabellate, or obtusely ovate, relatively shorter and broader than those of the foliage leaflets.—(JAPANESE CLIMBING-FERN.)—Coastal Plain, roadsides, woods, and creek-banks, Fla.[1] to La. and N. C. Nat. of E. Asia.—Spores mature in summer and fall.—Fig reduced.

The great majority of the species of *Lygodium* are natives of the Old World, largely Asiatic. Some typically Asiatic genera of plants, also have one or more representatives in eastern North America. The preceding species, *Lygodium palmatum*, represents such a case. The present species, naturalized from Asia, gives us two species of *Lygodium* for the southeastern states. The native species is more wide-spread geographically, but the range of the introduced one will doubt-less increase as ferns become more widely cultivated. The present species was described from Japanese specimens, under *Ophioglossum*, in 1784. There is no possibility of confusing these two climbing-ferns, as the one (*L. palmatum*) has palmately compound leaves, while the other (*L. japonicum*) has pinnately compound leaves as already recorded in the Key.

FAMILY 6. **OSMUNDACEAE**

CINNAMON-FERN FAMILY

Tall leafy terrestrial plants, with creeping, suberect or erect rootstocks. Leaves erect or spreading: blades 1- or 2-pinnate: veins free, mostly forked, extending to the margins of the leaflets:

[1] First collected in Florida at Aspalaga Bluff by Herman Kurz and E. T. Wherry, 1932.

petioles winged at the base. Sporophyls occupying a whole leaf or combined with a foliage leaf. Sporangia naked, large, globose, mostly stalked, borne on modified contracted leaflets, or in clusters (sori) on the lower surface of the leaflets, opening in 2 valves by a longitudinal slit; ring few-celled or wanting. Prothallia green. —There are three genera in this family, the following, and two others in the Old World.

1. OSMUNDA L.

Leaves in large crowns, erect, from a thickened, creeping or erect rootstock: blades once-pinnate or twice-pinnate, some wholly spore-bearing, or some partly, either near the middle or at the apex, the spore-bearing blades or leaflets very much contracted and devoid of chlorophyl (red or brown). Sporangia short-stalked, thin, reticulate, opening in halves, a few parallel thickened cells near the apex representing the rudimentary transverse ring. Spores copious, greenish.—Besides the following species, four or five additional ones occur in other parts of the world.—The genus is based on *Osmunda regalis* L.—The name is Saxon for the god Thor.—Spores mature in spring and summer or all year southward.—For notes on varieties and forms, see Am. Fern Jour. 25: 98–100. 1935.

Foliage leaves with 2-pinnate blades, some of them terminating in a compound sporophyl: veins mostly twice-forked.   I. REGALES.
Foliage leaves with 1-pinnate blades: sporophyls various, either occupying the middle part of a foliage leaf or a complete separate leaf, in either case 2-pinnate: veins mostly once-forked.   II. CINNAMOMEAE.

I. REGALES

Leaves borne in a crown on the rootstock, the leaflets (pinnules) separated, decidedly serrulate.   1. *O. regalis.*

II. CINNAMOMEAE

Sporophyls and foliage-leaves wholly different, the spore-bearing pinnae cinnamon-colored: leaflets of the foliage leaves with a tuft of tomentum at the base.   2. *O. cinnamomea.*
Sporophyls partly different from the foliage-leaves, the green and ultimately brown spore-bearing pinnae borne on the middle of the rachis, with normal foliage pinnae below and above them: leaflets of the foliage leaves without a tuft of tomentum at the base.   3. *O. Claytoniana.*

1. O. regalis L. Rootstock erect, at least partly so, often forming a tussock: leaves clustered, erect, often stiffly so, 6–20 dm. tall, the foliage leaf and sporophyl combined; blades 2-pinnate, broad and open, the leaflets separated, elliptic, 1.5–8 cm. long, serrulate and some-

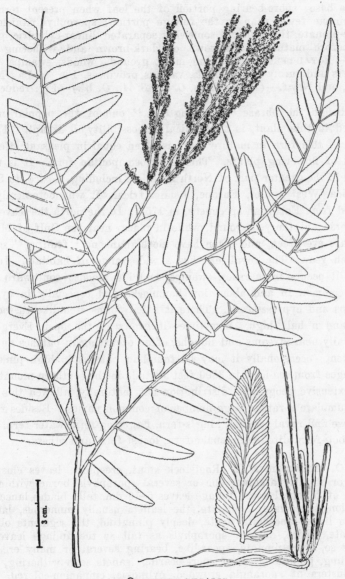

OSMUNDA REGALIS

3 cm.

times crenately lobed near the base, sessile or slightly stalked, oblique at the base; spore-bearing portion of the leaf when present terminal, the pinnae fewer than in the foliage portion: sporophyl panicle-like, thrice-pinnate, the divisions somewhat separated, linear-cylindric, greenish before maturity, red-brown or dark-brown and withering with age.—(ROYAL-FERN.)—Wet and moist grounds, woods, swamps, bogs, thickets and rarely in pinelands, various provinces, Fla. to La., Nebr., Sask., and Newf.—(*W. I., Mex., C. A., S. A., O. W.*)—Fig. reduced.

Although the phrase ''flowering-fern,'' one of the popular names applied to this plant, is a botanical impossibility, it is apt. For, a patch of this fern in mature spore is often equal in pleasant effect to a bed of flowering plants. This is a cosmopolitan fern. It is to be found in the greater part of North America, including Mexico, to South America, West Indies, Europe, Asia, Africa. It was botanically described from European specimens, in 1753. In the north the leaves are not persistent the year round, while in places near the Gulf of Mexico they are evergreen, and often have more than one ''fruiting'' season in each year. The royal-fern has a wide range of habitats. In the north it occurs in marshes, swamps, and low woods; southward it is most common in and about low hammocks and especially in cypress swamps and cypress-heads. There it often forms stem-like tussocks a foot and a half high. Sometimes it grows in the open Everglades especially near streams and sloughs, often occurring in patches an acre in extent; occasionally it may be found in patches in high pineland. It ranges from sea-level to 3800 feet altitude in the southern mountains. The extensive geographic distribution has, naturally, allowed this fern to accumulate a rather large number of common names. Besides royal-fern, we find royal-osmund, king's-fern, flowering-fern, water-fern, tree-fern, bog-fern, ditch-fern, snake-fern, locust-fern, and others.

2. O. cinnamomea L. Rootstock stout, creeping: leaves clustered erect or slightly arching, one or several sporophyls borne within the crown of foliage leaves; foliage leaves 5–16 dm. tall; blades lanceolate to oblong-lanceolate, 1-pinnate, the leaflets usually numerous, lanceolate to linear-lanceolate, acute, deeply pinnatifid, the segments oblong or ovate, entire, obtuse: sporophyls as tall as the foliage leaves or nearly so, twice-pinnate, spear-like, bearing several or many erect or ascending, pinnate pairs of spore-bearing leaflets soon withering, with the clusters of sporangia crowded, cylindric, cinnamon-colored, soon withering.—(CINNAMON-FERN.)—Swamps, low woods, moist thickets, and stream-shores, various provinces, Fla. to Tex., N. M., Minn., and Newf.—(*W. I., Mex., C. A., S. A., Asia.*)—Fig. reduced.

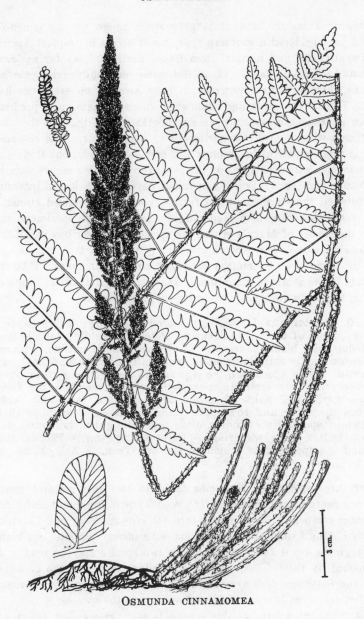

OSMUNDA CINNAMOMEA

Judging from its latitudinal geographic range the cinnamon-fern should be considered a southern type, for it occurs in tropical America, both continental and insular, from Brazil northward, as far as Minnesota and Newfoundland. If it did come originally from northern regions where it is not evergreen, it later assumed an evergreen habit in the Florida peninsula and southward where its main spore-producing season is frequently as much as six months earlier than in the north, sometimes with several ''flowering'' stages in a year. The cinnamon-fern is often plentiful in swamps and open wet woods, but it does not occur in such extensive areas as the royal-fern. It also occurs naturally in Europe and Asia. Forms sometimes develop with leaves intermediate between the sterile and the fertile types. It is named cinnamon-fern from the color of its sporangia. The original specimens came from the colony of Maryland and the species was described in 1753.

The cinnamon-fern reaches a greater altitude than the other two species of *Osmunda*. Specimens occur at nearly (or quite) 6000 feet altitude in the southern mountains. In different parts of its range this fern is known as swamp-brake, bread-root, fiddle-heads.

3. O. Claytoniana L. Rootstock stout, creeping: leaves clustered, arching, some of them spore-bearing about the middle; foliage leaves 6–20 dm. tall; blades lanceolate to oblanceolate in outline, 1-pinnate, the leaves usually rather numerous, lanceolate to linear-lanceolate, acute or acutish, deeply pinnatifid, the segments ovate to oblong-ovate, obtuse, entire or shallowly toothed: sporophyls often taller than the foliage leaves, bearing 1–7 pairs of spore-bearing pinnate, ascending, leaflets between the lower and the upper plain and longer leaflets, with the clusters of sporangia cylindric, close together, green, becoming dark-brown, brittle, early withering.—(INTERRUPTED-FERN.)—Woods, thickets, and swamps, various provinces, Ga. and Tenn. to Ark., Minn., and Newf.—(*Asia.*)—Fig. reduced.

Our three species of *Osmunda* fall into two very natural groups. The one contains the royal-fern (*O. regalis*) with bipinnate leaf-blades, the other comprises the cinnamon-fern (*O. cinnamomea*) and Clayton's-fern (*O. Claytoniana*), both of them with merely pinnate leaf-blades. Although the royal fern and the other two species may be readily distinguished by their foliage leaves, the foliage leaves of the cinnamon-fern and Clayton's fern are very much alike. However, the sporophyls are distinctive, as is shown in the above key to the species.

The interrupted-fern, as this species is sometimes called, has a wide geographic distribution, which lies mainly east of the Mississippi River and north of Georgia. It must be considered as a northern type. It

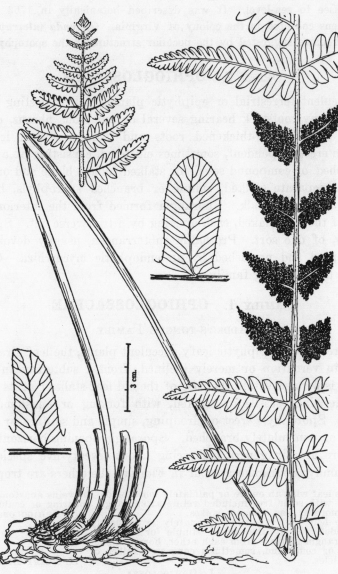

OSMUNDA CLAYTONIANA

also occurs in Asia. It ranges from 6000 feet in North Carolina and Tennessee to sea-level. It was described botanically in 1753 from specimens collected in the colony of Virginia. *Osmunda interrupta* is another name suggested by the peculiar structure of the sporophyl.

ORDER 2. **OPHIOGLOSSALES**

Succulent terrestrial or epiphytic plants, each consisting of a short fleshy rootstock bearing several or numerous fibrous, often fleshy or tuberous-thickened roots and one or several leaves. Leaves erect or pendent, sometimes clustered, consisting of a simple, lobed, or compound sessile or stalked foliage blade and one or several separate stalked, simple or branched sporophyls, borne upon a common stalk. Sporangia formed from the interior tissues of the leaf, naked, each opening by a transverse slit. Spores yellow, of one sort. Prothallia subterranean, usually devoid of chlorophyl and nourished by an endophytic mycorrhiza.—Comprises the following family:

FAMILY 1. **OPHIOGLOSSACEAE**

ADDER'S-TONGUE FAMILY

Terrestrial or epiphytic leafy succulent plants, the leaf straight, erect in vernation or merely inclined, from a subterranean bud which is formed within the base of the old leaf-stalk or at its side. Foliage blade sessile or stalked, with forking or anastomosing veins. Sporophyls erect or drooping, simple and solitary or clustered, or paniculately branched. Sporangia opening horizontally. —There are six genera embracing about seventy-five species in this family: four genera occur in Florida; the others are tropical.

Foliage leaf with an entire or palmately lobed blade, the veins anastomosing and with some free included veinlets : sporangia cohering or coalescent in more or less elongate spikes. I. OPHIOGLOSSA.
Foliage leaf with 1–4-times pinnately or ternately divided blade, the veins simple or forking : sporangia distinct from each other, borne in simple or compound, sometimes congested spikes or panicles. II. BOTRYCHIA.

I. OPHIOGLOSSA

Plants terrestrial : leaf erect ; foliage blade relatively small, entire : sporophyl solitary, erect. 1. OPHIOGLOSSUM.
Plants epiphytic : leaf pendent ; foliage blade typically palmately lobed : sporophyls usually few or

several, pendent from the side of the leaf-stalk
below the blade or from the base of the blade.   2. CHEIROGLOSSA.

II. BOTRYCHIA

Leaf-segments succulent, and crenulate, fimbriate, or
serrulate, the epidermal cells straight: veins several-times forked: bud for the following year
enclosed in the base of the common stalk.   3. BOTRYCHIUM.

Leaf-segments membranous, pinnatifid, the epidermal
cells curved: veins mostly once-forked: bud for
the following year exposed along one side of the
stalk.   4. OSMUNDOPTERIS.

1. OPHIOGLOSSUM L.[1]

Terrestrial, low, often diminutive plants, with small erect, oblique, or
horizontal, fleshy, sometimes tuber-like rootstocks, and fibrous, naked
roots. Leaves solitary or 2–6 together, erect, consisting usually of a
cylindric common stalk bearing at its summit a simple entire, broad or
narrow, sessile or short-stalked foliage blade and a single erect sporophyl with a long stalk and a terminal spike formed of 2 rows of globose
coalescent sporangia. Spores copious, sulphur-yellow. Bud for the following season borne at the apex of the rootstock, exposed, free.—
(ADDER'S-TONGUES. ADDER'S-FERNS. RATTLESNAKE-FERNS.)—Comprises more than fifty species, widely distributed. Besides the following,
five or six other species occur in North America. The name of the genus
is Greek, in allusion to the tongue-like narrow tip of the sporophyl.
The often apparent scarcity of the adder's-tongues is due largely to the
small size of the plants, simple structure, and close association with
other herbaceous vegetation.

At the base of the foliage blade several (3–13 or more) equal or unequal
     veins arise and extend with branches throughout the blade.
   Veins equal in thickness or substantially so.   I. ISONEURA.
   Veins unequal, the midvein decidedly thicker
     than the laterals and with strong branches.   II. HETERONEURA.
At the base of the foliage blade a strong vein ex-
   tends, arises and branches widely thus occupy-
   ing nearly or quite the entire blade.   III. MONONEURA.

I. ISONEURA

Rootstock cylindric.
   Plants large, usually from 12 to 20 cm. tall:
     midvein usually unbranched.
     Basal veins 13 or more: primary areolae
       broad with many included veinlets:
       blade apiculate.   1. O. Engelmanni.
     Basal veins 7–11: areolae narrow, with
       few included veinlets: blade not apicu-
       late.   2. O. vulgatum.
   Plants small, usually under 8 cm. tall: all
     veins usually forking repeatedly: basal
     veins 3–5: areolae irregular with very few
     included veinlets: blade ovate, acute at
     the apex.   3. O. tenerum.
Rootstock globose, 0.5–1.4 cm. in diameter: plants
   1.5–15 cm. tall: foliage blades usually cordate
   or deltoid ovate.   4. O. crotalophoroides.

[1] Text contributed by Edward P. St. John.

II. Heteroneura

Midvein straight or nearly so and extending to
the apex of the foliage blade, its branches
ascending and not much curved : connecting
veinlets usually straight.

Plants large, usually 10–20 cm. tall : foliage
blade usually deltoid-ovate with truncate
or cuneate base, obtuse to acute at the
apex, the basal veins 5–7 : rootstock
cylindric.   5. *O. floridanum.*

Plants small, usually under 5 cm. tall : rootstock cylindric : foliage blades ovate, horizontal, sessile, 2–8 mm. long, succulent,
slightly concave, apiculate at apex, the
basal veins 3 : areolae without included
veinlets : sporophyl very slender : spike 1
mm. or less in thickness.   6. *O. Pumilio.*

Midvein often not extending to the apex of the
blade, its branches curved : connecting veinlets curved or irregular : plants usually 3–9
cm. tall : rootstock ovoid : basal veins 5–7 :
primary areolae large with many included
veinlets : spike usually 1 mm. or less in thick-
ness and up to 2 mm. long.   7. *O. dendroneuron.*

III. Mononeura

Plants small, 3.5–5 cm. tall : foliage blade orbicular-ovate to broadly ovate, sessile, somewhat
clasping, apiculate, a strong vein arising at
base of blade with few spreading branches
which occupy nearly or quite the entire blade :
rootstock globose or ovoid.   8. *O. mononeuron.*

1. O. Engelmanni Prantl. Rootstock cylindric or subcylindric:
leaves usually 2–5 together, 0.5–3 dm. tall : foliage blade usually near
the middle, sessile, bright-green, glabrous, elliptic or rarely ovate or
obovate, 3–9 cm. long, apiculate at the apex, more or less cuneate at
the base: basal veins 13 or more running well up toward the tip of the
blade, connected laterally thus forming large and rather wide areolae;
areolae with numerous very slender included veinlets: spike 1.5–3.5 cm.
long, apiculate: sporangia globose, 10–27 along each side of the rachis
or rarely fewer: spores pitted.—Shaded hillsides, banks, rocks, thickets,
cedar-glades, and limestone ledges, various provinces, Fla. to Tex., Calif.,
Kans., and Va.—(*Mex.*)—Spores mature in spring and early summer.

Many years, perhaps half a century, elapsed between the discovery
and the describing of this species. In 1893 when named the plant had
been definitely reported only from Texas and Missouri. The original
specimens were collected at Comanche Springs, Texas. Subsequent exploration discovered the fern in the area bounded by Virginia, Texas,
California, and Missouri. A much later discovery in northern Florida
added the southeastern corner of the United States to its geographic
range. Recently it has been found in the Oligocene Island region of
Florida. The wide geographic range is also reflected in the altitudinal
range, for a maximum of 2000 to 3000 feet seems to be the record.

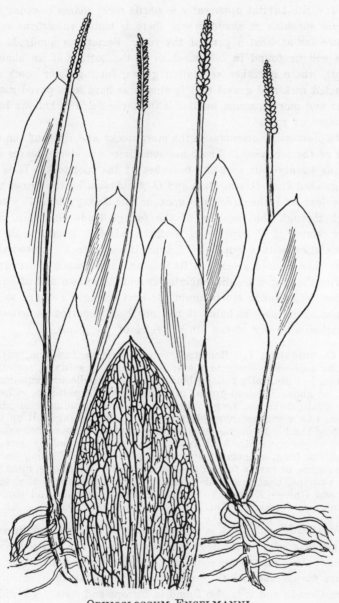

OPHIOGLOSSUM ENGELMANNI

Its favorite habitat apparently is sterile rocky places in cedar woods, either in sunshine or shade, where there is highly calcareous soil and moisture for at least a part of the year. Sometimes hundreds of the plants will be found in full sunshine at the bottom of an abandoned rock-pit, where no other vegetation grows, forcing their roots among compacted rock and gravel that is almost as hard as a paved road. A similar and more common habitat is in sterile fields in hollows between low ridges of rock.

Ophioglossum Engelmanni is the most stocky and rigid of the *Ophioglossa* of the southeast. There are sometimes five sterile leaves and as many as twenty-four root-like branches of the rootstock. It is easily distinguished from *O. vulgatum* and *O. floridanum* by the firmer texture of the leaf and the apiculate apex of the foliage blade. Curiously enough through the venation of the foliage blade this fern is most closely related to *O. capense* of southern Africa. Whatever its habits in association with a symbiotic fungus, it seems to be somewhat more regular than related species in its seasonal appearance above ground; but after the spores are disseminated it soon dies down and often leaves no trace until growth starts again the next spring. Perhaps as a consequence of its ascetic habit it has not been reported as growing in association with any of the other species of the genus.

2. O. vulgatum L. Rootstock subcylindric or fusiform, with few, cord-like somewhat elongate roots: leaves usually solitary, sometimes 2 together, 1–4 dm. tall: foliage blade near the middle or sometimes well below or above it, deep-green, glabrous, sessile, spatulate, elliptic, or rarely ovate, 3–12 cm. long, obtuse at the apex, gradually or abruptly narrowed to a cuneate base: basal veins 7–11, running well up toward the tip of the blade, connected laterally, thus forming rather small and narrow areolae; areolae with few very slender included veinlets: spike 1.5–3.5 cm. long, apiculate: sporangia globose, 10–27 along each side of the rachis, or rarely fewer: spores reticulate.—Meadows, open woods, bogs, swamps, pastures, and thickets, various provinces, Fla. to Tex., Que., and Ont.—(*Eurasia.*)—Spores mature in spring and summer.— For notes on forms, see Am. Fern. Jour. 25: 97.   1935.

Ophioglossum vulgatum is a northern type of fern and during the Ice Ages may have been forced southward far enough to reach northern Florida.[1] It is rare so far south and is there largely replaced by *Ophioglossum floridanum* and *O. Engelmanni*. In the north it extends into eastern Canada and it is also found in Europe and Asia. Its wide geographic range is paralleled altitudinally by its occurrence from 2500

[1] First found in Florida by John LeConte in the earlier part of the nineteenth century.

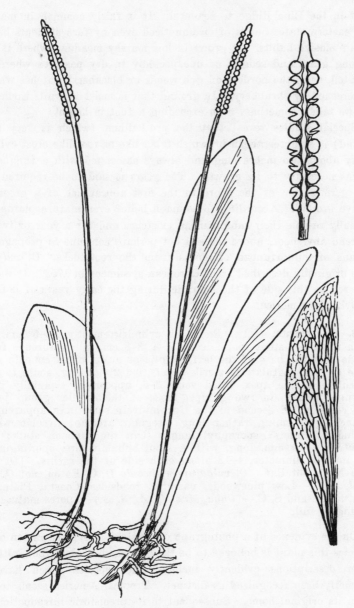

OPHIOGLOSSUM VULGATUM

feet in the Blue Ridge to sea-level. It is fairly common in many of the eastern states but is often unnoticed even by fern students because of its elusive habits. It grows in low marshy meadows where it hides among grass and sedges, or unexpectedly in dry pastures where it is stunted, or at the borders of rich woods or blackberry patches where it is screened by shrubbery. In ground that is moist it fruits earlier and grows taller, sometimes even exceeding a foot in height.

Special studies reveal that the prothallium (which is very rarely found) is a subterranean brownish tuber-like or root-like erect cylindric body about two inches long and always associated with a fungus that seems necessary to its growth. Ten years is said to be required from the germination of the spore to the first appearance of a green leaf above ground. According to common belief even mature plants occasionally resume their subterranean existence and for a year or two fail to send any shoots above the soil but perhaps continue to propagate by means of subterranean offshoots from the rootstocks. *O. vulgatum* was originally described from European specimens in 1753. It was discovered on this side of the Atlantic during the early years of botanical activity in America.

3. O. tenerum Mett. Rootstock cylindric, mostly 2.5–5 mm. long, with relatively stout roots: leaves 1–4, 3–8 cm. tall, glabrous: foliage blade near the base of the leaf, elliptic or ovate, often cuneate at the base or even spatulate in sterile plants, 0.6–2 cm. long, acute to short-apiculate at the apex, basal veins 3–5, appearing, especially in the younger plants, in two groups, those of the smaller group joining the veins which ascend to the tip; midvein sometimes apparent and branching, forming rather long irregular areolae; areolae without included veinlets: sporophyl longer than the common stalk: spike stoutish, 3–10 mm. long, with a stout subulate tip: sporangia 0.5–0.8 mm. in diameter, 4–12 along each side of the rachis. [*O. pusillum* Nutt. not Raf. *O. vulgatum nudicaule* D. C. Eaton, not *O. nudicaule* L.f.]—Low pinewoods, pastures, roadsides, Coastal Plain, pen. Fla. to La. and S. C.—(*Cuba, Mex., C. A., S. A.*)—Spores mature from spring to fall.

On the evidence of a photograph of Mettenius' type specimen of this species this plant is believed to be the one which he described, although later descriptions evidently include other species which have not formerly been recognized as distinct. Tropical America seems to have been its original home. Subsequent to its prehistoric introduction into Florida it failed to spread beyond the southeastern corner of the Coastal Plain, where it ranges near sea-level from southern Florida to Louisiana

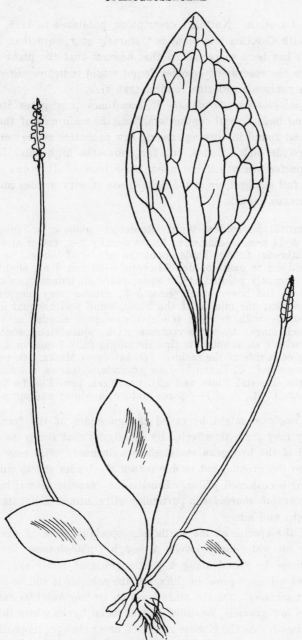

OPHIOGLOSSUM TENERUM.   × 2

and South Carolina. Nuttall's description, published in 1818, records that in South Carolina this plant is "scarcely ever more than an inch high." It has been suspected on that account that the plant is commoner than the records of colonies found would indicate. Recent discoveries in peninsular Florida confirm that view.

Like *Ophioglossum floridanum* it sometimes propagates itself by underground buds several centimeters from the main axis of the plant. It is oftenest found in openings among saw palmettos at the borders of pineland ponds and marshes, not far above the high-water line. It seems to prefer sandy soil but needs some humus. It grows on bare ground in full sunlight, or in the light shade of wiry grasses and other thin herbaceous growth.

4. O. crotalophoroides Walt. Rootstock globose or subglobose, tuber-like, 5–14 mm. in diameter: leaves usually 2–4, rather stout, 2–15 cm. tall, glabrous: foliage blade about the middle of the leaf or usually below it, elliptic to ovate or deltoid-ovate, 8–30 mm. long, slightly acuminate or abruptly pointed at the apex, rounded, truncate, subcordate, or cordate at the base: basal veins, 5–7; areolae very unequal, long and narrow near the middle of the blade, small and unequal near the margin, usually with no free veinlets: sporophyl slender or stoutish, usually much longer than the common stalk: spike stout, conic, 4–12 mm. long, with a stout subulate tip: sporangia fully 1 mm. in diameter, 3–12 along each side of the rachis. [*O. bulbosum* Michx. *O. vulgatum crotalophoroides* D. C. Eaton.]—Low grounds, meadows, old fields, and grassy slopes, Coastal Plain and adj. provinces, pen. Fla. to Tex. and S. C.—(*Mex., C. A., S. A.*)—Spores mature in winter and spring.

The *Ophioglossa* might be called the gnomides of the fern world. Apparently they are little affected by cataclysms that sweep the surface of the soil if the hypogean rootstock is uninjured. Fire may denude and blacken the ground, but in due season the tender shoots will again rise in their accustomed places. Erosion may deposit several inches of soil, but *O. crotalophoroides* in particular will continue to lift its slender stem to light and air.

Most of the species of the southeast, especially those of diminutive size, grow on water-made levels, although *Ophioglossum floridanum* will sometimes be found along a gentle grade of moist soil; and *O. Engelmanni* will even grow on cliffs, but the colonies it will be observed occupy flat terraces. On the other hand *O. crotalophoroides* favors, in addition to low grounds, locations on rich moist banks where the soil is easily displaced. As the globose rootstock never changes its position the ascending axis has to adjust itself to surface conditions; and the

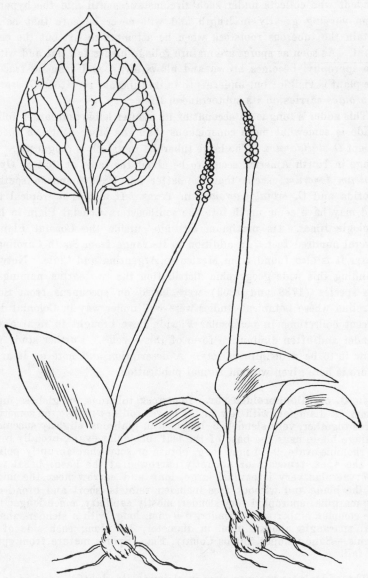

OPHIOGLOSSUM CROTALOPHOROIDES

student who collects under such circumstances will find the hypogean stem varying greatly in length and will never be sure that he will obtain the tuberous rootstock when he attempts to lift out the entire plant. As soon as spores are mature foliage blades fall flat and wither, the sporophyl becomes brown and blows away, and soon no trace of the plant is visible; but underneath in its tuberous rootstock *O. crotalophoroides* carries on its subterranean life.

This adder's tongue on account of its stouter habit and larger foliage blade is somewhat more conspicuous than the other southern species, except *O. floridanum.* The large tuberlike rootstock is diagnostic. The range in North America seems to be about the same as that of *Ophioglossum tenerum* except that the latter has been found in southern Florida and *O. crotalophoroides* in Texas. It also is a tropical type and may have come north into the southeastern Coastal Plain in later geologic times. Its maximum altitude outside the Coastal Plain is several hundred feet. In addition to its range from South Carolina to Texas it is also found from Mexico to Argentina and Chile. Notwithstanding this wide geographic distribution the two earlier namings of the species (1788 and 1803) were based on specimens from South Carolina where botanical studies were well under way in Colonial days. Recent collections in peninsular Florida have brought to light a very slender and often diminutive form of this species. Further study may show it to be a definite variety. A description and note on it and a figure is here given without formal publication.

4a. O. crotalophoroides var. Rootstock tuberous, subglobose, up to 7 mm. in diameter, with few roots: leaves solitary or two, or sometimes three together, very slender, 5–10 cm. tall, glabrous, slightly succulent: foliage blade near the base of the leaf, orbicular-ovate, broadly ovate, or rhombic-ovate, 9–15 mm. long, obtuse or somewhat abruptly pointed at the apex, truncate or abruptly narrowed at the base: basal veins 5–7; aerolae very irregular, large, long and narrow near the middle of the blade and without free included veinlets, short and broad near the margins: sporophyl very slender, mostly capillary, much longer than the common stalk: spike slender, 6–9 mm. long, with a slender-subulate tip: sporangia about 1 mm. in diameter, 3–7 along each side of the rachis.—Sandy slopes, Citrus County, Fla.—Spores mature from spring to fall.

The adder's-tongue was slow in claiming its rightful position in the Florida flora. A form of *Ophioglossum vulgatum* was found in the northern part of the state more than a century ago. Shortly before the middle of the past century collections of both *Ophioglossum tene-*

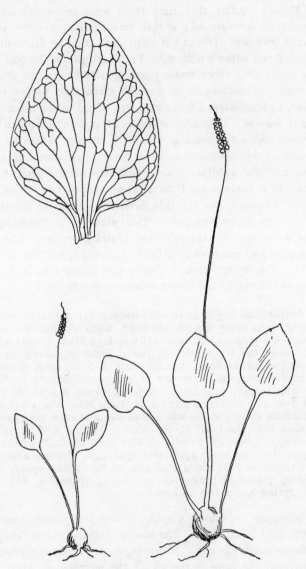

OPHIOGLOSSUM CROTALOPHOROIDES var.

rum and *O. crotalophoroides* were made in the Apalachicola River region of Florida. After that time there were occasional collections, especially of *O. tenerum* and a then unrecognized novelty, since described as *O. Pumilio*. It was not until 1935 that the distribution and abundance of the adder's-tongue in Florida began to become evident. Within a short time three undescribed species have been discovered, and the earlier collections of *O. Pumilio* given their proper standing. In addition, *Ophioglossum Engelmanni* was added to the list which now totals eight species. The more widespread eastern American species, *Ophioglossum vulgatum*, remains the most elusive. Three or four of these species of *Ophioglossum* occur in great abundance, and curiously enough in artificial habitats. The specimens of the present variety were found in a shallow road material-pit, about four miles east of Floral City, Florida.[1] So far this variety remains the rarest of the endemic Florida adder's-tongues. This plant is provisionally interpreted as a variety of *Ophioglossum crotalophoroides*. The leaf is usually smaller and much more delicate in texture, and the stalk more thread-like. The foliage blade is flat or less folded than in *O. crotalophoroides*, and the spike has a very slender subulate tip.

5. O. floridanum E. St. John. Rootstock subcylindric, very short when young, with many almost capillary, much elongate roots: leaves solitary or 2–5 together, 1–2.5 dm. tall: foliage blade usually above the middle or near the top, yellowish-green, glabrous, sessile or with a broad short petiole-like base, rhombic-ovate, 2–5 cm. long, obtuse at the apex, abruptly narrowed, truncate or somewhat cordate at the base, with the midrib alone running through the blade to near the tip, with a row of two or few large aerolae on each side, and smaller broad areolae between them and the small ones along the margin; basal veins 5–7, running into the base of the blade; aerolae with very few included veinlets: sporophyl usually shorter than the stalk of the foliage blade: spike 1–4 cm. long, apiculate: sporangia globose, about 1 mm. in diameter, yellow, 7–31 along each side of the rachis: spores pitted.— Moist grassy places in pinewoods and along roadsides, Fla.—Spores mature in spring and rarely in summer.

Adder's-tongues are elusive plants. Scarcely any other ferns are so easily overlooked in the field. The simple leaf and entire foliage-blade offer little to catch the eye. However, a well-directed *Ophioglossum* hunt discovered the present species on the morning of April twelfth, nineteen hundred and thirty-five. The discoverers wrote concerning it: "Your letter of the eleventh [1935], inquiring if we had collected

[1] Discovered by Robert P. St. John, March 30, 1936.

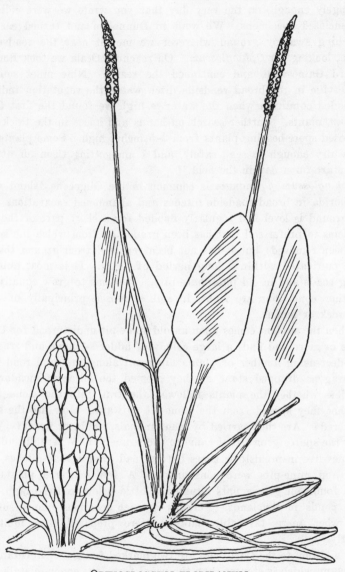

OPHIOGLOSSUM FLORIDANUM

Ophioglossum vulgatum in Florida was received on the thirteenth. Strangely enough, on the very day that you wrote we were collecting the enclosed specimens. We went to Dunnellon and turned eastward searching swampy ground wherever we met it near the roadside to Ocala, looking for *Ophioglossum*. On reaching Ocala we took Route 41 toward Gainesville, and continued the search. Nine miles south of Gainesville in the broad roadside ditch where the vegetation indicated a flooded condition when the water is high we found the first *Ophioglossum* plants. Further search on hands and knees in the thick grass disclosed spore-bearing plants from 2–5 inches high. Some plants seem to be dry enough to send safely, and I am getting them off at once, as I start for a day in the field.''

Ophioglossum floridanum is common in the Oligocene Island region of Florida in broad roadside ditches and abandoned excavations where the ground is level and regularly flooded for a short part of the year. It seems to prefer soil that has been graded or from which the surface has been removed: but it has not been reported from ground that has been cultivated within a long period of years. It is most abundant along roads and in old phosphate pits. It seems to grow equally well, if other conditions are right, in soil composed principally of either lime-rock or humus.

When the student comes upon an old stone-pit undisturbed for twenty years or more and finds a large colony of adder's-tongue and traces an ever-decreasing number of plants filing out along the sand road where the wagons dropped stone as they crossed the adjacent meadows, he wonders whether the plants followed the trail into the stone-pit, or whether they spread from the stone-pit outward. How are the spores scattered? Are they carried by men, animals, winds, or water? Where were the spores grown that came to the stone-pit? Where did adder's-tongues live in prehistoric times before road grades, road-ditches, road-pits, and mine-pits were constructed? A few scattered plants have been found on grassy flats situated a little below extreme high water near ponds in pinelands. Perhaps in such locations plants survived and when more favorable habitats were prepared then multiplied greatly.

In addition to the type there are two marked forms—**O. floridanum f. favosum,** which is stouter than the usual form, the common stalk sometimes over 2 mm. in diameter: leaf 6–10 cm. tall: foliage blade symmetrical, broadly deltoid-ovate, often apiculate or nearly so, broadly cuneate or subcordate at the base: basal veins usually 3: areolae

more regularly hexagonal than in the typical form and much more
uniform in size, the included veins frequent, often nearly subdividing
the larger areolae: spores maturing in May.—Roadside ditch 8 miles
south of Gainesville, Florida, occupying a few square yards at one end
of a colony of the species and at other stations. **O. floridanum f. reticulosum,** a slender plant, the common stalk sometimes less than 1 mm. in
diameter: leaf 12–20 cm. tall: foliage blade deep-green, ovate-lanceolate,
blunt or rounded at the tip, gradually narrowed or acute at the base,
usually curved to one side: basal veins usually 7, the adjacent veins
parallel with the midvein for a short distance: areolae much smaller
and narrower than in the typical form: spores apparently maturing in
late summer, sparingly as late as December.—In an abandoned clay-pit
near Weed's Landing Bridge, east of Floral City, Florida; occasional
at the more southern stations for the species and perhaps occupying
damper soil than the typical form.

In some colonies *Ophioglossum floridanum* propagates freely through
its root system.   A location was found where the plant grew abundantly
in alluvial soil unencumbered with rocks or roots of trees.   A hole was
excavated and from its side a sheet of metal was pushed underneath
the plants and parallel to the surface.   When the turf was lifted and
carefully washed as many as eight plants were found to be connected.
Just how extensively the plants are joined is uncertain, for the roots
are very brittle and a group can scarcely be lifted without breaking;
but probably the inter-connection is far-reaching.

    6. **O. Pumilio** E. St. John.[1]   Rootstock fusiform or cylindric, with
several slender roots: leaves mostly solitary or 2 together, mostly 3
cm. tall or less: foliage blade mostly below the middle, horizontal,
bright-green, glossy and succulent, sessile or nearly so, elliptic to oval,
sometimes narrowly so, 2–8 mm. long, apiculate, gradually or abruptly
narrowed at the base, with the midrib alone running through to the
tip, with a row of long areolae between the midrib and the one or two
rows of shorter aerolae near the margin: basal veins mostly 3; areolae
with few or no included veinlets: stem of the sporophyll capillary,
mostly longer than the stalk of the foliage blade, spike stout, 4–6 mm.
long, acute or apiculate: sporangia subglobose, about 0.5 mm. in diameter, 5–9 on each side of the rachis.—Flatwoods, above flood level, in

[1] OPHIOGLOSSUM **Pumilio** E. St. John, sp. nov., rhizomate e fusiformi
cylindrico, erecto: foliis singulis binatisve, more 2–4 cm. longis; lamina
ovata, sessili, 2–8 mm. longa; venis basalibus 3: areolis paucioribus, venulis
inclusis nullis: sporophyllo gracillimo: spica longe apiculata.   In planitie
Serenoibus repentibus frequenti, per semitam qua ad "The Cove" itur, in
oriente sole a Floral City, in Florida, E. P. St. John, 5.I. 1937, *578* in part.,
typus in herb. Hort. Bot. Noveboracensis.

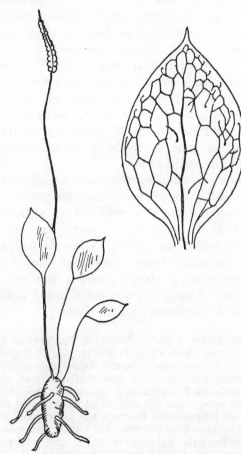

OPHIOGLOSSUM PUMILIO. ×4

openings between saw-palmetto, N.E. and pen. Fla.—Spores mature from spring to fall.

Students have searched in a general way for months throughout the Southeast for *Ophioglossum* and have not found a specimen. They were handicapped by not knowing habitats or season. Nevertheless those who failed had reason to feel chagrin, for in spite of not being seen or described *Ophioglossa* grow by millions throughout central Florida and adjacent regions.

Ophioglossa in the southeast grow on unattractive ground—not such as ferns are supposed to like. It should be level except for *Ophioglossum crotalophoroides* and *O. Engelmanni* which will climb banks or cliffs. Excepting the habitats of the latter fern it must be moist and often is subject to temporary flooding such as occurs in many roadside ditches, and in old stone-pits where heavy rains rush down the sides, making temporary ponds and leveling the bottom with eroded material. One can ride along a highway and note probable habitats and while mistakes are frequent one often chooses correctly. Then where a favorable spot is located perhaps hands and knees are needed, for the simple leaf is small and hard to see, and there is no pronounced color to attract.

The plants of *Ophioglossum Pumilio* are especially elusive, for they are the smallest species in the southeast. Mature fruited plants have been found with foliage-blades only 2 mm. long. It grows in such locations as are favored by *O. tenerum* but perhaps further out from the palmetto and in more sun. This species was found at Rosewood, Florida, as early as 1877[1] and was independently collected near Fort Myers, Florida, in 1916,[2] nearly forty years later. These specimens were referred to *O. tenerum*. It was not suspected as being an undescribed species until independently collected in various localities in Florida in 1936.[3] This species is related to *Ophioglossum floridanum* by the vertical rootstock and the venation, but it is a much smaller plant. From *Ophioglossum tenerum*, with which it has been confused, it differs by the vertical cylindric or fusiform rootstock, more succulent leaf, subterranean stalk of the horizontal foliage blade, and in its venation.

[1] Discovered by A. P. Garber, November, 1877.
[2] Collected by Jeanette P. Standley, September 4, 1916.
[3] Collected at Yulee, and at various stations in the Oligocene Island region, Florida, by Edward P. St. John; also near Yulee by Mary W. Diddell.

7. **O. dendroneuron** E. St. John.[1] Rootstock ovoid to short with many strong rootlets: leaves 1–5, 3.5–9 cm. tall: foliage blade bright-green, elliptic or rarely ovate, 1–3 cm. long, 0.5–1 cm. wide, acute at apex, cuneate at the base: basal veins 5–7, the midvein rarely extending to the apex, much more prominent than the laterals, its branches curved and connecting veinlets curved or irregular; primary areolae large with many included veinlets: sporophyl slender: spike elongate, up to 1 mm. thick and 1–1.8 cm. long, with long apiculate tip.—About pinewoods ponds and roadside ditches, pen. and N. Fl.—Spores mature in late spring and summer.

Like several others of the small *Ophioglossa* of the southeast this plant seems to be found only in the acid soil of the low pinewoods. While it is sometimes found in association with other species a single collection at one station of about 1000 plants showed no more than a score that were not immediately referable to this species. It is found in the vicinity of ponds or marshes, occupying ground not much above or below high water mark, and sometimes in shallow excavations that are subject to temporary flooding. It seems never to grow under trees or shrubs, but is sometimes found among tufts of tall grass that give deep shade before the ferns mature. Apparently these are plants which were well established before habital conditions changed. It is probable that the abundance of this and related species in long undisturbed artificial excavations is due to relief from competition with vegetation of stronger growth. After *Ophioglossum floridanum* this species seems to be the most abundant of the genus in the Oligocene Island region of Florida. It is to be expected that it will be found beyond the boundary of that state as soon as careful search is made.

8. **O. mononeuron** E. St John.[2] Rootstock globose or ovoid, 2–6 mm. in diameter, the roots up to 1 mm. thick: leaf 3.5–5.5 cm. tall, relatively stout: common stalk 2–6 mm. long, mostly hypogean: foliage blade deep-green, very broadly ovate to orbicular-ovate, 5–14

[1] OPHIOGLOSSUM **dendroneuron** E. St. John, sp. nov., rhizomate ex ovato cylindrico: foliis solitariis vel binatis ternatisve, 3.5–9 cm. longis; lamina elliptica raro ovata, sessili, 1–3 cm. longa; venis basalibus 5–7; areolis primariis magnis, venulis plurimis inter se confluentibus: sporophyllo gracillimo: spica longe apiculata. Ad marginem stagni in pinetoro, in occasu soliis a via qua e Lecanto ad Crystal River, in Florida, itur. E. P. St. John, 10.XII. 1936, *568*, typus in herb. Hort. Bot. Noveboracensis.

[2] OPHIOGLOSSUM **mononeuron** E. St. John sp. nov., rhizomate brevi globoso vel ovideo; frondibus solitariis vel 2, 3.5–5.5 cm. altis; lamina late ovata vel suborbiculata, basi brevi angustata sicut petiolo ornata, plerumque 3–9 mm. longa; areolis paucis, sensim minoribus e centro laminae ad marginem; spica longe apiculato-aristata basi non angustata; sporangilis 6–8-jugis, 5 mm. diametro.—Circa milia passuum duo, se. Crystal River, Citrus County, Florida, 10.XII. 1936, E. P. St. John, typus in herb. Hort. Bot. Noveboracensis.

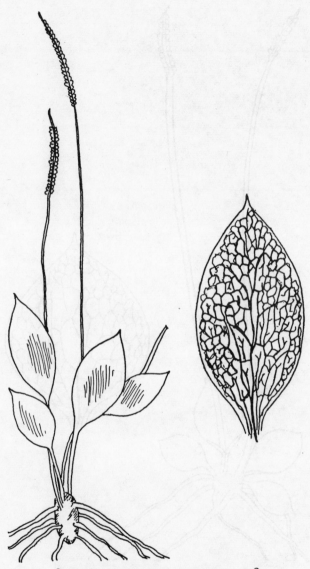

OPHIOGLOSSUM DENDRONEURON.   ×2

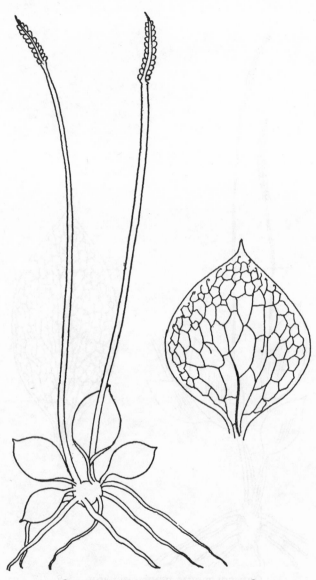

OPHIOGLOSSUM MONONEURON.　×2

mm. long, 3–9 mm. broad, apiculate, broadly cuneate at the somewhat clasping base: midvein prominent in the lower part of the blade, giving off a few spreading and forking branches which, with their ramifications, occupy nearly or quite the entire blade; weak marginal veins in some plants appearing to be branches of the midvein, in others joining it slightly below the base of the blade; central areolae large and one-half to one-fourth as broad as long, surrounding aerolae successively smaller to the margins; free included or marginal veinlets infrequent: sporophyl 3.5–5.5 mm. long, up to 1 mm. thick: spike with long slender apiculate tip, with 6–8 pairs of sporangia about 5 mm. in diameter.—Sandy soil in flatwoods, usually among saw palmettos, Citrus County, Fla.—Spores mature in autumn.

This small and apparently rare species has been collected at several stations in Citrus County, Florida, always associated with *Ophioglossum crotalophoroides*, *O. tenerum*, *O. dendroneuron*, or *O. Pumilio*, with none of which does it seem to intergrade. It is probable that extensive field work will show it to be widely, if sparingly, distributed, at least in the Oligocene Island region.

The tendency of various species of the northern *Botrychia* to grow in association is paralleled among the *Ophioglossa* of the southeast. None of the species that have been recently discovered in Florida are exempt from it. *Ophioglossum floridanum* is rarely absent from large colonies of the smaller species, and *O. crotalophoroides* and *O. dendroneuron* show the tendency to a marked extent. It is known that the survival of some of the species is dependent upon a symbiotic relationship with a fungus. Possibly the explanation of the social habit may be found in the presence in certain areas of a single species of fungus which establishes a beneficial relationship with plants of the various species of *Ophioglossum*.

2. CHEIROGLOSSA Presl.

Epiphytic, pendent plants, the scaly or chaffy rootstocks with long fleshy roots. Leaves solitary or several together, consisting of an elongate common stalk bearing at its summit a broad, typically palmately lobed foliage blade and one to several short-stalked spikes of sporangia along the upper part of the common stalk and the base of the blade. Leaf-blades broad, palmately lobed. Larger veins anastomosing, the elongate areolae with an anastomosing and rarely free veinlet. Sporangia in two rows, more or less strongly coalescent: spores yellow.—The following species is the only known representative of this genus.—The genus was based on *Ophioglossum palmatum* L.—The name is Greek in allusion to the hand-like lobing of the foliage blade.

1. **C. palmata** (L.) Presl. Roots cord-like: rootstock tuberous, covered with fine woolly chaff or scales: leaves fleshy, kelp-like, tender; foliage blade 10–30 cm. long, frequently shorter than the common stalk, palmately divided into 2–9 erect or broadly spreading lobes, or individually entire and lanceolate, narrowly or broadly cuneate at the base: sporophyls 2–16, or rarely 1, usually 2.5 cm. long or more, the cylindric or cylindric-conic spike usually longer than the stalk: sporangia in 8–60 pairs. [*Ophioglossum palmatum* L.]—(HAND-FERN.)—On trees, often among the bases of the leaves of the cabbage-tree or palmetto, pen. Fla.—(*W. I., Mex., C. A., S. A.*)—Spores mature throughout the year.—Fig. reduced.

The habit and habitat of the hand-fern are such that it would not commonly be recognized as a fern. The clusters of succulent curiously lobed leaves dangling under the crown of a palm tree are in no way suggestive of the common conception of a fern-plant. The hand-fern grows in insular and continental tropical America. The species was described under the genus *Ophioglossum* in 1753 from specimens collected in Santo Domingo. It was discovered in Florida in 1875 along the Caloosahatchee.[1] It has since been found at many localities, as far south as Cape Sable. Its various habitats are but little above sea-level. The plants are very sensitive to fire, and since forest-fires and prairie-fires are becoming more frequent in districts where they formerly were rare, this fern is fast disappearing from localities where it once was abundant. So destructive have been the fires that in many localities where comparatively few years ago the hand-fern could be gathered literally by the wagon load it is now extinct. The few stations now known to fern students are guarded with great secrecy. Evidently a prehistoric immigrant from tropical America, its geographical connection with the center of distribution is still intact. Its favorite habitat in Florida is the cabbage-tree (*Sabal Palmetto*). Before the cold climatic conditions of the Ice Age came, the hand-fern may have followed the cabbage-tree up along the Atlantic Coast. At present it does not extend north of the Florida peninsula.

3. BOTRYCHIUM Sw.

Fleshy terrestrial plants with erect rootstocks bearing clustered fleshy, sometimes tuberous-thickened roots. Leaves 1 to 3, erect, con-

[1] First found in Florida by A. W. Chapman.

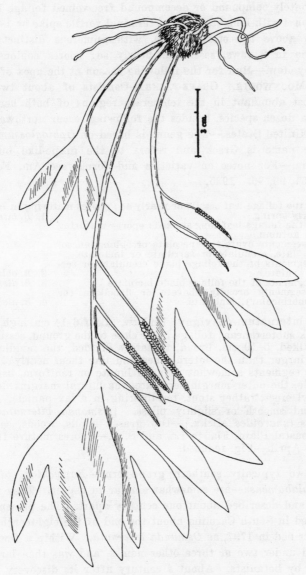

CHEIROGLOSSA PALMATA

sisting of a short cylindric common stalk bearing at its summit a
1–3-pinnately compound or decompound free-veined foliage blade and
a sporophyl with long stalk and a terminal fertile spike or 1–4-pinnate
panicles above the sterile blade, with numerous distinct globular
sporangia in 2 rows, sessile or nearly so: spores copious, usually
sulphur-yellow.—Bud for the following season at the apex of the rootstock.—MOONWORTS. GRAPE-FERNS.—Consists of about twenty species, most abundant in the temperate regions of both hemispheres.
Nearly a dozen species, besides the following, occur northward in the
eastern United States.—The genus is based on *Ophioglossum Lunaria*
L.—The name is Greek and refers to the grape-like bunches of
sporangia.—For notes on varieties and forms, see Am. Fern Jour.
25: 45–51, 95, 96. 1935.

Blade of the foliage leaf sessile or nearly so : spores maturing in late winter
   or early spring.   1. *B. biternatum.*
Blade of the foliage leaf long-stalked : spores maturing
   in autumn.
   Leaf-segments ovate to lanceolate or oblong-lanceo-
      late, crenulate or serrulate or laciniate.
      Segments of the foliage blade crenulate or ser-
        rulate.   2. *B. obliquum.*
      Segments of the foliage blade laciniate.   3. *B. dissectum.*
   Leaf-segments broadly obovate or flabellate (or
      suborbicular), fimbriate.   4. *B. alabamense.*

   1. **B. biternatum** (Savigny) Underw. Leaf 6–14 cm. high, the common stalk subterranean; foliage blade close to the ground, sessile or very
short-stalked, 5–10 cm. broad, ternately divided, the middle division
slightly larger than the lateral ones and like them nearly 3-pinnate;
ultimate segments somewhat rounded lunate or reniform, usually 5–6
mm. wide, the outer margin serrulate, the lateral margins decurrent:
sporophyl erect, rather stout, terminating in a lax panicle, 1–3.5 cm.
long: bud smooth or slightly pilose. [*Osmunda biternata* Savigny
Botrypus lunaroides Michx.]—Dry grassy knolls, woods, sandy pastures, Coastal Plain, Fla. to La. and S. C.—Spores mature from February to April.—Fig. reduced.

   The two typically southern grape-ferns—*Botrychium biternatum*
and *B. alabamense*—are somewhat similar in aspect. They were discovered and described about one century apart. The present species
discovered in South Carolina about the end of the eighteenth century,
was described in 1797, as *Osmunda biternata*. Within a few years it
appeared under two or three other names, and was then largely lost
sight of by botanists. About a century after its discovery in South
Carolina the plant was discovered in Alabama. Later it was found
to range as far west as Louisiana. The extremes of its geographic
range are Florida, Louisiana, and South Carolina, while its maximum

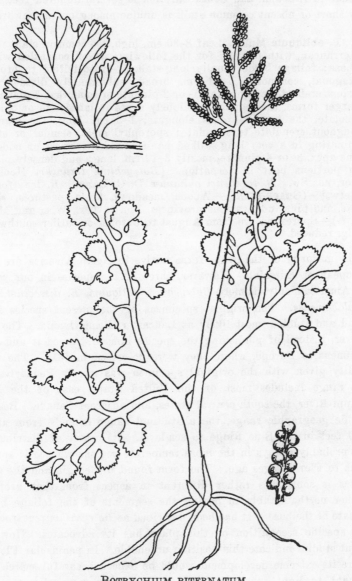

BOTRYCHIUM BITERNATUM

altitude in Alabama and South Carolina is several hundred feet. Its
very short or absent common stalk is unique among our moonworts.

2. B. obliquum Muhl. Leaf 8–30 cm. high, the common stalk short,
subterranean, with the bud for the following season concealed within
its base; foliage blade usually long-stalked, ovate-deltoid to broadly
pentagonal, commonly 5–13 cm. broad, subternately divided, the
divisions stalked, nearly equal, 1- or 2-pinnate or somewhat 3-pinnatifid
in larger forms, the segments obliquely ovate to lanceolate or oblong-
lanceolate, the terminal ones elongate, 1–2 cm. long, the margins
throughout crenulate to serrulate: sporophyl erect, slender or stout,
terminating in a very long-stalked panicle, which is erect or nodding
at the apex, 3- or 4-pinnate, mostly 3–13 cm. long: bud densely pilose,
both portions bent in vernation. [*Botrychium ternatum* Hook. &
Baker, not Sw. *B. ternatum obliquum* D. C. Eaton. *B. tenuifolium*
Underw.]—(Grape-fern.)—Woods, meadows, fields, pastures, river-
banks, and pinelands, various provinces, Fla. to Tex., Wis., and Me.—
(*W. I.*)—Spores mature from August to October or earlier southward.
—Fig. reduced.

The majority of the grape-ferns native in North America are also
European or Eurasian. However, three of the species in our range
are American only, namely *Botrychium obliquum*, *B. dissectum*, and
B. alabamense. The original specimens of the present species were
found and studied, most likely at Lancaster, Pennsylvania. The discoverer, instead of publishing the species himself, named it and sent
specimens to Europe, where they were described in 1810. The type
locality given with the original specimen was merely Pennsylvania.
The range includes most of the United States east of the Mississippi River, the south central states, and adjacent Canada. Besides
a wide geographic range, the altitudinal range extends from about
6000 feet in the Blue Ridge to sea-level. Its center of distribution
was probably always in the more temperate regions whence it spread
south to Florida ages ago. The form found in Georgia and the Gulf
States is sometimes rather different in aspect from that growing
farther north, notably in having the segments of the foliage blade
cuneate at the base. It has been described as *Botrychium tenuifolium*.
The specific recognition of this plant has its advocates. However
recent studies indicate this position untenable. In peninsular Florida
where its extreme development would be expected, careful search has
brought to light specimens with leaf-segments more elongate and
narrower at the base than those of typical *Botrychium tenuifolium*,
as well as those with leaf-segments broader and shorter than those of

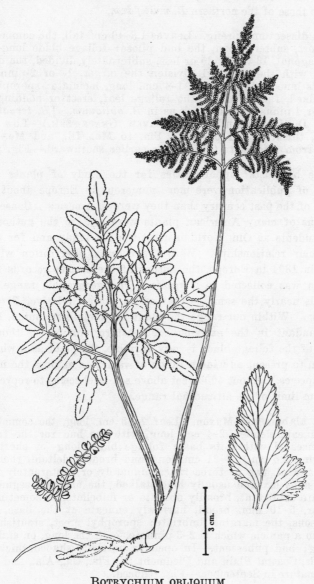

3 cm.

BOTRYCHIUM OBLIQUUM

typical *B. obliquum,* in fact, some so broad and short that they almost resemble those of the northern *B. multifidum.*

3. **B. dissectum** Spreng. Leaves 1.5–40 cm. tall, the common stalk very short, subterranean, the bud pilose: foliage blade long-stalked, subpentagonal, 13 cm. wide or less, subternately divided, the divisions stalked, with the terminal division the larger, 1- or 2-pinnate, the segments lanceolate to ovate, 1–4 cm. long, laciniate: sporophyl very long-stalked, far exceeding the foliage leaf, erect or nodding at the tip, 3- or 4-pinnate: bud much as in *B. obliquum.* [*B. ternatum dissectum* D. C. Eaton.]—(CUT-LEAVED GRAPE-FERN.)—Low woods, swamps, thickets, and pastures, Fla. to Mo., Ill., and Me.—Spores mature from August to October, or earlier southward.—Fig. reduced.

Active botanists' opportunities for the study of plants and for vehicles of publication were more numerous in Europe about the beginning of the past century than they were in America. Consequently, specimens of many American plants were sent to the authorities or plant students at Old World institutions for study and for opinions as to their relationships. With the original description which appeared in 1804 in Europe, the author of the species records that the specimen was collected in Virginia. The geographic range of this species is nearly the same as that of its nearest relative, *Botrychium obliquum.* Within our range the plant is widely distributed, but it is less abundant in the extreme southeastern portion. Although the cutting of the foliage blade is very variable, the plant as a whole does not seem to present as wide a range of variation as does the next preceding species. About 4000 feet above sea-level seems to represent the maximum limit of its altitudinal range.

4. **B. alabamense** Maxon. Leaf 7–38 cm. long, the common stalk subterranean, slender, 2–4 cm. long, with the bud for the following year concealed within its base: foliage blade long- or short-stalked (averaging 2.5 cm.), 5–21 cm. long and broadly deltoid, rhombic, or subpentagonal, two or three times pinnately or subternately divided, the divisions lax and usually long-stalked, the ultimate segments approximate or distant, broadly obovate or flabellate, or sometimes suborbicular, 5–10 mm. broad, narrowly cuneate at the base, adnate, chartaceous, the margins fimbriate: sporophyl erect, stoutish, terminating in a panicle which is 2–3-pinnate, 7–10 cm. long, on stalks 5–27 cm. long: bud pubescent.—In open or partially shaded thickets and pinelands, Coastal Plain and Piedmont, N. Fla., Ga., Ala., and N. C.— Spores mature in September.—Fig. reduced.

There are more kinds of grape-fern characteristic of the North than of the South, but the endemic southern species are more conspicuous,

BOTRYCHIUM DISSECTUM

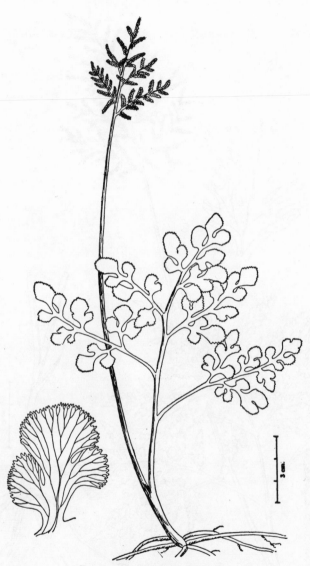

BOTRYCHIUM ALABAMENSE

especially by their greater spread of foliage blades and larger sporophyls. The present species and *B. biternatum* are particularly distinctive by the numerous broadly rounded lobes of the foliage blades. This Alabama grape-fern was discovered at Spring Hill, near Mobile, Alabama, about the beginning of this century, at an altitude of about 200 feet, and described in 1906. However, specimens were collected at an earlier date, 1900, in the Piedmont of Georgia at an altitude of about 1000 feet. The geographic range is not extensive as specimens have been found in only four states, Florida,[1] Alabama, Georgia, and North Carolina. In Alabama the plants grow in thickets under cedars and yaupon, or under yaupon hedges about abandoned fields and pastures. In Florida and Georgia the pineland is the usual habitat. The plants often grow in colonies.

4. OSMUNDOPTERIS (Milde) Small[2]

Terrestrial, fleshy, medium-sized plants, with rootstocks, bearing fibrous naked roots. Leaves mostly solitary, conspicuous, the base of the stalk open along one side containing the bud; foliage blade membranous, ternate, with the primary divisions once or twice pinnate, with the epidermal cells flexuous: sporophyl long-stalked, with a twice or thrice pinnate panicle high above the sterile blade: spores numerous, mostly yellow.—Consists of the following species widely distributed and in several forms.—The genus is based on *Osmunda virginiana* L.—The name is a compound of *Osmunda* and *pteris*, Greek for fern.

1. **O. virginiana** (L.) Small. Leaf 8–80 cm. high, the common stalk stout or slender, comprising one-half to two-thirds the length of the plant and mostly aerial, with the bud for the following season exposed along one side: foliage-blade nearly or quite sessile, spreading, thin, deltoid, 1–4 dm. broad, nearly as long, ternate, the short-stalked primary divisions 1-pinnate or 2-pinnate, the segments 1- or 2-pinnatifid; ultimate segments elliptic, lanceolate, or ovate, toothed at the apex; sporophyl erect, long-stalked, terminating in a panicle which is 2–3-pinnate, with slender branches: bud pubescent. [*Osmunda virginiana* L. *Botrychium virginianum* Sw. *Botrychium gracile* Pursh.]—(RATTLESNAKE-FERN.)—Rich woods, thickets, and meadows, various provinces, C. Fla. to Tex., Calif., Idaho, and N. B.—(*W. I., Mex., Eu., Asia.*)—Spores mature in June and July.—Fig. reduced.—For notes on varieties and forms, see Am. Fern Journ. 25: 96–97. 1935.

[1] First collected in Florida by Herman Kurz, Nov. 28, 1936.
[2] *Osmundopteris* (Milde). Basis infirma petioli rima longa verticali aperta; segmenta secundaria anadroma; cellulae epidermidis flexuosae. Typus *Osmunda virginiana* L.

OSMUNDOPTERIS VIRGINIANA

The rattlesnake-fern is the best known species of the *Botrychium* group, at least to the amateur fern student, largely on account of its large lace-like foliage blades. Its geographical range, too, is extensive, including North America north of Central America, Europe, and Asia. In altitudinal distribution the range extends from about 5000 feet in the Blue Ridge to sea-level. The plants require, or at least thrive best in a climate with alternating hot and cold seasons. This may account for the fact that it becomes rarer southward where its range extends into the central part of the Florida peninsula. There, too, the plants are dwarf and agree with the form described as *Botrychium gracile*. In and about the Linnaean period of botany the names of several political divisions of North America occurred frequently in botanical nomenclature. The Carolinas, Virginia, Pennsylvania, and Canada were the colonies most frequently commemorated by the specific names of species. These colonies had active botanists as residents, most of whom were in communication with the botanists of the Old World. The rattlesnake-fern was first found in the colony of Virginia in the early part of the eighteenth century and described in 1753.

ORDER 3. **SALVINIALES**

Aquatic herbs or mud-inhabiting when habitats become partly dry, with horizontal or creeping stems, or floating plants. Leaves various, sometimes filiform, or with dilated blades, entire, lobed, or 2–4-foliolate. Spores of two kinds, microspores and megaspores, contained in sporocarps, with both kinds of spores in one sporocarp or the different kinds in separate sporocarps. Megaspores germinating into simple prothallia which bear archegones. Microspores forming still simpler prothallia bearing antheridia, emitting antherozoids.—Consists of the following two families only.

Plants rooting in muddy bottoms: stems (rootstocks) creeping or horizontal: sporocarps uniform, containing both megaspores and microspores: leaves filiform or with 2- or 4-foliolate blades, the leaflets dilated. Fam. 1. MARSILEACEAE.

Plants floating: stems pinnately branched: sporocarps of two kinds, small ones containing a megaspore, and larger ones containing pedicelled microsporangia: leaves with entire or 2-lobed blades. Fam. 2. SALVINIACEAE.

FAMILY 1. **MARSILEACEAE**

PEPPERWORT FAMILY

Perennial herbaceous plants rooting in mud and usually partly submerged, with slender often elongate branching rootstocks. Leaves erect, spreading, or floating, with 2-foliolate or 4-foliolate blades, or merely filiform. Asexual propagation carried out by sporocarps which are borne on peduncles arising from the rootstock near the leaf-stalk, or consolidated with the leaf-stalk. Each sporocarp contains both megaspores and microspores. Megaspores germinate into prothallia that bear mostly archegonia; microspores develop into prothallia that bear antheridia.—The family comprises three genera and more than sixty species of wide geographic distribution. Most of the species belong to the genus *Marsilea*.

Sporocarps ovoid or ellipsoid : leaves with 2- or 4-foliolate blades.
                                                           1. MARSILEA.
Sporocarps globose : leaves filiform.   2. PILULARIA.

1. **MARSILEA** L.

Marsh or aquatic, anchored plants, either submersed or emersed. Leaves commonly floating on the surface of shallow water; blades slender-petioled, 4-foliolate. Leaflets broad, with many fine veins forming long and narrow areolae. Peduncles shorter than the petioles, arising from near their bases or more or less adnate to them. Sporocarps ovoid or ellipsoid, formed of two vertical valves each with several transverse compartments (sori), 2-valved at maturity and emitting a band of elastic tissue, which bears the sporangia on a number of short lobes.—PEPPERWORTS.—Contains more than fifty species of wide distribution. Four native species occur in the south central states, while a naturalized species occurs in the northeastern United States.— The genus is based on *Marsilea quadrifolia* L.—The name is in honor of Giovanni Marsigli, an Italian botanist.—Our species are introduced from west of the Mississippi River.—Spores mature all year under favorable circumstances.

Leaflets decidedly pubescent beneath : raphe short, with acute teeth or the
   lower one blunt.   1. *M. vestita*.
Leaflets glabrous or nearly so : raphe long, with long
   hooked teeth.   2. *M. uncinata*.

1. **M. vestita** Hook. & Grev. Rootstock slender: leaves pubescent, except the upper side of the leaflets; petioles 5–13 cm. long, slender; leaflets spreading, the blades obovate, 7–12 mm. long or smaller, entire or toothed: sporocarps ellipsoid, 4–8 mm. long, 3–6 mm. wide; raphe with a short and blunt lower tooth and an acute and sometimes curved upper one, densely covered with soft spreading or ascending narrow hair-like scales: sori 6–11 in each valve.—(WATER-CLOVER.)—Ponds, ditches, and moist places, central peninsular Florida, where introduced from western North America; also various provinces, Tex. to B. C. and Kans.—(*Mex.*)

None other of the fern-allies so closely resembles certain flowering plants by its leaves, as does the *Marsilea*. One of the popular names of the plant, water-clover, attests to this statement. The North American species of *Marsilea* form a peculiar group, well distinguished from the species of the Old World by the large purple stomata of the capsule, which is always solitary at the base of the petiole, and by the two large conspicuous teeth of the raphe. This species was the first of the genus discovered in North America. It was collected by Douglas on the Columbia River in Oregon and was named in 1831. This pepperwort roots in either clay or sand, and thrives in ponds and ditches, growing there equally well even when the water dries up for a part of the year. It was discovered in Florida in 1891.

2. **M. uncinata** A. Br. Rootstock very slender: leaves glabrous or nearly so; petioles 6–20 cm. tall; leaflets spreading, the blades entire, 10–30 mm. wide, and about as long: sporocarps ellipsoid to subglobose, 5–8 mm. long, 4–6 mm. wide; raphe long, terminating in 2 approximate teeth, the upper longer and mostly hooked, finely wrinkled and with slender hair-like scales: sori 13–14 in each valve.—(WATER-CLOVER.)— Swamps and ditches, Coastal Plain and adj. provinces, La. and Tex.; also Tenn., where naturalized.

Most of our pepperworts are limited naturally to the southcentral part of the United States. From this center species apparently migrated in one way or another to eastern and more northern localities. In addition a European species has long been naturalized in the more northern Atlantic seaboard. *M. uncinata* was first referred to under its present name in 1839. In 1847, the following information concerning it appeared: "*Marsilea uncinata* was discovered in 1835, on the margin of small swamps in the deep bottom woods on the Arkansas River, not far below Little Rock, Arkansas, growing with *Azolla caroliniana*. It is a much larger plant than those of our other species, nearly naked, with long petioles, (5 to 9 inches) and fan-

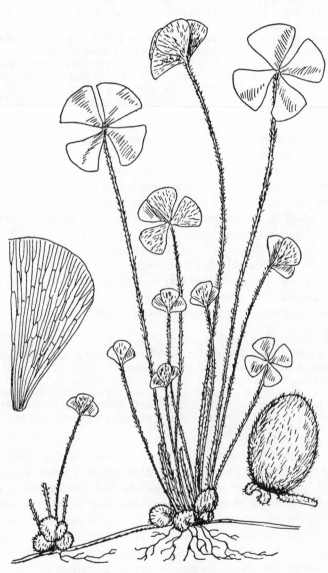

MARSILEA VESTITA

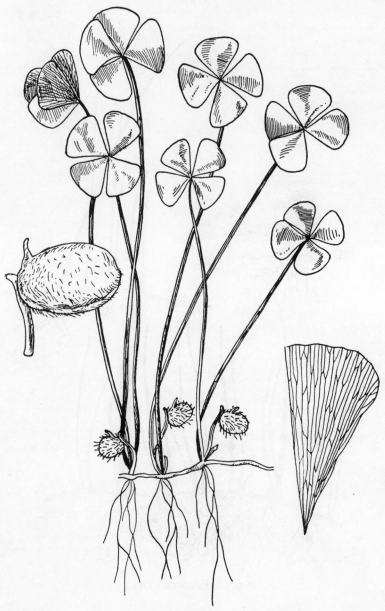

MARSILEA UNCINATA

PILULARIA AMERICANA

shaped leaflets 6 to 10 lines long; the rhizoma produces many fascicled branchlets which are paleaceous at tip. The shape of the capsule (sporocarp) and the larger number of sori in it, readily distinguish it from the others.''

2. PILULARIA L.

Aquatic plants with slender creeping rootstocks and few filiform leaves. Sporocarps globose, longitudinally 2–4-celled, dehiscing from the apex; cavities with parietal cushions bearing microsporanges above and numerous megasporanges below. Megaspores solitary.—About 6 species of wide geographic distribution mainly in the Old World.—The genus is founded on *Pilularia globulifera* L.—The name is Latin, alluding to the small ball-like sporocarps.

1. **P. americana** A. Br. Leaves filiform, 2–6 cm. long: sporocarps 2 mm. in diameter, attached by the side to a short descending peduncle, 3–4-celled: microspores 13–17, not constricted at the middle.—(PILL-WORT.)—Shallow pools and wet depressions in rock, Piedmont, Ga.; also in Ark. where originally discovered and in W. N. A.—(*S. A.*)

A pillwort was unknown in North America in the early days of botanical study. It was not until the earlier half of the past century that a specimen was collected in Arkansas. Later the genus was discovered on the Pacific Coast. There have been unsuccessful attempts to rediscover the plant in Arkansas. Without special search the species was found in Barrow County, Georgia, in 1901; and has recently been discovered in Walton County, adjacent to Barrow. There the plants are associated with isoetes and sedges and grow in shallow depressions in granite in soft mud or soil of flour-like consistency. They are extremely inconspicuous as the leaves are often only 3 or 4 cm. long and closely resemble juvenile isoetes or grasses and are hidden by the taller growth. The rootstocks run above the corms of the isoetes and produce the sporocarps just beneath the surface of the ground. To this habit of growth may be laid, in part at least, the apparent rarity of pillworts. The species was named in 1863, being described from the specimens collected in Arkansas.

FAMILY 2. **SALVINIACEAE**

SALVINIA FAMILY

Small floating plants, with more or less elongate and some-times pinnately branching stems bearing apparently 2-ranked leaves: blades entire or 2-lobed. Sporocarps soft, thin-walled, often borne 2 or more on a common stalk, 1-celled, with a central simple or branched receptacle, which bears one or more megasporangia containing a single megaspore, or stalked microsporanges, each containing numerous microspores, the sporocarps containing megaspores often larger than those containing microspores. Megaspores develop into prothallia bearing archegonia, while microspores grow into prothallia that bear antheridia.—The family comprises the two following genera.

Leaves minute, imbricate on pinnately branching stems.   1. AZOLLA.
Leaves large (1–1.5 cm. long), 2-ranked and spreading on
    mostly simple stems.   2. SALVINIA.

1. AZOLLA Lam.

Minute moss-like reddish or green floating plants, commonly resembling *Hepaticae*, often densely matted. Stems pinnately branched, covered with minute imbricate 2-lobed leaves, and emitting long rootlets beneath. Sporocarps of two kinds borne in the axils of the leaves, the smaller ovoid or acorn-shaped, containing a single megaspore at the base, and a few minute bodies above it, the larger globose or globose-ovoid, containing many stalked sporangia borne in a cluster, each comprising several masses of microspores.—Comprises few, about five, species of wide geographic distribution.—The genus is based on *Azolla filiculoides* Lam.—The name is Greek and signifies killed by drought.

1. **A. caroliniana** Willd. Plants greenish, or reddish, 7–25 mm. wide, or sometimes smaller, deltoid or triangular-ovate, sometimes irregular, the stems pinnately branching: leaves with ovate lobes, their color varying with the amount of sunlight, the lower usually reddish, the upper green with a reddish border; megasporangia 1.5–2 mm. long: megaspores minutely granulate, with three accessory bodies: microsporangia about 0.5 mm. long, relatively narrower than the megasporangia: masses of microspores armed with rigid separate processes. —Still water, ponds, pools, lakes, and shores of streams, mostly Coastal Plain and adj. provinces, Fla. to Tex., Calif., B. C., Ont., and Mass.— (*W. I., Mex., C. A., S. A.*)—Spores mature all year southward.

Free-floating fern-plants are not common in our range. Those of the present genus and of the following one, both fern-allies, and two species of *Ceratopteris* constitute the group. *Azolla* floats on the surface of the water and in still bodies of water it propagates rapidly and commonly forms carpets dense enough to conceal the water. It is

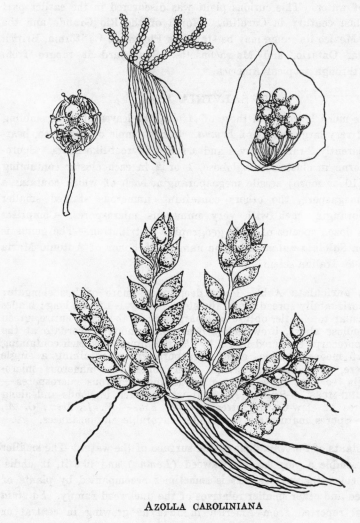

AZOLLA CAROLINIANA

in fact sometimes called mosquito-fern because it prevents the growth of mosquitoes in pools. The color of the foliage ranges from green to red or brown, and thus often makes large areas of the colors over sheets of water. This curious plant was discovered in the earlier part of the last century in Carolina. North of the Rio Grande and the Gulf of Mexico its range may be stated as Florida to California, British Columbia, Ontario, and Massachusetts. Southward it ranges from Mexico through tropical America.

2. SALVINIA Adans.

Plants much larger than those of *Azolla*, the leaves often resembling those of very large plants of *Lemna*. Stems simple or nearly so, bearing apparently 2-ranked leaves and a series of root-like fibers. Sporocarps borne in clusters, subglobose, 1 or 2 in each cluster containing many (10 or more) sessile megasporangia, each of which contains a single megaspore, the others containing numerous stalked smaller microsporangia, each with very numerous microspores.—Comprises about a dozen species of wide geographic distribution.—The genus is based on *Salvinia natans* L.—The name is in honor of Antonio Maria Salvini, an Italian scientist.

1. **S. auriculata** Aubl. Plant deep-green, more or less elongate: leaves horizontally spreading on the stem, mostly 1–1.5 cm. long: blades suborbicular to elliptic, obtuse or emarginate at the apex, entire, green and papillose above, brown-hairy beneath, rounded or cordate at the base: sporocarps clustered in 4's to 8's, the upper ones each containing up to 25 megasporangia, each megasporangium containing a single megaspore, the other sporocarps each containing numerous microsporangia, each of these in turn containing numerous microspores.— (FLOATING-MOSS.)—Still or stagnant water, often in ponds and along the shores of slow-flowing streams, pen. Fla.—(*W. I., Mex., C. A., S. A.*)—Spores mature all year under favorable circumstances.

The plants of *Salvinia* float on the surface of the water. The smaller races resemble a very large duckweed (*Lemna*) and like it, if undisturbed, cover the surface. It is sometimes accompanied by plants of duckweed and other smaller relatives of the duckweed family. *Salvinia* was first reported from America in 1814 as growing in central or western New York. Later it was found at widely separated stations at some of which it was considered to be native, at others it was known to be naturalized. It was discovered in Florida in 1928 in the Saint Johns River and some of its tributaries. How it was introduced into

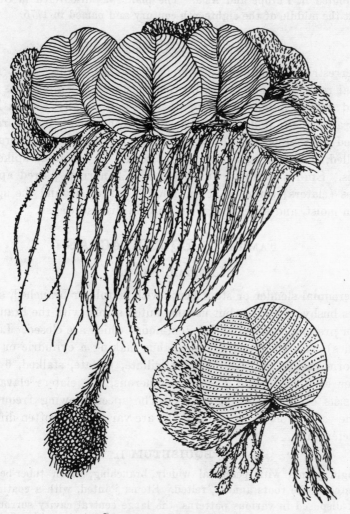

SALVINIA AURICULATA × 2.

the Saint Johns watershed is not known. Water birds are responsible for its distribution into ponds throughout the peninsula. It is widely distributed in Europe and Asia. The plant was discovered in Guiana about the middle of the eighteenth century and named in 1775.

Order 4. EQUISETALES

Terrestrial, sometimes uliginous, rush-like plants, with horizontal rootstocks and jointed, grooved stems, the internodes provided with a double series of cavities and usually with a large central one, the nodes provided with diaphragms. Leaves represented by toothed sheaths at the nodes of the stem. Sporanges 1-celled, clustered underneath the scales of terminal spike-like cones. Spores uniform, furnished with 2 narrow paired appendages (elaters) attached at the middle, coiling around the spores when moist, and spreading when dry, in diverse ways.

Family 1. EQUISETACEAE

Horsetail Family

Perennial slender or stout herbs with simple or branched, sometimes bushy, cylindric, but usually fluted stems, with the branches, when present, whorled at the stem-nodes which are closed. Leaves (scales) with their edges joined, thus making a cylindric or funnelform sheath. Sporophyls verticillate, peltate, stalked, 6 or 7 under each cone-scale. Spores numerous, the elaters clavate.— Consists of the following genus.—The species, owing frequently to the vacillation of the water-table, are variable and often difficult to determine.

1. EQUISETUM L.

Rigid plants with perennial widely branching, often tuber-bearing rootstocks, the roots annual, felted. Stems jointed, with a coating of silex disposed in various patterns, the large central cavity surrounded by a series of small cavities situated under each groove. Sporangia opening along the inner side where they discharge the green spores.— Represented by about 25 species, of very wide geographic distribution. —The genus is based on *Equisetum fluviatile* L.—The name is Latin, signifying horsetail, in allusion to the copious branching of the stems of some species.—Our species fall into two natural groups: the one with horizontal rootstocks which annually send up a series of branches simple at the base (the first group of one species) the other in which the branching rootstock merges into the branching bases of the perennial stems (the second group, of two species.)

Stems annual, appearing in spring, dying down in fall, the sterile ones, at least, branched: spikes (cones) rounded at the apex.
                                                                    I. EQUISETUM.
Stems perennial, evergreen, simple or with few irregular branches: spikes (cones) apiculate.   II. HIPPOCHAETE.

I. EQUISETUM

Spore-bearing (cone-bearing) stems appearing before the sterile ones, succulent and early withering, sometimes only at the apex.   1. *E. arvense.*

II. HIPPOCHAETE

Stems smooth or nearly so: stem-sheaths funnelform. 2. *E. laevigatum.*
Stems tuberculate-roughened: stem-sheaths cylindric or nearly so.   3. *E. praealtum.*

1. E. arvense L. Stems annual, with scattered stomata, the fertile appearing in early spring before the sterile: cone-bearing stems 1–2.5 dm. high, not branched, soon withering, light-brown, their loose scarious sheaths mostly distant, whitish, ending in about 12 brown acuminate teeth; cone ovoid to cylindric, 1.5–3 cm. long, obtuse: sterile stems green, rather slender, 0.5–6 dm. high, 6–19-furrowed, with numerous long mostly simple whorled 4-angled or rarely 3-angled solid branches which stand erect or are strongly ascending, their sheaths 4-toothed, the stomata in two rows in the furrows.—*E. arvense serotinum* is an occasional form with a cone terminating the normally sterile plant.— HORSETAIL.—Sandy or clayey soil, meadows, wet woods, stream-banks, lake-shores, cultivated grounds, and railroad embankments, various provinces, N. C. to N. Ala., Calif., Alas., Lab., and Greenl.—(*Eurasia.*)— Spores mature in spring.

The common horsetail is the most widely distributed species of *Equisetum*, at least in North America. It is also known to a greater number of people than the other species. This wide acquaintance is due to the fact that the plant grows in cultivated sandy grounds, dumps, roadsides, and cinder piles as well as in its natural haunts. The plants seem to thrive not only in soil almost devoid of nourishment, but to grow more luxuriantly there. The original specimens came from Europe and were named in 1753. It was said to grow on shores of lakes and rivers. It inhabits similar localities in North America.

2. E. laevigatum A. Br. Stems 3–15 dm. high, simple or little branched, pale-green, persistent, 14–30-furrowed, the ridges almost

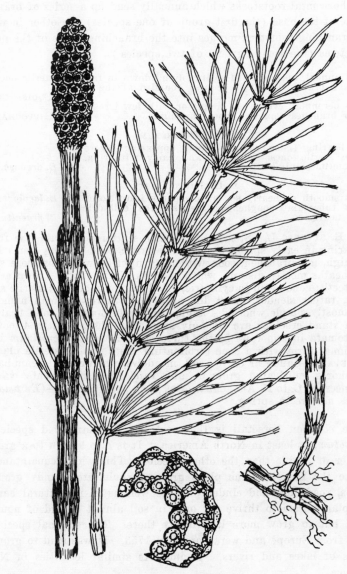

EQUISETUM ARVENSE

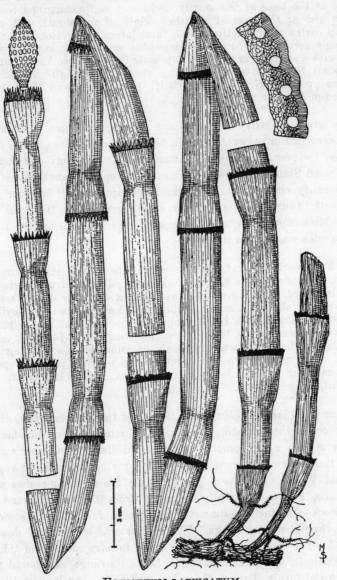

EQUISETUM LAEVIGATUM

EQUISETACEAE

smooth: leaf-sheaths elongated and enlarged upward, with a black girdle at the base of the mostly deciduous, white-margined teeth and rarely also at the base of sheaths; ridges of the sheath with a faint central carina and sometimes with faint lateral ones: stomata arranged in single series; centrum very large, the wall of the stem very thin: cone with a sharp firm tip. [*E. hyemale intermedium* A. A. Eaton.]— (SMOOTH SCOURING-RUSH.)—Along streams, especially in clay soil, various provines, N. C. to La., Calif., B. C., Ont., and N. J.—Spores mature in summer and fall.

The great majority of our North American species of *Equisetum* also occur in Europe or Asia or in both of these regions. The present species, however, is peculiarly American. It is widely distributed in the United States and southern Canada, except the northeastern parts. The locality cited with the original description is ''On poor clayey soil, with *Andropogon* and other coarse grasses, at the foot of the rocky Mississippi hills, on the banks of the river, below St. Louis.'' The species was named in 1844.

3. **E. praealtum** Raf. Stems rough-tuberculate, stout, evergreen, 1–3 m. high, sometimes 2.5 cm. in diameter, 10–48-furrowed, simple or little branched, the ridges roughened with a single or double series of transversely oblong siliceous tubercles: leaf-sheaths short-cylindric, appressed, marked with black girdles at the base and at the bases of the dark caducous lobes, the ridges of the sheath 3- or 4-keeled; centrum very large: branches when present, occasionally cone-bearing: cone tipped with a firm tip.—(SCOURING-RUSH.)—Wet places, especially alluvium along streams, low woods, and flats, Fla. to La., Calif., B. C., and Ont.—Fig. reduced.

There is no lack of silex in the tissues of the scouring-rush, as there is in those of the preceding species. This mineral is so abundant that the stems of it were formerly used in rural districts in this country to scour tinware and other utensils. This practice was also in vogue in the Old World. This is a giant among the scouring-rushes or the horsetails, for stems, really branches from the underground stem (rootstock), an inch in diameter and eleven feet tall are sometimes found throughout its range. The species was named and described in 1814. The original specimens are said to have come from ''Islands of the Mississippi in Louisiana.'' Later its range was found to extend to California, British Columbia, and Ohio. As late as 1932 the southeastern corner of the United States was added to the geographic range by the discovery of the plant in Florida.

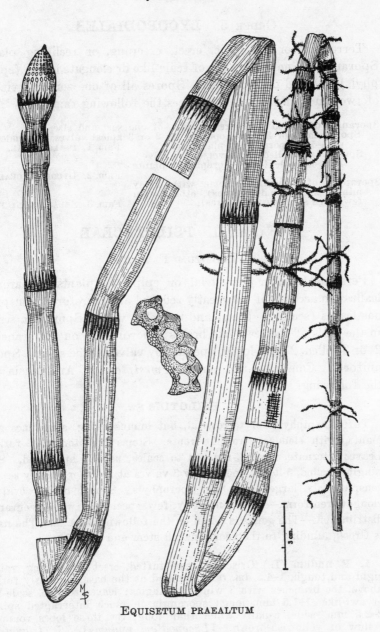

EQUISETUM PRAEALTUM

Order 5. **LYCOPODIALES**

Terrestrial or epiphytic, erect, creeping, or reclining plants. Sporangia borne in the axils of scale-like or elongate leaves (sporophyls), 1-celled or 2–3-celled. Spores all of one sort and size or of two kinds and sizes.—Embraces the following families:

Sporangia of one kind: spores minute, of one sort and size.
  Sporangia 2- or 3-celled, opening by 2 or 3 apical valves, subtended by scale-like sporophyls: plants scaly. Fam. 1. Psilotaceae.
  Sporangia 1-celled, transversely 2-valved, hidden in leaf-like sporophyls: plants leafy. Fam. 2. Lycopodiaceae.
Sporangia of two kinds, some with many minute spores (microspores), others with few large spores (megaspores). Fam. 3. Selaginellaceae.

Family 1. **PSILOTACEAE**

Psilotum Family

Perennial slender terrestrial or epiphytic plants, apparently leafless on account of the greatly reduced and therefore inconspicuous leaves (scales). Stems and branches wiry. Sporangia sessile in the axils of the scale-like bracts (sporophyls) on the branches, 2- or 3-celled, 2- or 3-lobed, opening by valves at the apex. Spores uniform. Comprises two genera, *Tmesipteris* of Australasia and the following.

1. **PSILOTUM** Sw.

Tufted, epiphytic or terrestrial, but humus-loving, sometimes stiff plants, with slender coral-like roots. Stems dichotomously forked. Leaves alternate, remote, reduced to scales, usually appressed. Sporangia 3-celled, 3-lobed, opening by 3 valves at the apex, closely sessile, conspicuously larger than the sporophyls. Spores mealy, oval or elongate-reniform.—Represented by few species of wide geographic distribution.—The genus is based on the following species. The name is Greek, alluding to the nearly naked stem and branches.

1. **P. nudum** (L.) Griseb. Stems tufted, erect or nodding, rather rigid and tough, 1–4.5 dm. tall, 3-angled at the base, copiously forked above, the branches with 3 wing-like angles: leaves remote, scale-like or awl-like, 1–1.5 mm. long; sporangia in much interrupted spikes, 2–2.5 mm. wide, usually wider than long, the three lobes rounded, yellow or yellowish-brown. [*Lycopodium nudum* L. *P. triquetrum* Sw. *P. floridanum* Michx.]—(Whisk-fern.)—Hammocks and cypress-

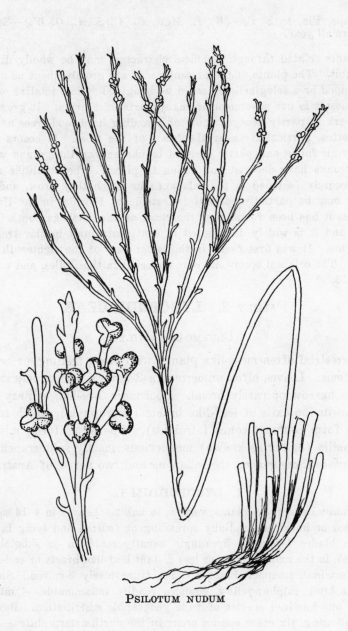

PSILOTUM NUDUM

swamps, Fla. to S. C.—(*W. I., Mex., C. A., S. A., O. W.*)—Spores mature all year.

Plants related through technical characters may be wholly diverse in habit. The plants of the present genus are grossly about as unlike a lycopod or a selaginella as could be imagined. This relative of the clubmosses is not uncommon in many parts of Florida. It grows on the bark in partly decayed spots on standing hardwood trees and on palmettos, particularly near the bases of the trees. It occurs commonly on fallen and partly decayed trunks and on the ground where tree-trunks have decayed and fallen to pieces. The coral-like roots are securely fastened in the substance in which they grow, and the plant may be partially parasitic. Outside of Florida, in the United States, it has been found near the coast as far north as South Carolina, and it is widely distributed in continental and insular tropical America. It was first found in the latter part of the eighteenth century. The original specimens were collected in the Indies, and named in 1753.

FAMILY 2. LYCOPODIACEAE

CLUBMOSS FAMILY

Terrestrial often moss-like plants, with erect, trailing, or creeping stems. Leaves often numerous in 2–several series, persistent: blades narrow or rarely broad. Sporangia 1-celled, solitary and hidden in the axils of leaf-like bracts (sporophyls), which sometimes form compact cones (strobiles). Spores uniform, minute. Prothallia (as far as known) monoecious, mostly subterranean.— Comprises three genera, the following and two native of Australia.

1. LYCOPODIUM L.

Perennial evergreen plants, various in habit. Leaves in 4–16 series, crowded or imbricate, radially spreading or twisted and lying in one plane: blades 1-veined. Sporangia usually reniform or subglobose, 1-celled, in the axils of more or less distant leaf-like bracts or collected into terminal, compact, bracted cones, transversely 2-valved. Spores of one kind, sulphur-yellow, copious, readily inflammable.—Contains about one hundred species of wide geographic distribution. Besides the following, six other species occur in the northeastern states.—The genus is based on *Lycopodium clavatum* L.—The name is Greek, meaning wolf's-foot, used perhaps in some fancied allusion to some part of the plant.

Sporophyls not closely associate in terminal cones: plants gemmiparous in the upper leaf-axils.
    Plants terrestrial.
        Stems and branches erect or stiffly upcurved from a short rootstock, tufted or densely matted: leaves entire or with an occasional minute tooth-like process on the side, not broadened above the middle.   **I. SELAGINES.**
        Stems and branches diffusely assurgent or widely spreading from an elongate rootstock or creeping base: leaves toothed, broadened above the middle.   **II. LUCIDULA.**
    III. DICHOTOMA.
    Plants epiphytic.
Sporophyls closely associated in terminal cones: plants not gemmiparous.
    Sporophyls similar to the foliage leaves: sporangia subglobose.   **IV. PROSTRATA.**
    Sporophyls specialized, unlike the foliage leaves: sporangia compressed and reniform.
        Cones erect, elongate, few, terminating erect branches or peduncles: leaves with spreading teeth.
            Stems prostrate and creeping, without leafy aerial branches, the elongate erect cone-bearing branches arising directly from the prostrate stem.   **V. CAROLINIANA.**
            Stems subterranean or aerial, with numerous erect or assurgent leafy branches.
                Leaves of the ultimate branches in 6 or more rows, spreading: cones sessile.
                    Main stem (rootstock) spreading deep in the ground: aerial branches few, tree-like.   **VI. OBSCURA.**
                    Main stem merely prostrate: branches numerous, not tree-like.   **VII. CLAVATA.**
                Leaves of the ultimate branches in 4 rows, appressed, mostly decurrent: cones peduncled.   **VIII. COMPLANATA.**
        Cones nodding, short, numerous, borne at the at the tips of spreading branches and branchlets: leaves with appressed teeth.   **IX. CERNUA.**

I. SELAGINES

Leaves ascending or appressed, acuminate.   1. *L. Selago.*
Leaves spreading or partly reflexed, attenuate.   2. *L. porophilum.*

II. LUCIDULA

Plants with diffusely assurgent or widely spreading stems and branches which are copiously clothed with spreading or reflexed shining leaves borne in irregular zones.   3. *L. lucidulum.*

III. DICHOTOMA

Plants pendent from the trunks and branches of trees.   4. *L. dichotomum.*

IV. PROSTRATA

Sporophyls less than 6 mm. long, incurved, often only slightly toothed at the apex.   5. *L. appressum.*

Sporophyls more than 8 mm. long, not incurved,
    usually much toothed.
    Stems mostly recurved or arching : leaves in many
      ranks, spreading radially.   6. *L. alopecuroides.*
    Stems prostrate : leaves twisted, lying in one
      plane.   7. *L. prostratum.*

V. Caroliniana

Creeping plant with the main stem leafless on the
    under side, but there rooting freely, the lateral
    leaves widely spreading.   8. *L. carolinianum.*

VI. Obscura

Rootstock subterranean, giving off, irregularly, erect
    tree-like copiously leafy branches.   9. *L. obscurum.*

VII. Clavata

Branches from the main stem irregular, mostly
    forked, copiously leafy, some of the branchlets
    terminating in a long peduncle which is topped by
    a cone or a cluster of cones.   10. *L. clavatum.*

VIII. Complanata

Ultimate branches conspicuously flattened : leaves of
    the under row greatly reduced, minute, triangu-
    lar-cuspidate.   11. *L. flabelliforme.*
Ultimate branches narrower and less flattened :
    leaves of the under row scarcely smaller, acicular. 12. *L. tristachyum.*

IX. Cernua

Ultimately diffuse plants with copiously leafy
    branches and branchlets which end in nodding
    short cones.   13. *L. cernuum.*

1. L. Selago L. Stem and branches rigidly erect from a short slender curved base, several times dichotomous, the vertical branches forming compact even tufts or mats 5–15 cm. high: leaves uniform, crowded, appressed or ascending, narrowly deltoid-lanceolate or somewhat acicular from a broader base, shining, pale-green or yellowish, 4–8 mm. long, usually entire, acute: sporophyls (below the summit) a little shorter than the foliage leaves: plant often gemmiparous above. —(Fir-clubmoss.)—Rocks and shaded cliffs, Blue Ridge, N. C. and Tenn. and various provinces, Pa. to Mich., Wash., Alas., Lab., Greenl., and Me.—(*S. A., Eurasia.*)—Spores mature in summer and fall.

The genus *Lycopodium* is represented in eastern North America by about sixteen species. The great majority of them are common to both the North and the South. Two species are confined to the southeastern states, while four in the northeastern states do not reach the North Carolina-Virginia state line. The original specimens of *Lycopodium Selago* were of European origin and the species was named in 1753. The plant is also Asiatic. In the New World the geographic range extends from Arctic America southward gradually gaining altitude until it reaches the high mountain summits over 6000 feet in the

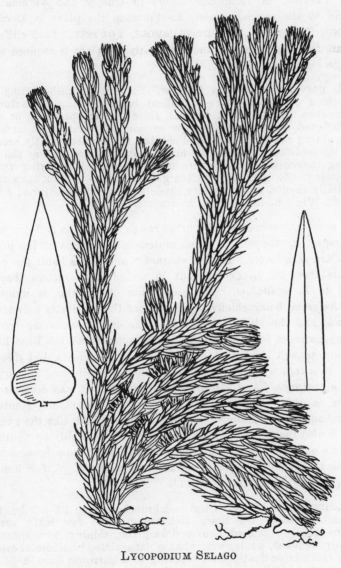

LYCOPODIUM SELAGO

southern Blue Ridge. Patagonia represents its southern limit in South America. A subspecies occurs in Quebec and Vermont. In addition to the common name, fir-clubmoss, the plant is known as FIR-MOSS, TREE-MOSS, UPRIGHT CLUBMOSS, FOX-FEET. Cold cliffs and rocks are the usual habitats, and apparently the plant is confined to the older geologic formations.

2. **L. porophilum** Lloyd & Underw. Stem and branches rising 5–10 cm. from a curved or short-decumbent base, 1–3-times dichotomous, the branches densely leafy, vertical, close: leaves spreading or somewhat deflexed, 4–7 mm. long, entire or minutely denticulate, arranged in alternating zones of longer and shorter, the former slightly broadest above the middle, attenuate, the latter distinctly broadest at the base, tapering thence to an acuminate apex: sporophyls tapering from a broad base to the apex: plant often gemmiparous.—(ROCK-CLUBMOSS.) —Partially shaded rocks, usually sandstone, various provinces, Ala. to Ind. and Wis.—Spores mature in summer and fall.

The usual habitats of our lycopods range from rocks and dry woods to swamps. As the specific name indicates, the plants of the present species are rock-lovers. In this character and in its habit the plants resemble those of *L. Selago*, but in technical characters they are related to *L. lucidulum*. The geographic distribution is unique in North America, being chiefly in the central United States between the highlands and the Mississippi River. The other rock-loving lycopod, *L. Selago*, ranges southward only on the summits of the Blue Ridge. Curiously enough this plant eluded not only botanists, but also collectors, in a region where there was much plant collecting activity for nearly a century. Then within seven years after it was discovered in Indiana, in 1891, it was successively found in Wisconsin, Kentucky, and Alabama. The petrographic range of the plant, like the geologic range, is also limited, for as far as known it occurs only on weathered sandstone outcrops. It has not been found on the older igneous rocks to which the preceding species seems to be confined. A few hundred feet represents its maximum altitude.

3. **L. lucidulum** Michx. Stem and branches rising 1.5–2.5 dm. from a decumbent base, 1–3 times dichotomous, the few leafy vertical branches loosely clustered: leaves dark-green, shining, wide-spreading or finally deflexed, acute, somewhat oblanceolate, broadest above the middle, there erose-denticulate, tapering to a narrower base, 8–11 mm. long, arranged in alternating zones of longer and shorter leaves: sporophyls shorter than the foliage leaves and less denticulate, or entire: plant often gemmiparous.—(TRAILING-EVERGREEN. STAGHORN-MOSS.) —Low, cool, often damp woods, Blue Ridge, S. C. and Tenn., and

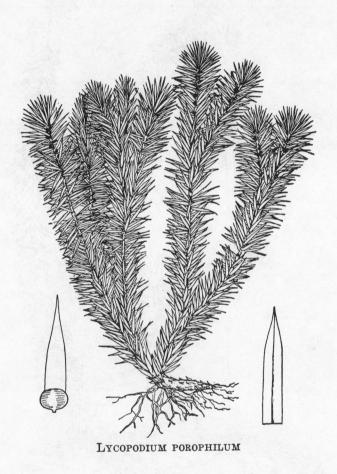

LYCOPODIUM POROPHILUM

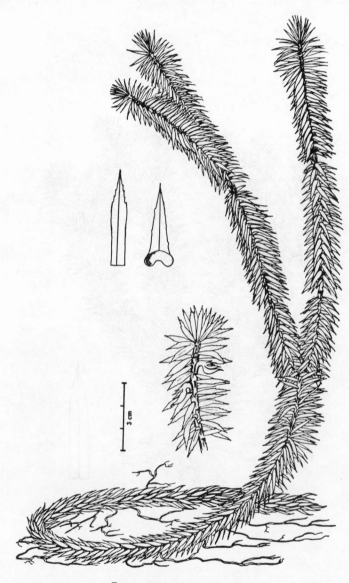

3 cm

LYCOPODIUM LUCIDULUM

various provinces to Iowa, B. C., Alas., and Newf.—Spores mature in summer and fall.—Fig. reduced.

The preceding species, *Lycopodium Selago* and *L. porophilum* are cliff or rock dwellers, so to speak. The present species, their most closely related one in our area, is a woods-plant. It is also much larger, and of quite different aspect. The author of the species in naming and describing it, recorded (1803) that the plant ranged from Canada to the Carolina mountains. Since this original record was made the geographic range has been extended so that it includes boreal North America south to South Carolina and west to Iowa. Plants grow at an altitude of about 6000 feet in North Carolina. Besides the common name trailing-evergreen, the plant is also known as SHINING CLUBMOSS and MOONFRUIT-PINE.

4. **L. dichotomum** Jacq. Plant epiphytic, pendent from the trunks or branches of trees, the stem stout, green, one or several times forked, mostly 1–5 dm. long: leaves uniform, laxly ascending, not twisted, mostly 1–2 cm. long, 6–10-ranked, rather crowded; blades acicular-attenuate, sessile, 0.5–1 mm. wide, usually deep-green, somewhat shining, with the midrib prominent: sporophyls similar to the foliage leaves: sporangia reniform, 1.5–2 mm. wide.—Trees, coniferous, broad-leaved, or palms, Big Cypress Swamp, Fla.—(*W. I.*)—Spores mature all year.—Fig. reduced.

Some plants, ferns, bromeliads, and orchids, which formed certain habits and selected certain habitats, adhere to them. Just why a lycopod like the present one should have selected in past ages an arboreous habitat is not to be known. But today *Lycopodium dichotomum* sticks to its epiphytic habitat while related species may be found on the ground beneath the trees. They will not exchange habitats. It is the most robust of all our lycopods. This lycopod is widely distributed in the West Indies. It was not until the spring of 1934[1] that it was found this side of the Gulf Stream. The Big Cypress Swamp is a natural locality for this lycopod, for it has for associates such West Indian ferns as the epiphytic *Cheiroglossa palmata* and the terrestrial *Dryopteris submarginalis;* also various epiphytic bromeliads and orchids. *Lycopodium dichotomum* was discovered on Martinique in the eighteenth century and named in 1762. It seems strange that specimens have not been found on the mainland of Central America and Mexico.

[1] First collected in Florida by C. A. Mosier and J. B. McFarlin, April 15, 1934.

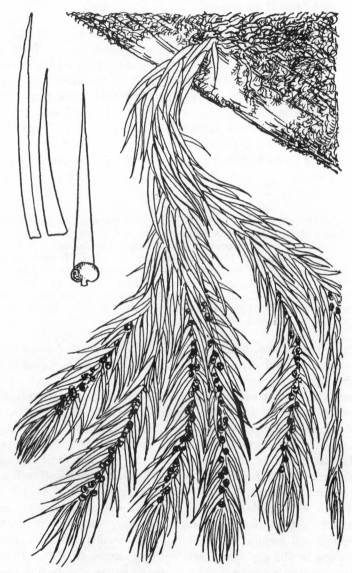

LYCOPODIUM DICHOTOMUM

5. L. appressum (Chapm.) Lloyd & Underw.   Stem and branches when present, mostly prostrate and creeping, 1.5–5 dm. long, very leafy: cauline leaves usually curved upward; blades lanceolate, 6–7 mm. long, saliently toothed: cone-bearing branches slender, arising directly from the stem, 1–3.5 dm. tall, with incurved or appressed narrow leaves, those near the base usually sparingly toothed, those above nearly or quite entire: cone slender, often elongate-cylindric, 2–7 cm. long: sporophyls lanceolate, acuminate, mostly incurved, appressed, obscurely toothed at base: sporangia less than 1 mm. long, subglobose, slightly narrower than the dilated base of the sporophyl. [*L. Chapmani* Underw.]—Moist soil near streams, low pinelands, and sandy bogs, Coastal Plain and adj. Piedmont, Fla. to La. and N. Y.— Spores mature in summer and fall or all year southward.

The genus *Lycopodium* occurs in all our plant provinces, some species in only one province, others in all six.   The present species may be found in two provinces which are contiguous to each other. This lycopod is intermediate in habit, as well as technical characters, between *Lycopodium carolinianum* and the following species.   It is less stiff in port than the former and more stiff than the following. The leaves of the peduncle are placed close together and rather loosely imbricate.   The leaves of the prostrate-creeping stem and branches are very numerous and are not distinctly distichous as they are in *L. carolinianum*.   It was discovered in Florida about the middle of the last century and named as a variety in 1883.   It occurs in the Coastal Plain, and locally in the adjacent Piedmont, and consequently does not reach any great altitude.

6. L. alopecuroides L.   Stem and branches stout, mostly recurved and more or less arching, 3–6 dm. long, densely leafy throughout: cauline leaves very numerous, spreading in all directions; blades narrowly lanceolate or linear-lanceolate, mostly 6–8 mm. long, irregularly saliently toothed: cone-bearing branches stout, 2–3 dm. tall, arising usually from the arches of the stem, copiously leafy, the leaves nearly similar to those of the stem, but narrower, lax or ascending: cones very stout-cylindric, 2.5–10 cm. long: sporophyls similar to the leaves of the peduncle, but much longer, broader and few-toothed at the base, ascending, spreading, or finally reflexed: sporangia globose.—(FOX-TAIL LYCOPOD.)—Wet pinelands, bogs, and borders of swamps, Coastal Plain, Fla. to Miss. and N. Y.—(*S. A.*)—Spores mature all year southward.—Fig. reduced.

Lycopods exhibit great contrasts in traveling ability.   Some stay at home, so to speak, others go almost the limit, either in latitude or longitude.   The range of the present species is extensive in latitude. The fox-tail lycopod, while plants of the next preceding species some-

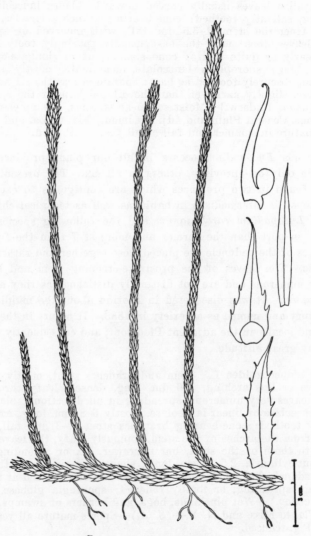

LYCOPODIUM APPRESSUM

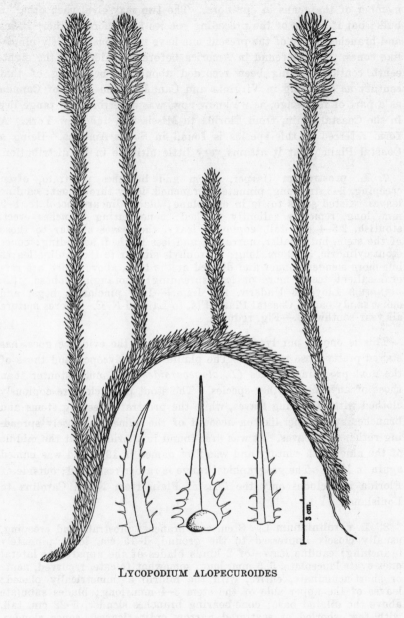

LYCOPODIUM ALOPECUROIDES

times equal it in size, is in general the most conspicuous terrestrial member of the genus in our flora. The two may rival each other in bulk; but if plants of the preceding species have more feathery stems and branches, those of the present one have more conspicuously plume-like cones. It was found in America before the middle of the eighteenth century, having been recorded about the beginning of that century as occurring in Virginia and Canada. The claim of Canada as a part of the range, as we know now, was an error. Its range lies in the Coastal Plain, from Florida to Mississippi and New York. A form referred to this species is found in South America. Being a Coastal Plain plant it attains very little altitude in its distribution.

7. **L. prostratum** Harper. Stem and branches prostrate, often creeping, 2–3 dm. long, pinnately branched, leafy throughout: cauline leaves twisted so as to lie in one plane; blades linear-lanceolate, 8–9 mm. long, remotely saliently toothed: cone-bearing branches erect, stoutish, 2.5–4 dm. tall, copiously leafy, the leaves similar to those of the stem, but smaller, narrower, and less toothed, ascending: cones stout-cylindric, 3–12 cm. long: sporophyls similar to the cauline leaves but more slender, longer and dilated at the base, above which are several salient teeth, more or less spreading: sporangia globose. [*L. pinnatum* Lloyd & Underw. not Lam.]—Low pinelands, bogs, and moist sandy banks, Coastal Plain, Fla. to La. and N. C.—Spores mature all year southward.—Fig. reduced.

This is one of our lycopods that, as far as the evidence goes, has stayed pretty close to home. The plants of this lycopod and those of the next preceding species (*L. alopecuroides*) are much stouter than those of any of our other species. The stout peduncles are copiously clothed with ascending leaves, while the prostrate creeping stems and branches are feather-like on account of the numerous loosely spreading rather soft leaves. It was first found in Florida about the middle of the nineteenth century and was first named in 1900 and was named again in 1906. The geographical range is rather restricted; outside of Florida it includes only the Coastal Plain from North Carolina to Louisiana.

8. **L. carolinianum** L. Stem and branches prostrate and creeping, usually closely appressed to the ground, 1–15 cm. long, pinnately branching: cauline leaves of 2 kinds blades of the apparently lateral ones ovate-lanceolate, 5–6 mm. long, somewhat falcate, recurved, acute or short-acuminate, entire, with the midrib asymmetrically placed; leaves of the upper side of the stem 3–4 mm. long; blades subulate above the dilated base: cone-bearing branches slender, 5–22 cm. tall, with few whorled or scattered narrow entire leaves: cones slender-

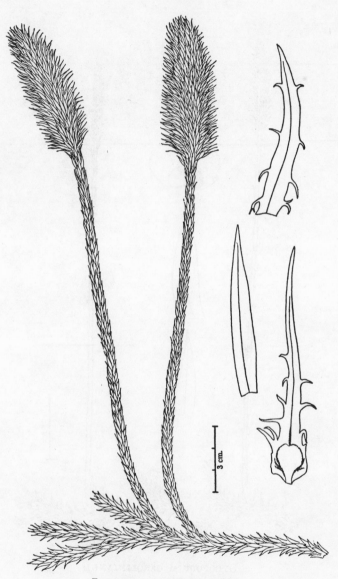

LYCOPODIUM PROSTRATUM

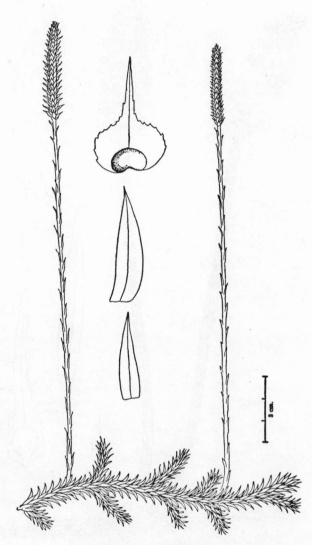

LYCOPODIUM CAROLINIANUM

cylindric, 1–5 cm. long, decidedly thicker than the supporting branch: sporophyls triangular-ovate in outline, acuminate, usually shallowly toothed all around: sporangia compressed, reniform, narrower than the dilated bases of the sporophyls.—Sandy bogs, swamps, and damp pinelands, Coastal Plain, Fla. to Miss., La., and N. J.—Fig. reduced.

The activity among plant collectors in the Carolina colonies is evidenced by the many species bearing the name *carolina* or *caroliniana*. This like most of the other species, however, was later found not to be confined to the Carolinas, but ranges many hundred miles north and south in the Coastal Plain. The plants of this species are more slender than those of any of its relatives with approximately the same habit of growth. It differs from the other kinds in the relatively few and separate rigid leaves of the peduncles and the rigid short-tipped sporophyls which are closely imbricated at their bases. It prefers to grow in open sandy places where the stem and branches lie closely appressed to the ground with the leaves of the lower plane stiffly spreading as if two-ranked. It was first found in the Carolinas in the earlier part of the eighteenth century, for its author records it as coming from there, in naming it in 1753. Its geographical range extends northward in the Coastal Plain to New Jersey, consequently its altitudinal range is slight.

9. **L. obscurum** L. Main stem creeping horizontally, often deep in the ground, giving off a few distant upright aerial branches 1–2.5 dm. high, these tree-like with numerous bushy branches: leaves 8-ranked on the lower branches, 6-ranked on the terminal ultimate ones, linear-lanceolate, curved upward, twisted (especially above), the branches thus more or less dorsiventral: sporophyls broadly ovate, subulate, the margins scarious and erose. [*L. dendroideum* Michx.]—(GROUND-PINE.)—Woods, often coniferous, in dry or moist, but usually strongly acid soil, Blue Ridge and adj. provinces, Ga. and Ala. to Ind., Wash., Alas., Lab., and Newf.—Spores mature in summer and fall.—Fig. reduced.

The genus *Lycopodium* has, through the ages, developed different lines of descent. On the morphological characters shown along these lines the genus may definitely be divided into groups or subgenera. In the case of *Lycopodium*, at least in our region, these groups are very clear-cut. Some of them consist of but one species, while others comprise several. The present species stands alone. It varies little even at the extremes of its geographic range. It is very constant in the morphological characters and in its habit. It is a very outstanding plant and its peculiar habit of growth, a resemblance to miniature

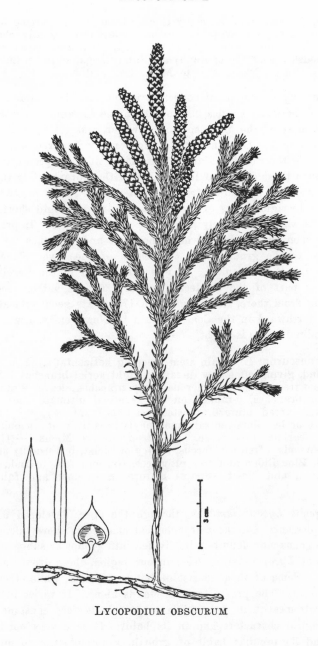

LYCOPODIUM OBSCURUM

coniferous trees, early suggested its popular name, ground-pine. Other popular names are SPIRAL-PINE, TREE-LIKE CLUBMOSS, BUNCH-EVER-GREEN, and CROWFOOT. The original specimens were collected at Philadelphia, Pennsylvania, in the earlier half of the eighteenth century and named in 1753. It occurs at 5000 feet altitude in the Blue Ridge of North Carolina.

10. L. clavatum L. Stem and branches creeping, 3–90 dm. long, stiff, with close-set or imbricate appressed, linear-lanceolate, denticulate, pungent leaves: branches from the main stem erect or ascending, 1–2 dm. long, branched, with very numerous, crowded, many-ranked, hair-tipped, linear-lanceolate leaves: cones narrowly cylindric, 2–7 cm. long: sporophyls deltoid or ovate-deltoid, bristle-tipped, with erose scarious margins.—(RUNNING-PINE.)—Dry or moist woods, various provinces, N. C. to Mich., Minn., Wash., Alas., and Lab.—(*Trop. Am., Eurasia, O. W.*)—Spores mature in summer and fall.—Fig. reduced.

Like many plants of ancient types this lycopod is circumboreal in its distribution. The original specimens came from Europe and were named in 1753. The species was found in North America during the early years of botanical activity, and later its geographic range was shown to be very wide, extending from the highlands of North Carolina northward and westward. It is represented in tropical America, Europe, and Asia. Like the Christmas-greens this plant thrives in dry woods, and produces remarkably long stems, when the scant supply of moisture and sterile soil are considered. Besides the wide geographic range extending through many plant provinces, the altitudinal range is great. The maximum elevation is fully 6000 feet in the Blue Ridge of North Carolina. As a result of its wide distribution many popular names have become associated with this plant, viz.: RUNNING-MOSS, BUCK'S-GRASS, FOX-TAIL, STAGHORN-MOSS, SNAKE-MOSS, GROUND-PINE, CREEPING-JENNIE, BUCK'S-HORN, WOLF'S-CLAWS, TOAD'S-TAIL. The plant is, apparently not abundant in the southeastern highlands, but when the remaining botanically unexplored mountain peaks are visited, it may be found on the summits of many of them.

11. L. flabelliforme (Fernald) Blanchard. Stems and branches horizontal, wide-creeping, flattish above, with many erect irregularly forked aerial branches or branchlets, the branches broadly flattened, 2–3-forked, the divisions few, or often numerous and fan-like, leafy throughout: leaves 4–ranked, minute and (excepting those of the under row) imbricate and decurrent, those of the upper row narrow and in-curved, of the lateral rows broad, with spreading tips and of the under row triangular-cuspidate, spreading: cone-bearing branches slender, 2–

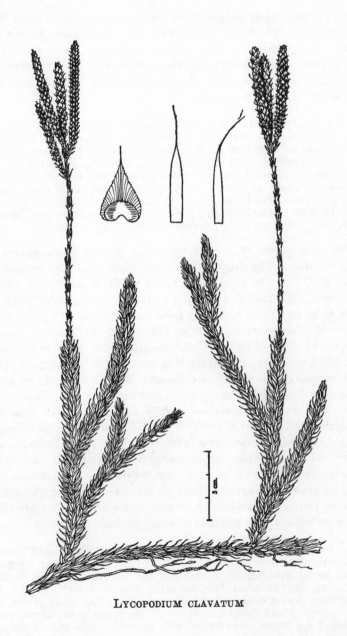

LYCOPODIUM CLAVATUM

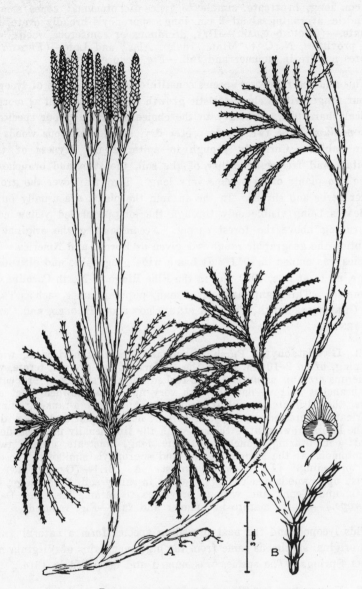

LYCOPODIUM FLABELLIFORME

13 cm. long, bracteate, simple to twice-dichotomous: cones slender, cylindric, averaging about 2 cm. long: sporophyls broadly ovate, acuminate.—(GROUND-CEDAR.)—Dry, deciduous or coniferous woods, various provinces, N. C. to Minn., Idaho, Alas., and Lab.—(*Eurasia.*)—Spores mature in summer and fall.—Fig. reduced.

This and the following species constitute a natural group of lycopods in our range, with a characteristic growth and habit as well as morphological characters. Contrary to the choice of many of our species of *Lycopodium*, these two plants prefer dry, often coniferous woods for their habitat. Curiously enough in spite of the dryness of their habitats and frequent sterility of the soil, the stem and branches of these two plants often become very long. They trail over the ground under herbs and shrubs. In the autumn the plants are usually buried in leaves being visible only through the long-peduncled yellow cones protruding above the forest carpet. Accompanying the original description the geographic range was given as Europe and America. The species was named in 1911. It has a wide geographic and altitudinal range, up to at least 4000 feet in the Blue Ridge of North Carolina and Tennessee. This plant has received many popular names, such as, TRAILING CHRISTMAS-GREEN, FESTOON-PINE, CROWFOOT, HAGBED, and CREEPING-JENNIE.

12. **L. tristachyum** Pursh. Stem and branches horizontal, widely creeping, often 2–10 cm. below the surface of the ground, terete, with numerous erect or assurgent much-forked aerial branches or branchlets, the branches narrow, flattish, with very numerous crowded erect divisions, the ultimate ones leafy throughout: leaves 4-ranked, minute, imbricate, appressed, strongly decurrent, nearly equal and alike, those of the lateral rows a little thicker, with the tips usually incurved downward: cone-bearing branches 7–13 cm. long, bracteate, usually twice-dichotomous at the summit: spike and sporophyls similar to those of the preceding. [*L. Chamaecyparissus* A. Br.]—(GROUND-PINE.)—Dryish open woods or clearings, usually in sandy soil, Blue Ridge, Ga., N. C., and Tenn., and various provinces to Minn., Me., and Del.—(*Europe.*)—Spores mature in summer and fall.—Fig. reduced.

This lycopod and the next preceding species form a natural group. The original specimens came from the high mountains of Virginia near Sweet Springs. The species was named and described in 1814.

13. **L. cernuum** L. Stems procumbent, arching, reclining, or ascending, 2–9 dm. long, with numerous relatively short spreading, arching, or recurved, divided lateral branches and branchlets, these very leafy throughout and with many short simple or branched divisions: leaves

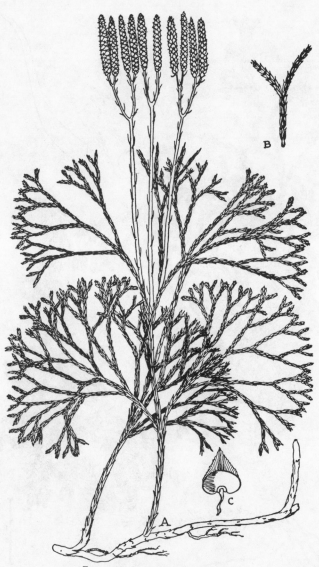

LYCOPODIUM TRISTACHYUM

LYCOPODIUM CERNUUM

numerous; blades acicular, 3–5 mm. long, spreading and upwardly curved or incurved: cones terminal upon many of the ultimate branches, sessile, nodding, cylindric to ovoid, 4–7 mm. long: sporophyls ovate-hastate or hastate, acuminate, lacerately sharp-toothed, much shorter and broader than the leaves: sporangia minute, much narrower than the bases of the sporophyls.—(STAGHORN-LYCOPOD.)—Wet or moist banks, bogs, and hammocks, Coastal Plain, Fla. to Miss., La., and Ga. —(*W. I.*, *Mex.*, *C. A.*, *S. A.*)—Spores mature all year.—Fig. reduced.

Several species of *Lycopodium* in the Gulf States are much alike in appearance but the staghorn-lycopod differs in habit as well as technically from all our other kinds. It is usually more or less vine-like and has a much-branched stem, which like the branches is copiously clothed with ascending or upwardly curved leaves. The cones are short and dense, and instead of being borne erect, they are borne nodding from the tips of the branches and branchlets. The existence of this plant in Florida was not known, apparently, until after the middle of the last century. This is a tropical plant and it is abundant in continental and insular tropical America.

FAMILY 3. **SELAGINELLACEAE**

SPIKE-MOSS FAMILY

Annual or perennial, often moss-like, leafy plants, with usually much-branched stems. Leaves scale-like, uniform and several-ranked, or of 2 kinds and in 2 planes. Sporangia 1-celled, of 2 kinds, disposed in 4-sided cones, solitary in the axils of bracts, some (megasporangia) containing 4 megaspores; others (microsporangia), containing numerous microspores, which develop into small prothallia, those from the megaspores bearing archegones, those from the microspores bearing antherids.—Consists of the following genera.

Leaves soft, of two kinds, borne in two planes, the lateral ones the larger
  and two-ranked; blades not bristle-tipped: diffuse or prostrate plants
  with creeping stems and branches.   1. DIPLOSTACHYUM.
Leaves stiff, all alike, several-ranked and uniformly
  disposed; blades bristle-tipped: tufted plants with
  erect or ascending stems and branches.   2. SELAGINELLA.

1. **DIPLOSTACHYUM** Beauv.

Terrestrial or paludal, hepatic-like plants. Stem and branches prostrate or assurgent rooting and forming patches. Leaves borne in two planes, the lateral two-ranked, with a marginal border of elongate cells, shallowly serrulate, usually acute, smaller leaves appressed, more pointed than the lateral ones. Cones rather lax, the sporophyls relatively narrower than the larger foliage leaves. [*Selaginella* Beauv., in part.]—SPIKE-MOSSES.—Comprises several hundred species, widely distributed, but most abundant in the tropics.—The genus is based on *Lycopodium apodum* L.—The name is Greek, referring to the two-ranked leaves.

Leaf-blades with broad margins, acute or obtuse.
  Spike short (2–5 mm. long) ; bracts flexuous-
    attenuate.   1. *D. Eatoni.*
  Spike elongate (10–20 mm. long) ; bracts acumi-
    nate.   2. *D. ludovicianum.*
Leaf-blades with very narrow margins, acuminate. 3. *D. apodum.*

1. D. Eatoni (Hieron.) Small. Plants yellow-green, loosely or closely matted and appressed to the moss in which they root: stems and branches 1–4 cm. long: leaves of the lower plane spreading; blades ovate, oval-ovate, or broadly oblong, 1–1.5 mm. long, abruptly pointed, the margins obscurely bristle-toothed: leaves of the upper plane smaller, lanceolate, long-acuminate: spikes 2–5 mm. long; bracts ovate-lanceolate, long-acuminate, and awned, the edges with obscure bristles: megasporangia 0.3–0.4 mm. in diameter: megaspores reddish-orange, 20–22 μ in diameter, tubercled. [*Selaginella Eatoni* Hieron.]—About and in moist limesinks in hammocks and eroded rocky reefs, Everglade Keys, pen. Fla.—(*W. I.*)

Our spike-mosses have become quite selective as to habitats. Two of them thrive on wet clay or loam banks, a third one on rock. The plants of this species grow flat on the rock in and about lime-sinks in low or moist hammocks and in outlying rocky reefs. It is more common in hammocks along the Everglades and prairies and often persists in these spots after the shrubs and trees have been burned entirely away; it is also occasionally met with in the pineland hammocks particularly in the moister parts. It always occurs in small patches. It is at its best during the rainy season (summer) when patches the size of a silver dollar may be found; it is also capable of resisting long droughts (winter) when the patches gradually dry and shrink to the size of a nickel or a dime. However, they are always ready to expand when the rains begin. It was discovered in Florida in 1903 and named in 1918.

2. D. ludovicianum (A.Br.) Small. Plants dark-green, creeping at the base, thence ascending: stems and branches 15–30 cm. long, once or twice pinnately branched: leaves of the lower plane broadly ovate or orbicular-ovate, obtuse, with whitish minutely toothed margins,

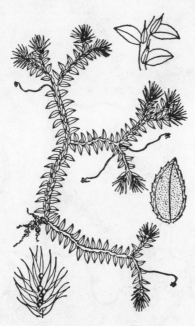

DIPLOSTACHYUM EATONI

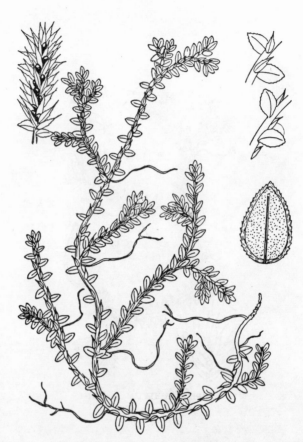

DIPLOSTACHYUM LUDOVICIANUM

those of the upper plane lanceolate, more closely toothed than those
of the lower, slender-tipped: spikes 1–2 cm. long, often somewhat
4-angled: bracts ovate-lanceolate, acuminate, minutely toothed above
the base: megasporangia about 1 mm. in diameter. [*Selaginella ludoviciana* A. Br.]—(LOUISIANA SPIKE-MOSS.)—Moist pinelands, about
swamps, and ditches, N. Fla. to La. and Tex.

Although the plants of this species have the same general habit as
those of *Selaginella apoda*, they appear to have less of the creeping
habit and consequently are more assurgent in growth. In very favorable habitats and in grassy places the plants either grow so luxuriantly
that the stems and branches are overcrowded and cannot lie prostrate
or they lean on the grass and climb through it. However, too little is
known about both the plant and its geographic distribution. The
Louisiana spike-moss may readily be separated from the following
species by the blunter leaf-blades in which the midrib stops short of
the tip and the wide margin of elongate cells, which is twice or thrice
the width of that of the following wide-spread species. It occurs only
in the coastal region from northern Florida to Louisiana and Texas.
It was first collected in Louisiana in the earlier half of the last century. The species has not been found in the Old World.

3. **D. apodum** (L.) Beauv. Plants pale-green, creeping, often
loosely matted: stems and branches 5–15 cm. long, flaccid, pinnately
branched: leaves of the lower plane ovate, acute or acutish, shortly
bristle-toothed on the margins, those of the upper plane lanceolate or
ovate-lanceolate, acuminate, short bristle-pointed, minutely toothed:
spikes 6–15 mm. long, obscurely 4-angled; bracts ovate or ovate-
lanceolate, acuminate, minutely toothed above the base, acutely keeled
above: megasporangia 0.5–0.6 mm. in diameter.—(CREEPING-SELA-
GINELLA. CREEPING-MOSS.) [*Lycopodium apodum* L. *Selaginella
apoda* Spring.]—Wet woods, meadows, muddy or mossy or grassy
places in and about swamps, along streams, and ditches, various provinces, Fla. to Tex., B. C., Ont., and Me.—Spores mature in summer and
fall or all year southward.—[S. A.]

The preceding plants have a very restricted geographic range in our
area. The present one covers southern Canada and the United States,
except the southwest. It thrives in almost any moist shaded spot.
However, this plant delights in a location on a steep bank where
water seeps from behind, and multiplies to such an extent as to form
a delicate ground-cover. The creeping-moss was discovered in
"Canada, Virginia and Pennsylvania" in the earlier half of the
eighteenth century and named in 1753. It has not been found in the
Old World.

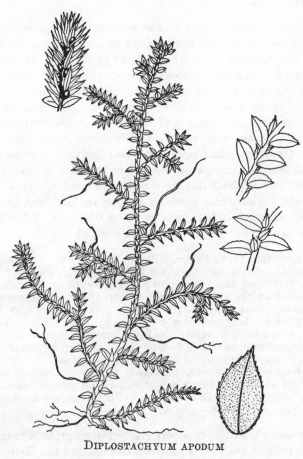

DIPLOSTACHYUM APODUM

2. SELAGINELLA Beauv.

Terrestrial, often epipetric or arenicolous, moss-like plants. Stems and branches erect or ascending, often densely clustered and tufted, but more or less rooting at the nodes. Leaves borne in several ranks, lax or closely imbricated, all alike, without a border of elongate cells, spiny-toothed, bristle-tipped. Cones compact, the sporophyls broader than the foliage leaves.—SPIKE-MOSSES.—Comprises several hundred species, widely distributed.—The genus is based on *Lycopodium selaginoides* L. The name is a diminutive of the lycopod.

Plants of the higher lands, mainly Blue Ridge and adjacent provinces.
    Young leaves with firm, straight, persistent, apical bristles about half
        as long as the blades or less.   1. *S. rupestris.*
    Young leaves with delicate twisted or contorted,
        more or less deciduous apical bristles as long
        as the blade or nearly so.   2. *S. tortipila.*
Plants of the lower lands, mainly Coastal Plain, rarely
    Appalachian Plateaus.
    Young leaves with stiff apical bristles nearly or
        quite as long as the blades, rather evenly and
        strongly ciliate.   3. *S. acanthonota.*
    Young leaves with weak apical bristles about half
        as long as the blades or less, unevenly and
        weakly ciliate.   4. *S. arenicola.*

1. S. rupestris (L.) Spring. Plant dark-green; stem and branches creeping, 5–10 cm. long, often densely tufted, zigzag, ascending at the tips; primary branches short; leaves closely imbricate, about 8-ranked; blades about 2 mm. long, deeply channeled dorsally, with 5–9 or more cilia on each side, the apical bristle about 1 mm. long: persistent cones 1–1.5 cm. long, sharply 4-angled: sporophyls erect; blades triangular-lanceolate, with shorter awns and more cilia than the leaves.—(DWARF-LYCOPOD. SPIKE-MOSS.)—Dry rocks, various provinces, Ga. to Mo., B. C., Ont., and Me.—Spores mature in summer and fall.

American true spike-mosses were scant in botanical literature up to the middle of the past century. The present species and *Lycopodium selaginoides* (*Selaginella selaginoides*) of our northeast, and also of Europe of the Linnaean period, being the total. This plant has a wide geographic distribution. Within its range only one species, the following, is liable to be confused with it. The original specimens came from Virginia and were named and described in 1753. It occurs as high as 3000 feet in the Blue Ridge.

2. S. tortipila A. Br. Plant with ascending or prostrate stems and branches closely tipped or loosely spreading about the edges of the tufts, 20 to 25 cm. long, 1.2–1.8 mm. thick, zigzag, leaves 8–13-ranked, imbricate, closely appressed on the shoots and branches, glaucous or in age becoming grayish or brownish, the body lanceolate to linear-

SELAGINELLA RUPESTRIS

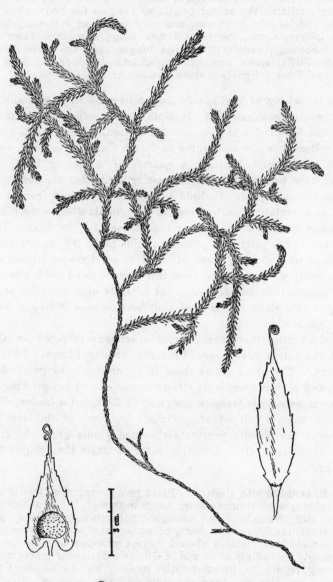

SELAGINELLA TORTIPILA

lanceolate from a long decurrent base, 1.5–2 mm. long, minutely and sparingly ciliate: the apical bristle as long as the body when young, fragile and largely deciduous, minutely spinulose, extremely tortuous. Cones inconspicuous, less than 5 mm. long; sporophyls lanceolate to ovate-lanceolate, usually somewhat longer than the leaves, minutely ciliate.—Cliffs, stony mountain tops, and damp rocks, Blue Ridge, N. C. and Tenn.—Spores mature in summer and fall.

The launching of this species might be considered sporadic, but it really was a renaissance of attempts at the proper understanding of the genus *Selaginella* as it occurs in our area. The original specimens were collected in the mountains of North Carolina in 1841, and were named and described nearly a quarter of a century later. Recent studies have brought out the interesting facts that the plants of this species are dimorphic. In 1902 a specimen of a plant from the North Carolina mountains was described as *Selaginella Sherwoodii*. The type specimens are very much stouter than those of *S. tortipila*. It seems now that in the clumps or patches of this plant the central portion is composed of a dense growth of short stout stems and branches, (*S. Sherwoodii*) while radiating from this center extend much more slender and elongate branches (*S. tortipila*).[1] Only high altitudes are to the liking of this plant. It is most abundant between 5000 and 6000 feet above sea-level.

In describing this species from specimens collected on Caesar's Head, the author gave a second locality, namely, Chimney Rock, North Carolina. The plant grows there in an unusually moist shaded situation, and is correspondingly slender-stemmed and low-growing. None of the diagnostic characters assigned to *Selaginella Sherwoodii* hold, however, when a full set of specimens from any of the localities are compared, for slender prostrate stemmed plants grow out from the bases of the same clumps, in the center of which the upright-stemmed ones grow.

3. **S. acanthonota** Underw. Plant pale-green, often less than 5 cm. tall, in depressed clumps: stem much branched, the branches densely tufted, stiff, decumbent and assurgent and rooting, especially near the base, stout, the branchlets short, often incurved, softly plumose at the tips, densely leafy: leaves when dry erect or somewhat appressed, erect or strongly ascending when wet, 8–10-ranked; blades lanceolate, 1–1.5 mm. long, ciliate, the apical bristles more or less deciduous at the tip: cones of less diameter than the stem and the branches, often yellow-tinged, 4-angled, 1–2 cm. long; sporophyls triangular-lanceolate, 1.5–2 mm. long, erect when dry, erect or appressed when wet, copiously

[1] See E. T. Wherry, Jour. S. Appal. Bot. Club 1: 65–69. 1936.

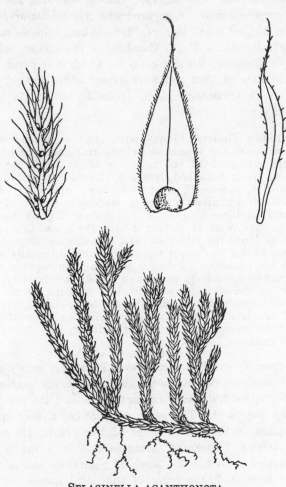

SELAGINELLA ACANTHONOTA

ciliate.—Dry sand, pinelands, sandhills, and scrub, pen. Fla. to N. C.—
Spores mature all year.

As compared with the plants of the following species those of this
species are stouter and more stocky. The clumps, also, are more depressed and usually denser. Compared with *Selaginella arenicola* this
species has a decided south to north distribution. Specimens of this
species were collected in North Carolina in the earlier half of the
past century. However, the specimens on which it is based were collected in that state in 1892 and were named and described a decade
later. This is an arenicolous plant, occurring in sand in pinelands,
sandhills, and scrub.

4. **S. arenicola** Underw. Plant with erect or ascending tufted,
often crowded stems and branches, brown, gray-green, or gray-brown
when dry, the clumps 5–12 cm. tall: the stems rigid, the branches
relatively few, freely branched, leaves 4–12-ranked, ascending or appressed when dry, appressed, erect or strongly ascending when wet:
blades lanceolate, sometimes narrowly lanceolate, mostly 1–1.5 mm.
long, thickish, papillose-roughened, flat above, slightly convex and
sulcate on the back, with 12 marginal cilia, the apical bristle up to 1
mm. long white above the yellowish base, spinulose-roughened, more or
less deciduous at the tip: cones terminal, 4-angled, usually somewhat
thicker than the branches, up to 3.5 cm. long: sporophyls about 1.8
mm. long, erect or ascending, sometimes loosely so when dry, strongly
ascending or appressed when wet; blade lanceolate, ovate, rhombic-
ovate or ovate-lanceolate, auriculate at the base, curved, each with a
short apical bristle and marginal cilia similar to those of the leaf-
blades but more numerous.—Scrub, sand-dunes, and dry pinelands,
Fla.—Spores mature all year.

Although specimens of this species were known for nearly a century
they did not receive a definite name until late in the past century—
1898. Moreover, its first name was untenable, and the present name
was promptly published. The scrub of Florida, a very specialized
plant association, is the typical home of this plant. Its occurrence
in the Appalachian Plateau of Alabama and in Texas is unusual.
Other specimens collected in the scrub of peninsular and of northern
Florida were later made the types of additional species—*Selaginella
funiformis* (1917) and *S. humifusa* (1918). A study of much material
from the general range involved indicates that the specific distinctions
attributed to the two species just cited are not sufficiently constant for
distinguishing characters. The plants grow in clumps of varying sizes
in the almost pure sand. They occur in the open or in the shade of

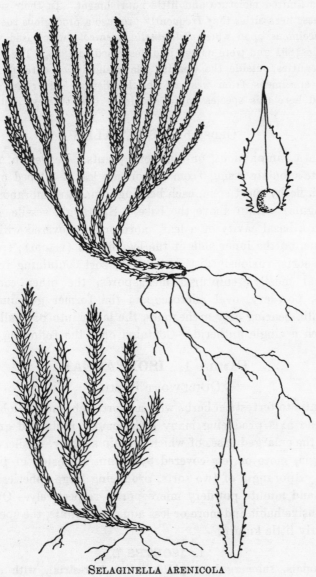

SELAGINELLA ARENICOLA

shrubbery. The clumps are often of great age. They grow where
there is limited moisture and little nourishment. In their search for
both these necessities they frequently produce a prodigious root-system.
The specimens upon which *Selaginella arenicola* was based were collected in 1891 and were named and described in 1898. The specimens
and localities outside the Coastal Plain should be carefully studied.
If the specimens from west of the Mississippi River are properly
referred here this species has a decidedly east to west distribution.

ORDER 6. **ISOETALES**[1]

Aquatic, amphibious, or uliginous plants. Leaves in a crown,
elongate-subulate rising from a more or less 2–3-lobed or rarely
5-lobed, fleshy short stem, each bearing a small membranous member (ligule) within above the base. Sporangia sessile, solitary,
each in a basal cavity of a leaf, more or less covered with a fold
of tissue, on the inner side of the leaf-blades (velum); sporangia
of two sorts, variously distributed; one sort containing few large
spherical mostly sculptured megaspores, the other containing
minute, powdery, oval microscopes; the former germinate into
prothallia bearing only archegones, the latter into prothallia bearing each a single antherid.—Contains only the following family.

FAMILY 1. **ISOETACEAE**
QUILLWORT FAMILY

Aquatic to terrestrial herbs with a short, unbranched, lobed, subterranean axis producing many dichotomous roots and grass-like
leaves, the enlarged bases of which contain solitary, sessile, adaxial,
sporangia, more or less covered by a thin extension of tissue or
velum. Sporangia of two sorts, producing large spherical megaspores and minute powdery microspores, respectively.—Owing to
their elusive habit and more or less aquatic habitats, the species are
popularly little known.

1. **ISOETES** L.
Perennials, submerged, amphibious, or terrestrial, with a 2- or
3-lobed, short fleshy axis or corm giving rise to numerous branched

[1] This treatment in the main follows the *Monograph of the Isoetaceae,*
Ann. Mo. Bot. Gard. 9 : 79–234. 1922, by Norma E. Pfeiffer.

roots and to a rosette of elongated, somewhat triangular or quadrangular leaves. Leaves with 4 transversely septate, longitudinal airchannels, with central fibrovascular bundle; peripheral groups of supporting cells present or absent, stomata present or absent. Ligule a small, delicate triangular extension of tissue on inner face of the leaf above the sporangium. Sporangium solitary, sessile, on adaxial side of leaf, contained within a basal cavity, and more or less covered by a membranous tissue, the velum, on the inner leaf face. Sporangia of two types, microsporangia and megasporangia, bearing respectively microspores and megaspores, which on germination develop gametophytes, the former with a single antherid, the latter producing archegones. Megaspores hemispherical at base, with equatorial ridge at center and three other crests joined at top of upper hemisphere, with variously sculptured walls. Microspores minute, powdery, usually oval.— About 68 species of wide geographic distribution.—The genus is based on *Isoetes lacustris*—(MERLIN'S GRASS, ISOETES).—The latter is from the Greek, apparently referring to the persistent green leaves.—Spores mature according to the stage of the water and the variation in the seasons.

Megaspores with tuberculate surface, or nearly smooth.
   Velum complete.
      Megaspores white or creamy.
         Sporangia subglobose, ellipsoid, ovoid or obovoid and only slightly longer than wide: ligule deltoid.
            Megaspores about 0.3 mm. in diameter, the faces minutely tubercled, the tubercles sometimes confluent.   1. *I. flaccida.*
            Megaspores about 0.5 mm. in diameter, the faces nearly or quite smooth.   1a. *I. flaccida Chapmani.*
         Sporangia much longer than wide, fusiform-obovoid: ligule lanceolate or triangular-lanceolate.   1b. *I. flaccida alata.*
      Megaspores gray when dry, black when wet.   2. *I. melanospora.*
   Velum very narrow, usually covering not more than one-third of the sporangium.   3. *I. Butleri.*
Megaspores with irregularly reticulate surfaces.
   Velum narrow, covering less than one-third of the sporangium.   4. *I. Engelmanni.*
   Velum covering one-third to two-thirds of the sporangium.   4a. *I. Engelmanni caroliniana.*

1. **I. flaccida** Shuttlw. Leaves 1–4 dm. long or rarely longer, erect, prostrate, or partly floating, slender, sometimes very slender, very much dilated on either side of the sporangium: ligule broadly deltoid, 1 mm. long or less, rather obtuse: sporangia ellipsoid, or slightly broadest above the middle or below it, 3–5 mm. long, completely covered by the velum: megaspores pale, about 300–500 μ in diameter or more, the apical face with few or several flattish central tubercles which are

distinct or partly confluent, the basal face with bold rounded ridges, sometimes anastomosing: microspores light-brown, 26–33 μ long.— Lakes, hammocks, wet pinelands, marshes, and sluggish pineland-streams, Coastal Plain, nearly throughout Fla., except the Florida Keys, and Ga.

The North American species of *Isoetes* fall into several groups. They may have developed from different immigrant ancestors. The southeastern species show relationship to South American species. Those species now isolated north and south of the tropics may have had a common tropical American ancestor. The spores could easily have been brought northward on the feet or in the craws of water-birds. This, the commonest species of *Isoetes* in the southeastern Coastal Plain, grows either submerged or more or less emersed, with the leaves erect or partly spread out on the mud. It was discovered in Lake Immonia north of Tallahassee, Florida, by Ferdinand Rugel, in 1842; and in more recent years it has been collected in southern Georgia. It was named in 1846. The plants vary greatly in size, but whether small or large, the leaves are usually more slender than those of the other southeastern species.

It occurs in several forms which are somewhat difficult for the inex-perienced student to distinguish. Indeed most species of *Isoetes* in habit and superficial characters resemble one another more closely than do most ferns. All species are alike in having short and stocky stems that give rise to leaves in a complicated spiral; crowns are con-cave and the centrally lowest part produces the newest leaves. Roots branch dichotomously and the corm is 2–3-lobed, corresponding to furrows in the stem. At the inner base of each fertile leaf is an elongated or round cavity, called the fovea, in which is produced a single sporangium, containing either microspores or megaspores. Above the sporangium, lying against the leaf, is an extension, or tooth, of thin tissue called the ligule; and covering the sporangium wholly or partly is a delicate membrane like an indusium—but of different origin—known as the velum. A cross-section of a leaf toward its base shows four air-channels (which have transverse partitions), a central vascular-bundle, and frequently 4–6 peripheral strands of sup-porting tissue. In the surface of the leaf toward the upper end are usually more or less numerous stomata.

Of these details of structure most distinctive characters seem to be the size and markings of megaspores which when mature can be ob-served with a magnification of about 50 to 60 diameters. The form of the velum and the extent to which it covers the sporangium also affords a fairly dependable detail. Another relatively consistent and reliable character is the lobing of the corm. Useful but less trustworthy for discrimination, on account of seasonal or ecological variation, are the shape of the ligule, the presence and number of peripheral strands of supporting tissue, the abundance and location of stomata, and the shape and habit of leaves. Only rarely are superficial appearance, size, habitat, and locality sufficient for identification.

Immaturity of structure, especially of megaspores, is one of the greatest obstacles to correct determination. The collector should not only refrain from removing the partly dried or decayed leaves but should try to keep some earth clinging to the roots. If the plant is secured out of season for ripened sporangia nearly always normal megaspores of the past year can be found either among leaf-vestiges or in attached soil if available.

1a. I. flaccida Chapmani Engelm. Leaves about 4.5 dm. long, mostly floating, stoutish, dilated on either side of the sporangium: ligule triangular, 4–5.5 mm. long, often acuminate: sporangia obovoid, about 4 mm. long, completely covered by the velum: megaspores about 500 μ in diameter, the faces sparingly tubercled, or with somewhat elongate ridge-like tubercles, or some of them nearly or quite smooth. [*I. Chapmani* (Engelm.) Small.]—Limestone spring near Marianna, Fla.

The geographic range of this quillwort is limited. Apparently the variety is rare. It was discovered, as the account states, in 1848, in a clear spring-fed stream arising under a ledge of lime-rock from a subterranean tributary of the Chipola River about one-third mile above the bridge at Marianna, Florida.

At various intervals during the near-century that has elapsed, botanists have searched vainly for specimens of *I. flaccida Chapmani* in the station so clearly described by the discoverer. Recently, a student equipped with hip-boots and hoe explored the region thoroughly. At first he traversed the sandy shallows and backwaters where he had learned by experience *Isoetes* are most likely to grow; then he carefully followed the bed of the stream to the river and examined the river swamp. His search was unsuccessful, and he had covered the entire locality except a few feet of narrow channel where the current had threatened to take him off his feet. Returning to that spot he discovered, where the stream flowed most rapidly, a row of six plants of *Isoetes* waving their leaves frantically in the swift and swollen current.   Two specimens were deposited in the New York Botanical Garden.

1b. I. flaccida alata N. Pfeiffer.   Leaves 1–4 dm. long, stout, stouter than those of either the preceding or succeeding species, mostly erect, scarious, winged near the base, and somewhat dilated on either side of the sporangium: ligule deltoid, 2.5–3.5 mm. long, acute or acutish: sporangia fusiform, 8–10 mm. long, completely covered by the velum; megaspores 290–500 μ in diameter, upper faces usually crowded with tubercles which may become ridge-like; lower face with bold rounded ridges so anastomosing as to give more or less irregularly reticulate effect.—Shaded pond-margins, cypress swamps, open miry places and sluggish pineland streams, Fla. and S. Ga.

The geographic ranges of the rarer quillworts are often little known, owing largely to the rather inconspicuous habit of the plants and the more or less inaccessible habitats.   The plants of this species resemble those of *Isoetes flaccida Chapmani* in the stout habit and *I. flaccida* in the small megaspores, but they may be distinguished from either by the fusiform sporangia and the prominent wings on the lower part of the leaves.   The type specimens were collected in 1900 by A. H. Curtiss at Riverland, Sumter County, Florida.

A student who recently searched far and wide without success for *Isoetes* found *I. flaccida alata* growing by thousands on his lawn. They resemble certain grasses and sedges so closely that they are not easily recognized; and on land irregularly flooded they appear and disappear so unexpectedly that they are not likely to attract attention. Though seldom observed, *Isoetes* of one species or another are common throughout the range of this book and are abundant in Florida.

They are most easily found in the southeastern states about ponds that have flat shores and are subject to regular seasonal variation in water-level, or in shallow wooded bays of such ponds, or on the bottom up to six feet in depth, where they may be seen from a boat if the water is clear, or where, if it is dark, they can be secured by persistent dredging.   Often where the water is turbid and full of weeds their presence is revealed by the work of predatory animals, such as ducks and other water-birds, carp, and muskrats, who in seeking the corms cause the leaves to float to the surface.   They also grow on the beds of slow-moving streams, and more rarely where the current is rapid, especially if the bottom is of firmly compacted soil.   They are frequent in temporary ponds, or hog-wallows, in grassy fields.   In the southeast (excepting *I. Butleri*) they are seldom found among rocks, but often where naked surface rock, especially granite, is crossed by runlets which moisten hollows filled with humus.

At stations where plants are submerged throughout the year and where conditions are little changed colonies seem to persist indefinitely; nor do colonies usually become extinct when drouth or drainage deprive normally submerged species of water for long periods and the sun bakes the soil. Although the plants temporarily disappear they usually regain their vigor after one or two wet seasons. *Isoetes* are perennials of slow growth. Young plants under normal conditions may require three or more years to attain maturity. Each autumn in temperate climates, or after each prolonged drouth, most of the roots and leaves and the outer portion of the stem fall away or decay. Only the small central cylinder, with perhaps a few of the sterile leaves, persists from year to year.

2. **I. melanospora** Engelm. Leaves 2.5–8 cm. long, tapering to the apex and almost setaceous, light-green, spreading where the water has dried up: ligule small, triangular: sporangia orbicular, 1–2 mm. long, covered by the velum: megaspores gray when dry, black when wet, 400–480 μ in diameter, the rough warts sometimes merging into short narrow ridges which rarely anastomose: commissural ridges thin, bladelike, microspores brown, 26–31 μ long, papillose to smoothish.—Depressions in granite rock, Piedmont, Stone Mountain and adjacent territory, Ga.

Among localities that harbor endemic species of plants, Stone Mountain, Georgia, is outstanding. Moreover, these several unusual plants grow on almost bare granite rock or in very scant accumulations of coarse soil resulting from disintegrating granite. The note with the original description of this *Isoetes* well expresses the peculiar habitat of the plants of some of these species. It is recorded that this species was discovered "In shallow depressions a couple of inches deep and a few feet in diameter, on the naked granite surface near the top of the mountain, where occasional rains and dews furnish temporary and precarious moisture, but where for weeks and even months the glaring sun, flashing on the naked rock, parches and bakes them." This, the smallest species in the southeast, was discovered by W. M. Canby in 1869 and was named and described in 1877.

Stone Mountain and Little Stone Mountain were thought to be the only stations for this species until it was recently found in depressions in granite rock near Winder, Barrow Co., Ga., and still more recently in adjacent Walton County. In these locations it grows abundantly where springs or spring-fed rivulets of clear water flow over naked granite and irrigate depressions filled to a depth of one or several inches with granitic sand and humus. It is usually associated with *Isoetes Engelmani caroliniana* and with sedges and sometimes with *Pilularia americana* which runs its rootstocks and sporocarps above the corms, for as usual the latter are deeply-seated. In most of the newer stations on account of the abundant moisture *I. melanospora* can be found throughout the growing season, but on Stone Mountain it utterly disappears from the surface in winter and in drouth. A visit in March to Granite Mt., Texas, a similar endemic station for the allied species *I. lithophila*, revealed similar conditions. In the depressions where it grows there was at that early season no surface indication of the plant.

The name *Isoetes* (first used in literature by Linnaeus) which means equal throughout the year, or not changing according to season, seems scarcely appropriate for such species as *I. melanospora* and *I. lithophila*. Even those species that remain always in deep water have their periods of leaf-producing and fruiting while those that are truly xerophilous sometimes drop all leaves and remain dormant through one or more dry seasons.

3. I. Butleri Engelm. Leaves 8–15 cm. long, erect or ascending, tapering to the apex: ligule elongate, cordate at base: velum very narrow: sporangia oblong or ellipsoid, 6–7 mm. long, brown-lined: megaspores variable, commonly 480–650 µ in diameter, or smaller, the numerous tubercles distinct or occasionally confluent: microspores 27–37 µ long, papillose.—Cedar glades, barrens, and limestone flats, various provinces, Tenn. to Okla., Kans., and Mo.

This quillwort was named in 1878 from plants collected in 1875 in Indian Territory, now Oklahoma, by G. D. Butler. It differs from all the other southeastern quillworts in being a terrestrial species, in having little or no velum, in being dioecious—that is individual plants produce either megaspores or microspores exclusively and are to that extent sexed—, and in being a lover of rocky places. Its range is confined to the several interior plant provinces where limestone dominates. Its favorite habitat is springy depressions in cedar and rock barrens where later in the season the earth becomes the driest of dry ground. As with other terrestrial *Isoetes* the sporelings appear in places subject to flood in spring and drouth in summer. The plants grow only during high water and then await a flood to grow. By May or June fruiting is mature, and the plants disappear by July.

As the leaves are nearly always out of water, they have numerous stomata. If one places bits of epidermis under the microscope stomata can be observed with a magnifying power of 150 to 250 diameters. In studying emersed species that have few stomata the epidermis should be taken from various locations, especially from the tips of leaves. A species like the European *I. lacustris,* which is always submerged, has no stomata, as the leaves are unable to reach the air.

I. Butleri is not closely related to the other three southeastern quillworts, but is closely connected with *I. melanopoda* with which it intergrades. The megaspore sculpture of the allied species is so much alike as to be scarcely distinguishable. The two occupy similar habitats and somewhat similar ranges but *I. melanopoda* has not yet been reported within the boundaries of the southeastern states.

Of the 68 known species of *Isoetes* 12 have been found in Asia, 10 in Africa, 15 in Europe, 9 in South America, 26 in North America, 22 in the United States, 10 in the northeastern states, 6 in the central states, 9 in the states west of the Rockies, and 4 in the southeastern states. After additional exploration and study the number occurring in the latter area will probably be increased.

4. I. Engelmanni A. Br. Amphibious, usually partly immersed when mature: corm 2-lobed; leaves light green, quadrangular, tapering, 15–50 cm. long, bearing abundant stomata: peripheral strands present or wanting: sporangia oblong or linear-oblong, unspotted: velum narrow: megaspores white, 400–570 μ in diameter, covered with honeycomb-like reticulations: microspores 21–30 μ long, mostly smooth.—Brooks, ponds, swamps, and ditches, rooting in mud, S. C. to Mo., and Me.

This fine quillwort was named in 1846, near the time of the launching of a number of North American species, for an American student of the genus by his friend Alexander Braun, an outstanding European contributor to our knowledge of *Isoetes.* The original specimens were collected in 1842 by George Engelmann and N. Riehl from a small pond near St. Louis, Mo. It has proved to be a species of wide geographical distribution and has apparently developed into several subspecies in the extensive range. It is fairly abundant from Maine as far west as the Mississippi River and Missouri and south to North Carolina and Georgia, where the type is inclined to give way to the varieties.

The plants are among the larger in the genus as regards the number of leaves, the length of leaves, and the size of corms. Specimens have

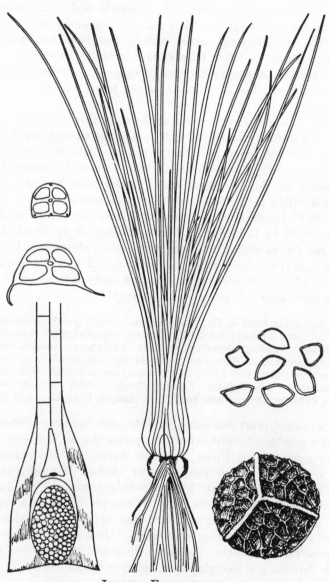

ISOETES ENGELMANNI

been seen nearly two feet long, having 200 leaves and corms 1–2 inches in diameter. Numerous stomata are observable in the light green foliage. Spores mature in the southeast in July. The plants grow in brooks or ponds, often entirely under water in the spring and completely exposed during summer drouth; and they have been found more rarely where they remain, under normal rainfall, entirely out of water throughout the year.

4a. **I. Engelmanni caroliniana** A. A. Eaton. Corm 2-lobed; leaves 15–25, up to 22 cm. long; peripheral strands 4, weak; stomata numerous; sporangium 7–9 mm. long, one-third to two-thirds covered by velum; megaspores 400–530 μ in diameter, with high reticulate ridges, much crisped and cut with an irregular margin, producing somewhat spiny effect; microspores 24–34 μ long, spinulose. Emersed or submerged in ponds, sluggish streams, or swamps, Georgia and North Carolina.

This variety was named in 1900 from specimens collected in Mitchell Co., North Carolina, in 1893. According to its author it has broader leaves than the type, a broader velum (covering one-half to two-thirds of the sporangium), more scattered megaspore sculpture, and brown microspores which are large and densely muricate. It occurs up to an altitude of 3000 feet near Columbus, North Carolina, and is found in nearly all of North Carolina and Georgia, excepting perhaps extreme west Georgia, the type locality for var. *georgiana*,[1] which Pfeiffer does not maintain. She cites the type-specimens of var. *georgiana* under the species.

[1] *I. Engelmanni* var. *georgiana* Engelm. Similar to the type; leaves few (in the only specimens seen 15, 10 to 12 inches long), rather slender; oval sporangium with narrow velum; macrospores larger, 0.48 to 0.46 mm. thick; microspores 0.028 to 0.031 mm. long, smooth. Variety *georgiana* comes from a mountain stream, the Horseleg Creek, a tributary of the Coosa River, Floyd Co., Georgia, in slow-moving water about a foot deep, *A. W. Chapman.*

GENERAL AND RESTRICTED DISTRIBUTION OF FERNS OF SOUTHEASTERN FLORA

Ferns of the southeastern flora, the general and restricted distribution indicated in column headings.[1]

Ferns of wide latitudinal or longitudinal distribution, or both, in the Southeastern Flora

Ferns of restricted distribution in the Southeastern Flora in one or few limited areas

Trichomanes Petersii (S) (Ar)
Trichomanes punctatum (T) (Cr) (Cp)
Trichomanes sphenoides (T)
Trichomanes lineolatum (T) (Cr) (Cp)
Trichomanes Krausii (T) (W) (Cr) (Cp)
Trichomanes Boschianum (S) (Ar)
Stenochlaena Kunzeana (W) (Cr) (E) (Cp)
Stenochleana tenuifolia (I) (W) (Cp)
Acrostichum aureum (T) (A) (P) (Cp)
Acrostichum danaeaefolium (T) (A) (P) (Cp)

Polypodium virginianum (N) (OW) (Ir) (E)

Polypodium Plumula (T) (W) (Cr) (E) (Cp)
Polypodium pectinatum (T) (W) (Cr) (E) (Cp)

Marginaria polypodioides (S) (Ir) (E)

Goniophlebium brasiliense (T) (E) (Cp)
Phlebodium aureum (T) (Cr) (E) (Cp)
Campyloneurum angustifolium (T) (E) (Cp)
Campyloneurum Phyllitidis (T) (E) (Cp)
Campyloneurum latum (T) (E) (Cp)
Campyloneurum costatum (T) (E) (Cp)
Phymatodes heterophyllum (T) (W) (Cp)
Pityrogramma calomelanos (T) (W) (Cp)
Vittaria lineata (T) (E) (Cp)
Paltonium lanceolatum (T) (E) (Cp)
Pycnodoria bahamensis (T) (W) (Cr) (Cp)

[1] Letters in parentheses means: G, generally distributed in our area. S, southern type. I, intermediate between north and south extremes. N, northern type. T, tropical type. Z, western type. OW, Old World included in distribution. C, occurs around the globe. A, aquatic ferns. P, palustral ferns. W, wood and grassland ferns. B, sphagnum bog ferns. Ar, acid rock, only or preferably. Cr, calcareous rock, only or preferably. Ir, indifferent as to kinds of rock. E, epiphytic ferns. Cp, Coastal Plain. Pp, Piedmont Plateau. Br, Blue Ridge. Av, Appalachian Valley.

Pycnodoria vittata (S) (W) (Cp)
(Cr)
Pycnodoria cretica (S) (OW) (W)
(Cr) (Cp)
Pycnodoria multifida (S) (W) (OW)
(Cr)

Pteris latiuscula (G) (W)

Pteris caudata (T) (W) (Cp)
Litobrochia tripartita (T) (P) (W)
(Cp)

Adiantum pedatum (OW) (W)

Adiantum melanoleucum (T) (W)
(Cr) (Cp)
Adiantum hispidulum (S) (W) (Cr)

Adiantum Capillus-Veneris (S) (OW)
(C) (W) (Cr)

Adiantum tenerum (T) (W) (Cr)
(Cp)
Hypolepis repens (T) (P) (Cp)

Cheilanthes tomentosa (S) (Ir)
Cheilanthes lanosa (I) (Ir?)

Cheilanthes alabamensis (S) (Cr)
Cheilanthes microphylla (T) (Cr)
(Cp)

Pellaea atropurpurea (Cr)

Pellaea glabella (N) (Cr)
Blechnum occidentale (T) (W) (Cp)
Blechnum serrulatum (T) (P) (E)
(Cp)
Woodwardia radicans (W) (Cp)

Anchistea virginica (G) (P) (W) (B)
Lorinseria areolata (G) (P) (W)

Phyllitis Scolopendrium (N) (OW)
(C) (Cr)
Asplenium serratum (T) (Cr) (E)
(Cp)

Asplenium pinnatifidum (I) (Ar)

Asplenium abscissum (T) (Cr) (Cp)
Asplenium dentatum (T) (Cr) (Cp)
Asplenium auritum (T) (E) (Cp)
Asplenium verecundum (T) (Cp)
(Cr)
Asplenium subtile (T) (Cr) (Cp)
Asplenium biscaynianum (T) (Cr)
(Cp)
Asplenium scalifolium (T) (Cr)
(Cp)
Asplenium suave (T) (Cr) (Cp)
Asplenium Curtissii (T) (Cr) (Cp)
Asplenium cristatum (T) (Cr) (Cp)
Asplenium plenum (T) (Cr) (Cp)
Asplenium pumilum (T) (Cr) (Cp)

Asplenium Trudelli (I) (Ar)
Asplenium montanum (I) (Ar)
Asplenium cryptolepis (I) (Cr)
Asplenium ebenoides (I) (Ir)
Asplenium Trichomanes (N) (Ir)

Asplenium heterochroum (T) (Cr)
(Cp)

Asplenium resiliens (S) (OW) (Cr)
Asplenium platyneuron (G) (W) (Ir)
Asplenium Bradleyi (I) (Ar)
Homalosorus pycnocarpus (N) (OW)
(P) (W)
Athyrium asplenioides (G) (W)
Athyrium angustum (N) (W)

Diplazium acrostichoides (N) (OW)
  (W)
Camptosorus rhizophyllus (I) (Cr)

Tectaria heracleifolia (T) (W) (Cr)
  (E) (Cp)
Tectaria minima (T) (W) (Cr) (Cp)
Tectaria Amesiana (T) (W) (Cr)
  (Cp)
Tectaria coriandrifolia (T) (W) (Cr)
  (Cp)
Cyrtomium falcatum (OW) (S) (Cr)
Meniscium reticulatum (T) (P) (Cp)
Meniscium serratum (T) (P) (Cp)
Goniopteris reptans (T) (W) (Cr)
  (Cp)
Thelypteris panamensis (T) (W)
  (Cp)

Thelypteris noveboracensis (N) (W)
Thelypteris Thelypteris (G) (OW)
  (P) (W)

Thelypteris macilenta (T) (W) (Cp)
Thelypteris augescens (T) (W) (Cr)
  (Cp)
Thelypteris patens (T) (W) (Cr)
  (Cp)
Thelypteris unca (I) (W) (Cr)
  (Cp)

Thelypteris simulata (N) (P) (W)
  (B)

Thelypteris saxatilis (S)
  (W) (Cr)
Thelypteris ovata (T) (W) (Cr) (Cp)

Thelypteris normalis (T) (W) (Cr)
  (Cp)

Thelypteris gongylodes (T) (P) (W)
  (Cp)
Thelypteris versicolor (T) (W)

Thelypteris dentata (T) (W) (Cp)

Thelypteris reducta (T) (W)
Thelypteris tetragona (T) (Cr) (Cp)
Thelypteris submarginalis (T) (P)
  (W) (Cp)

Dryopteris marginalis (N) (W) (Ir)
Dryopteris cristata (N) (OW) (P)
  (W)

Dryopteris Clintoniana (N) (P) (W)
Dryopteris celsa (I) (W)
Dryopteris separabilis (I) (P)
Dryopteris atropalustris (I) (P)
Dryopteris australis (I) (P)
Dryopteris Goldiana (N) (W)
Dryopteris Boottii (N) (W) (P)

Dryopteris ludoviciana (S) (P) (W)
  (Cp)

Dryopteris intermedia (N (W)
Dryopteris spinulosa (N) (OW) (P)
  (W)

Dryopteris campyloptera (N) (W)
  (Br)

Dryopteris ampla (T) (W) (Cr) (Cp)
Dryopteris setigera (T) (P) (W)
  (Cp)

Polystichum acrostichoides (G) (W)
Phegopteris hexagonoptera (G) (W)

Phegopteris Phegopteris (N) (Ir)
  (W)

Cystopteris fragilis (N) (OW) (C)
   (Ir)
Cystopteris bulbifera (N) Cr)

Woodsia obtusa (I) (Ir)

Dennstaedtia punctilobula (N) (W)

Onoclea sensibilis (G) (OW) (P) (W)

Ceratopteris deltoidea (T) (A) (Cp)

Lygodium palmatum (I) (P) (W) (B)
Lygodium japonicum (S) (W) (P)
Osmunda regalis (G) (OW) (C) (P)
Osmunda cinnamomea (G) (OW) (C)
   (P)
Osmunda Claytoniana (N) (OW) (C)
   (P) (W)
Ophioglossum vulgatum (G) (OW)
   (C) (P) (W)

Ophioglossum Engelmanni (S) (W)
   (Cr)
Ophioglossum tenerum (T) (W) (Cp)
Ophioglossum crotalophoroides (T)
   (P) (W) (Cp)

Botrychium biternatum (S) (W)
Botrychium obliquum (G) (W)

Osmundopteris virginiana (G) (OW)
   (C) (W)

Azolla caroliniana (T) (A) (Cp)

Equisetum arvense (N) (OW) (C)
   (W)

Equisetum praealtum (G) (P) (W)

Lycopodium lucidulum (N) (P) (W)

Nephrolepis exaltata (T) (P) (W)
   (Ir) (E) (Cp)
Nephrolepis cordifolia (T) (P) (W)
   (Cr) (E) (Cp)
Nephrolepis biserrata (T) (P) (W)
   (Cr) (E) (Cp)

Woodsia ilvensis (N) (OW) (C) (Ar)
Woodsia scopulina (N) (Ar)

Sphenomeris clavata (T) (Cr) (Cp)

Dennstaedtia adiantoides (T) (W)
   Cp)

Ceratopteris pteridoides (T) (A)
   (Cp)

Dicranopteris flexuosa (S) (W) (Cp)
Actinostachys Germani (T) (P)
   (W) (E) (Cp)
Anemia adiantifolia (T) (W) (Cr)
   (Cp)

Ophioglossum floridanum (S) (W)
   (P)

O. Pumilio (S) (W) (P)
O. dendroneuron (S) (W) (P)
O. mononeuron (S) (W) (P)
Cheiroglossa palmata (T) (E) (Cp)

Botrychium dissectum (G) (W)
Botrychium alabamense (S) (W)

Marsilia vestita (S) (A) (Cp)
Marsilia uncinata (S) (A) (Cp)
Pilularia americana (S) (A) (Ar)
   (Pp)

Salvinia auriculata (T) (A) (Cp)

Equisetum laevigatum (N) (W)

Psilotum nudum (T) (Cr?) (E) (Cp)
Lycopodium Selago (N) (OW) (C)
   (Ar) (Br)
Lycopodium porophilum (N) (Ar)

Lycopodium dichotomum (Cp) (E)

Lycopodium appressum (S) (P) (B)
Lycopodium alopecuroides (T) (P)
  (Cp) (B)
Lycopodium prostratum (S) (P)
  (Cp) (B)
Lycopodium carolinianum (S) (P)
  (Cp) (B)
Lycopodium obscurum (N) (OW)
  (W)

Lycopodium clavatum (N) (C) (W)
  (Br)
Lycopodium flabelliforme (N) (OW)
  (W)
Lycopodium tristachyum (N) (OW)
  (W) (Br)
Lycopodium cernuum (T) (W) (Cp)
  (B)
Diplostachyum Eatoni (T) (Cr) (Cp)

Diplostachyum apodum (G) (P)
Diplostachyum ludovicianum (S)
  (P) (W)
Selaginella rupestris (N) (OW) (C)
  (Ar)

Selaginella tortipila (S) (Ar) (Br)
Selaginella acanthonota (S) (W)
  (Cp)
Selaginella arenicola (S) (W) (Cp)
Isoetes flaccida (S) (A) (Cp)
Isoetes flaccida Chapmani (Cp) (A)
Isoetes flaccida alata (Cp) (A)
Isoetes melanospora (S) (Ar) (Pp)
Isoetes Butleri (A) (Cr)

Isoetes Engelmanni (I) (P) (A)

GENERAL NOTES ON THE CULTIVATION OF SOUTHEASTERN FERNS[1]

It has been my experience that ferns do not take kindly to cultivation in the sense that word carries in ordinary gardening. They seem not to thrive if the soil about their roots is disturbed frequently. My practice has been to transplant them where conditions of soil, moisture (or lack of it) and either light or shade are as nearly similar as possible to the conditions under which they grow naturally. This may require taking up considerable soil with the roots when collecting the plants, if the soil where they are to be planted differs materially from that in which they are found. However, if it is of the usual type found in rich, shady woods almost any of the larger ferns will grow and thrive, provided they are given sufficient moisture and shade.

As to soil for transplanting; good woods loam is best suited to the great majority of species but it should not be finely sifted. With this should be mixed some of the finer litter, only partly decomposed, that is always present where wood ferns grow. I find this mixture not only desirable for the larger species but, by eliminating the coarser debris through screening or hand-picking, it is desirable for the smaller species as well. For epiphytic species a good substitute is material from well rotted logs, or such material mixed half and half with the loam-litter mixture mentioned.

While we have no species in our area that can be called purely xerophytic, we do have a few that will live in the open sun in quite arid conditions. If any of these species are transplanted to such situations they should be given some protection from the sun and watered occasionally until they become established.

From the following list of ferns for which cultural directions are given it will be noted that quite a few species are missing. Some are omitted because they are not considered particularly desirable for transplanting. Others, notably some of the rarer

[1] Contributed by William A. Knight. For additional notes on the cultivation of Florida ferns see Mary W. Diddell, Am. Fern Jour. 26: 1–10. 1936.

ones, are omitted because of the fact that they are rare and possibly in danger of extinction. Finally, still others, including most of the fern-allies, are omitted because of a lack of actual experience in cultivating them.

In the absence of a specific statement to the contrary, directions for the cultivation of each species may be assumed to apply for transplanting only within the natural range of that species.

Acrostichum aureum being a tremendous, coarse plant, an inhabitant of swampy areas only, and being subject to injury by frost, is totally unfitted for transplanting outside its natural range and even within that range requires damp or wet conditions, preferably in open sunlight or only partial shade.

Acrostichum danaeaefolium; transplant like *A. aureum*.

Adiantum pedatum, our northern maidenhair and one of the handsomest of the genus, transplants easily but should be given good woods soil in shade and a spot should be chosen for it where it will be given protection from winds. Unlike the other species of this genus it will tolerate soil with a reaction on the acid side.

Adiantum tenerum will not thrive out-of-doors north of its native habitat but it can be easily transplanted within that area to pockets in eroded limestone, to crevices in walls or to pots. For the latter some broken limestone should be added to the potting soil.

Adiantum Capillus-Veneris, the Venus-hair fern, while native as far south as the Florida peninsula, is also hardy even beyond our northern limits. It transplants readily under conditions similar to those prescribed for *Adiantum tenerum*. Placed where it can overhang damp lime rock, it is especially attractive.

Anchistea virginica bears a strong resemblance to the sterile portion of the cinnamon fern and is suited for transplanting to conditions somewhat similar to those advised for that species. It needs damp or preferably wet soil and will thrive in shade or sun. Its creeping rootstock is rather active, however, and this should be borne in mind should it be transplanted.

Anemia adiantifolia, an unusual southern species, is not advised for transplanting outside its native range except with protection from cold. Within its range it can be transplanted either to eroded limestone or to soil. In the latter case it seems to do best in humus although it often grows, naturally, in quite sandy areas or in sand-clay.

Asplenium abscissum, a desirable and attractive rock-plant, should be treated in the manner prescribed for *Asplenium verecundum* but does not take to transplanting as readily as *A. pinnatifidum* and *A. serratum*. Requires an alkaline reaction.

Asplenium Bradleyi, another attractive rock fern, is desirable for transplanting under same conditions as advised for *Asplenium pinnatifidum*. It, also, is an acid lover.

Asplenium cristatum should be treated in the same manner as *Asplenium verecundum* but is another plant that seems to take to transplanting less readily than some of the others. Requires an alkaline reaction.

Asplenium cryptolepis, the wall rue, is most definitely a calciphile and will not tolerate anything approaching acid conditions. It is native only in the northern portion of our range and is advised for transplanting only within its natural range. It requires treatment similar to that advised for *Asplenium pinnatifidum*, except as to soil reaction.

Asplenium Curtissii is another very desirable plant somewhat similar in character to *Asplenium verecundum*, but larger and not so delicate and lacy. It also transplants readily within its range but is not hardy outside of Florida. Transplant like *Asplenium verecundum*. Requires an alkaline reaction.

Asplenium dentatum, a small and rather delicate plant native in extreme southern Florida, is not advised for transplanting outside its habitat and, even there, preferably by lifting a rock on which the plant is already established.

Asplenium ebenoides is still another attractive species. It should be treated in the same way as *Asplenium pinnatifidum* except that it seems to prefer a more neutral soil. Being quite rare it would be well for beginners to avoid it until they have had some experience with ferns of this type.

Asplenium heterochroum, a southern species quite similar to *Asplenium resiliens*, transplants readily to lime conditions similar to those needed by that species, but is not advised outside its natural range.

Asplenium montanum is another desirable species for rock crevices, etc. Transplant only under conditions advised for *Asplenium pinnatifidum*. It, also, is an acid lover.

Asplenium pinnatifidum is native in the northern portion of our area, usually at some altitude, and is one of the species addicted to crevices in rocks that are definitely acid in their reaction. It is not advised for transplanting except within its natural range. This is one of the species that evidently needs to have its roots compressed. Hard water containing lime must be avoided at all costs.

Asplenium platyneuron is a desirable species for transplanting almost anywhere in our area from our northern border into northern Florida. It is suitable for rockeries and similar places but does best under some shade.

Asplenium resiliens is a very desirable type for rock crevices but is distinctly a lime lover. Aside from that feature transplant as with *Asplenium pinnatifidum*. It is a frequent associate of *Pellaea atropurpurea* and is advised for planting with it.

Asplenium serratum, one of the handsomest of our native ferns from the far south, bears a striking resemblance to its near relative the bird's-nest fern (*Asplenium nidus*) and deserves a place beside that species as a house or greenhouse subject. Growing as it does in deep shade, it should always be so placed that it will be protected from direct sunlight. For transplanting to pots it should have some material from rotten logs mixed with woods loam. Within its area it is easily transplanted to conditions similar to those under which it grows naturally but it will not stand transplanting out-of-doors north of its range, without protection.

Asplenium trichomanes is one of the most attractive of all the smaller species and, fortunately, is one of the easiest to transplant. While it is generally considered a lime lover it seems indifferent to soil reaction and thrives about as well in soil with at least a slight acid reaction as it does elsewhere. It is one of the best species for crevices in a rock wall but it should have some moisture and considerable shade.

Asplenium verecundum is one of the most beautiful of all the small rock spleenworts, its fronds being remarkably delicate and lace-like. Fortunately it transplants readily within its natural range, but unfortunately is not hardy and is not advised outside that area. The advice previously given for transplanting Florida rock ferns should be followed carefully, especially as to lime requirements.

Athyrium angustum is quite similar to the sister species mentioned and requires the same treatment when transplanted.

Athyrium asplenioides is an attractive species and is easily transplanted. It should be given fairly damp soil and considerable shade to maintain its best appearance. It will thrive in open sun but, in exposed places, it begins quite early in the year to show individual fronds that turn brown, giving a ragged, unkempt effect that is anything but pleasing. Even in shade this species is subject to this defect more than almost any other species, with the possible exception of *Dennstaedtia punctilobula*.

Blechnum serrulatum is very different from *Blechnum occidentale* and, while it ranges farther north than its relative, is not hardy beyond northern Florida. Being a swamp dweller it is not fitted for general transplanting but will grow in almost any damp soil, where it should be given considerable shade. It is quite a graceful plant when growing in the deep shade of swamps but becomes stiff and rigid in open sun.

Blechnum occidentale is an attractive species but is not hardy and is not advised for transplanting outside its natural range, except under protection. As it usually is found in a heavier soil than most ferns of its type, mixing of some clay with woods earth is advised for transplanting.

Botrychium dissectum, the dissected grape-fern, a close relative of *Botrychium obliquum,* is more attractive on account of its much dissected, lacy fronds. It is much less common than its sister plant and when found is usually associated with it. It also appears quite late in the year and assumes the same weathered bronze color after frost as does that plant.

Botrychium obliquum, the grape-fern, is an inhabitant of damp woods almost throughout our range. It transplants readily to similar situations and is an attractive species and well worth a place among other ferns of like habitat. It is one of the very last ferns to show new growth, frequently not appearing until late in July. However, it is evergreen and its fronds assume a weathered bronze after frost and persist all through the winter.

Camptosorus rhizophyllus is one of the very best of all the smaller ferns for use on damp rocks about shady pools or along stream banks. Growing in almost solid mats as it frequently does it is readily lifted from the rocks where it is usually found. While this species is commonly referred to as a ''calciphile'' it seems, at least in our area, to be rather indifferent to soil reaction.

Campyloneurum Phyllitidis is not hardy outside of peninsular Florida and transplanting north of that area is inadvisable. Within its range it can be transplanted in pots, in good woods earth or on rotting logs. For growing it as an epiphyte it can be transplanted to rough barked trees in the same way as *Polypodium pectinatum,* but it should have a damp position in shade.

Cheilanthes alabamensis, the handsomest of the genus, apparently requires soil with some alkaline reaction as it is invariably found on or near limestone. It is an excellent subject for pockets and crevices in a limestone wall but should have considerable shade, preferably with some moisture. Where so grown it maintains its beautiful, dark green hue to much better advantage.

Cheilanthes lanosa is a desirable species for planting about a rockery, on top of a wall, or in pockets or crevices in the face of a wall. It is of the "resurrection" type in that its fronds wither, curl and turn brown during continued dry weather but revive and turn green again after rains. If this is objectionable it should be planted only where it can be watered. It is fairly indifferent to soil reaction.

Cheilanthes microphylla is a more calcareous soil plant than *Cheilanthes alabamensis*, but is much more difficult to transplant and is not advised north of its natural range. Where good specimens are found growing in old shell mounds they can, by taking considerable material with the roots, be transplanted. However, more success will follow in cases where plants are found growing on small rocks that can be lifted bodily.

Cheilanthes tomentosa is suitable for situations similar to those named for *Cheilanthes lanosa*. It is also of the "resurrection" type and while also somewhat indifferent to soil reaction seems less inclined to acid conditions than does *C. lanosa*.

Cheiroglossa palmata, the hand-fern, while a very unusual and attractive species, is an extremely difficult subject to transplant; being an epiphyte and usually found well above the ground in the "boots" of palm trees it is difficult to reach. As the whole plant is quite succulent and easily injured and as its cord-like roots are well imbedded in woody matter, it is extremely difficult to remove intact. Even when so removed it requires extreme care in handling. Attempts at transplanting are not advised outside its native habitat and even there only in case a plant may be found under unusually favorable conditions.

Cyrtomium falcatum, one of the so called "holly"-ferns, while not a native, has become established on and in the crevices of lime rock walls in northeastern Florida. It seems to be fairly hardy considerably farther north but it should have some protection during cold weather. It transplants readily to pots and is very desirable for that purpose on account of its firm, dark green and shining foliage. It is also quite desirable for out-of-door planting in Florida, preferably on rock walls, but will maintain a much better appearance if given winter protection even in that climate.

Cystopteris bulbifera is much less common in our area than its sister species and is seldom found except on wet limestone cliffs. It will, however, live and thrive about other rocks but is at its best only where there is considerable moisture and at least some shade. Its long graceful fronds make it particularly desirable for planting among rocks along stream banks and about pools.

Cystopteris fragilis is one of the first ferns to show new growth in the spring. It is especially desirable planted in "mats" in the damper portions of shady woods or along the banks of streams and pools.

Dennstaedtia punctilobula is, within our range, largely confined to the mountains. There its favorite locations are pastures and open roadsides. It transplants easily but has some objectionable features, one being its tendency to spread and crowd out other plants and another being the fact that its fronds begin to turn brown quite early in the year. If given shade they remain green longer than in the open sun but even in shade they brown earlier in the year than almost any other species.

Diplazium acrostichoides is an inhabitant of rather rich, moist woods where it frequently associates with the narrow-leaved spleenwort, or gladefern (*Homalosorus pycnocarpus*). It transplants readily and should be given conditions such as those just mentioned. It is not as desirable as its associate and, in addition is very fragile and easily broken.

Dryopteris ampla, a semi-tree type of fern and a remarkably handsome one, is, unfortunately, decidedly tropical and is unfitted for transplanting outside extreme southern Florida.

Dryopteris campyloptera, the mountain species of the spinulose group, is much the largest and handsomest of the three. Unfortunately however, it is confined in its range to the higher mountains and is not adapted to transplanting to altitudes less than 2000 feet. Even at that altitude it does not thrive; at any rate not within our area.

Dryopteris cristata bears some resemblance to *Dryopteris marginalis* but, reversing its habitat, it is found only in the northern portion of our range—where it is far from common. It grows only in quite swampy areas and needs shade and very considerable moisture for successful transplanting.

Dryopteris Goldiana is, aside from two species of the far south, the largest of our shield ferns and a very handsome one as well. It transplants readily to moist woodlands where there is considerable shade.

Dryopteris intermedia is the commonest one of the spinulose ferns in our area and is a very handsome one as well. It is very desirable for transplanting, either as individual plants or for massing in groups.

Dryopteris ludoviciana is, unlike most of the more southern species, hardy even beyond the northern limits of our area. While in its native habitat it is found almost exclusively in swamps and low hammocks it will live and thrive in much less damp conditions. It transplants readily, preferably to fairly damp woods but should have considerable shade. It is practically evergreen and is a very desirable species indeed.

Dryopteris marginalis, in that portion of our area where it is native (from the upper Piedmont into the mountains), is one of the most desirable species of its type for transplanting. Its favorite haunts are among rocks, sometimes even in their crevices, and about buttresses of trees in fairly shady woods. It transplants easily but it should not be planted too deep; mature plants usually show several inches of the heavy rootstocks above the ground and it should be planted accordingly. Its fronds collapse in late fall but lie on the ground and remain green all winter.

Dryopteris setigera ranges pretty well toward the northern border of Florida. It is a very handsome species and is desirable for transplanting anywhere within its native area, but should be given protection from cold whenever frost is likely to occur. It should have good, rich woods soil and at least partial shade.

Dryopteris spinulosa is not often found in our area. It has a less lacy appearance than *Dryopteris intermedia* and not so desirable on that account.

Equisetum arvense. The best season for transplanting this species seems to be while it is dormant—preferably just before it begins to make new growth in the spring. As generous a portion of the rootstock as is possible to secure should be planted in damp sandy soil at a depth of several inches. It transplants much more readily to such situations than it does to the dry sand and cinders in which it sometimes occurs along railway tracks. Like some of the true ferns with creeping rootstocks it is not a plant that is particularly easy to grow, but when it does become established it frequently forms dense colonies. For that reason it is desirable for sandy stream banks that are subject to washing.

Goniopteris reptans. This is an especially desirable species for transplanting to damp limestone walls, in shade, anywhere within its natural range. It is very attractive in its almost vine-like aspect under such conditions. Transplant as with the limestone group of aspleniums, notably *A. verecundum*, but if mature plants are chosen most of the fronds should be snipped off.

Homalosorus pycnocarpus, a species more nearly approaching the wood ferns in general appearance than its book name would indicate, is desirable for transplanting to damp woods where it will have considerable shade.

Hypolepis repens is not hardy outside its native habitat and is not suitable for transplanting outside its range. Even within that area it is not advised except in low hammocks, swamps, or prairies, or places where some similar conditions exist. On account of its running rootstock it is apt to develop the same objections that apply to the two brackens (*Pteris*).

Litobrochia tripartita (the giant bracken) does not have a creeping rootstock and is free from the resulting objectionable feature of its common relatives. However, this fern is not adapted to transplanting, except to swampy areas in deep shade, in southern Florida where it is native. Small plants can be easily lifted and, if carefully handled, can be transplanted without removing the fronds.

Lorinseria areolata, while found under much the same conditions as the preceding species, will thrive in somewhat drier soil. Its sterile fronds bear a striking resemblance to those of the sensitive-fern (*Onoclea sensibilis*). It is suitable for transplanting in partial shade where it often forms an almost solid ground cover, somewhat as does the New York-fern (*Thelypteris noveboracensis*), but it needs damper conditions than does that species and an acid reaction must be assured for it to thrive.

Lycopodium. For transplanting any of the species that have a long running rootstock, as generous a piece as possible of such rootstock should be lifted, most of the "fronds" should be snipped off with sharp scissors and the root should then be planted, parallel to the surface of the ground at a depth slightly greater than that at which it grows in nature—preferably at about two or three inches; it should then be watered, and the ground firmed over it and not allowed to dry out until new growth starts. It does best in quite shady woods where there is always enough natural litter to prevent the soil from ever becoming thoroughly dry. For transplanting such types as *L. lucidulum,* much of the same plan should be followed but a really damp area, in rather deep shade, is essential.

Lygodium japonicum, one of the climbing ferns, while an introduced plant, has become established in some places from North Carolina to Florida and Louisiana. It does not transplant as easily as the native species. Its rootstock is much heavier and it seems necessary to plant a considerable section of it to get results. While it is much more vine-like than the native and has larger and lacier foliage, it is not so "evergreen" and even in Florida some of its leaves are always brown during the winter. However, it is a very attractive plant during the summer months. Not wholly hardy north of the range given.

Lygodium palmatum is found in isolated communities in our mountain region and much more frequently in the Cumberland Plateau. It transplants readily in both areas and will probably thrive at even lower altitudes. Its unusual character makes it especially desirable but it should be given fairly damp situations in some shade. It does best when planted in clumps beside small shrubs on which it can climb, although it should be remembered that it is not a true vine and the fronds reach a maximum length of only about three feet. Its sterile fronds remain green throughout winter and until new growth starts in the spring. It is the most acid loving of all our ferns, so keep lime water away from it.

Marginaria polypodioides, while common throughout almost the whole of our area, is a very attractive species and is interesting on account of its "resurrection" habit. It seems to prefer to grow on trees in the southern portion of our area (where most of the rock is limestone) and in the northern portion where acid rocks appear, it usually takes to them rather than to trees. Growing in sheets much as does the common polypody (*Polypodium virginianum*) it can readily be lifted and transplanted. If transplanted to rocks, those with an acid reaction should be chosen rather than limestone. For transplanting to trees a simple method is to place a sheet of the plants on an approximately horizontal limb and secure it in place by wires.

Nephrolepis biserrata can be transplanted as with *Nephrolepis exaltata* but it is not advised outside southern Florida.

Nephrolepis cordifolia, while not a native, has become well established in parts of northern Florida where it is hardy and not affected by cold. It grows both as an epiphyte and as a terrestrial plant. When planted on palm trees it soon covers all that portion of the trunk to which the leaf bases ("boots") adhere and it seems utterly indifferent to the kind of palm it uses as a host, flourishing equally well on native cabbage palmettos and on various species of date palms. If planted in the ground care should be taken to keep it away from desirable small plants as it is a real "place taker" and will completely overwhelm almost any herbaceous vegetation.

Nephrolepis exaltata transplants readily, within its range, and, with some protection, considerably farther north. It can be planted among the "boots" of palm trees (as advised for *Phlebodium aureum*), in pots or in eroded lime rock.

Onoclea sensibilis, whose sterile fronds bear a strong resemblance to those of the net-veined chain fern (*Lorinseria areolata*), is suitable for transplanting to conditions somewhat similar to those prescribed for that species. It will thrive without the moisture that plant needs but it does best in soil on the moist side and in shade. Its rootstock is a running one and that should be considered in selecting a location for it.

Ophioglossum. While the various species of this genus occur elsewhere under a rather wide range of conditions, within our area they usually are found in damp and rather heavy soil and, as a rule, in partial shade. Considerable further study will have to be made of the group as a whole before any explicit directions for transplanting can be given. For the present the only safe plan to follow is to lift the plants with as generous a portion as possible of the soil in which they are growing and transplant to conditions as nearly similar thereto as can be found. If, as seems probable, these plants need some form of thallophytic life in the soil about their roots no other plan of transplanting seems feasible.

Osmunda cinnamomea, the cinnamon-fern, like *Osmunda regalis* is a very common plant throughout practically our whole area and is

a handsome one as well.   It should be included in every fern garden.
While it will live in drier soil than *O. regalis* it needs the same damp,
or preferably wet, conditions and considerable shade to attain its best
growth.   While it will grow in the open sun it there tends to lose most
of its grace; the fronds become rigidly erect and lack the arching effect
they attain in shade.   It transplants readily but by no means easily.
Removing a mature plant from a boggy spot is something of an exca-
vating job and requires a heavy spade, a good deal of exertion and
frequently a pair of rubber boots as well.   While this species covers
the same range as *O. regalis* it attains a very considerable altitude,
sometimes occurring in almost solid stands in wet areas in the mountains at more than 5000 feet.

Osmunda Claytoniana, the interrupted-fern, is not addicted to such
wet conditions as are the other two members of the genus.   Within our
range it is usually found in woods and groves and not often in open
sunlight.   It transplants readily to similar situations.

Osmunda regalis, the royal-fern, while common throughout almost
the whole of our area, is nevertheless one of our handsomest species.
It should be included in every fern garden where there is a spot damp
enough to suit its requirements.   It grows about equally well in sunlight and shade but must have moisture, even a swamp being none too
wet for it.   It transplants readily but its rootstock is quite large and
is by no means easy to dig up intact.

Pellaea atropurpurea is an excellent subject for a rock garden or
for crevices in a rock wall.   It grows naturally almost exclusively on
limestone but seems somewhat tolerant to neutral soil or even to soil
with a slight leaning to the acid side.   It seems to do better with its
roots constricted than when planted in open ground.   It is evergreen
and hardy throughout our area and extends, occasionally at least, into
northern Florida.

Pellaea glabella is a smaller plant than the preceding; it grows in a
more compact clump and is a little more desirable on that account.   It
is quite rare in our area and is not advised for transplanting except in
the northern portion of our range.   It also insists upon having its
roots compressed and is advised for transplanting only on vertical limestone walls.   While, outside our area, it is sometimes found on sandstone, every such case that has been tested has shown the presence of
sufficient lime to neutralize the soil.   Hence the recommendation as to
limestone.

Phegopteris hexagonoptera is suitable for transplanting to much
the same conditions as the net-veined chain fern (*Lorinseria areolata*)
although it will stand soil a little less damp.   This is another species
whose running rootstock should be considered in transplanting, although it is not as troublesome, by any means, as the brackens.

Phegopteris Phegopteris is very rare in our area and is known only from quite high altitudes. It can be transplanted but is not advised, in our area, outside the mountains. While further north this fern develops fronds of as much as 18 inches in length, it seldom grows to half that size within our range. In fact in one small colony the largest frond found was less than 8 inches long and most of them were under 6 inches.

Phlebodium aureum is not hardy north of northern Florida and is not advisable for transplanting north of that region. While essentially an epiphyte it can be grown as a pot plant and is an attractive subject for that purpose. A wide pot or pan should be selected, the fronds should be snipped off and the rope-like rootstock should be coiled in the pot and covered with about one inch of soil which should be kept moist until new growth starts. For transplanting to palm trees, fronds should be removed and the rootstock worked well down between the bases of the leaves and the trunk of the tree, being careful to pack the fibrous matter which adheres to the leaf bases, well down about the rootstock.

Pityrogramma calomelanos, while not a native, has become established in at least one place in the lower lake district of Florida but, even there, it is seriously damaged by cold weather. It is an especially desirable plant on account of its handsome dark green, lacy foliage and the rather startling white, powdery covering on the under surface of the fronds. It transplants readily either to damp soil out-of-doors or to pots, but needs protection from cold even in the extreme south.

Polypodium pectinatum is not hardy north of the Florida peninsula and is not suitable for transplanting outside its range except with protection from cold. Within its range it transplants readily to ordinary woods soil or to rotting logs in shade. It is, at least occasionally, found on trees and quite frequently on lime rock. It does not grow in extensive sheets as does *Polypodium virginianum*, and, for transplanting to trees, individual specimens should be selected. The fronds should be cut off and the roots should be firmly placed in the deepest crevices of rough barked trees, with a bit of leaf mold, and kept damp until established. It is not advisable to attempt transplanting to rocks, except well eroded ones and preferably such as have pockets of sufficient size to take the entire root structure with sufficient soil.

Polypodium Plumula; transplant like *Polypodium pectinatum.*

Polypodium virginianum is an attractive species and transplants readily. Growing on rocks, as it usually does, and usually in dense mats, it can easily be lifted and transplanted to similar conditions. It does best in considerable shade. Evergreen and hardy.

Polystichum acrostichoides while one of our commonest is also one of the best of all our native ferns for general transplanting. As individual specimens, for amassing in groups, or for outlining paths through woods it is very desirable. It should be given good woods soil in considerable shade. Like some of the evergreen wood ferns, its fronds collapse late in the fall or early winter but lie on the ground and remain green until spring.

Psilotum nudum. This species is suitable for transplanting only to such situations as those in which we find it in nature. It may be removed in clumps from the bases of palmetto trees or from the bark of hardwoods by means of a sharp spade. These woody clumps, with the *Psilotum* roots imbedded in them may be attached by wiring, or other similar means, to the bark of a tree in some rather damp, shady spot.

Pteris caudata, the southern bracken, is limited in its range from southern Florida as far north as the vicinity of Ormond and is not recommended for transplanting north of the latter point. Transplant like *Pteris latiuscula.*

Pteris latiuscula, the common bracken, can be transplanted almost anywhere within our area north of southern Florida. For this purpose the fronds should be cut off at the ground and a section of the root-stock of two feet or more in length should be planted parallel to the surface of the ground at a depth of only a few inches. While it grows equally well in shade and sun it maintains a fresher, greener appearance later in the year when planted in shade. Anyone unacquainted with the habit of bracken (if there is such a person) is cautioned not to plant either this species or the following one anywhere near valuable shrubs, for if the bracken roots once creep into the roots of such plants they can be eradicated only by digging up the plants and extracting the bracken roots piece-meal. While this is a difficult plant to establish, when it does get a good start it is even more difficult to control. Consequently care should be exercised in selecting an area for planting it.

Pycnodoria cretica, one of the most attractive of the genus for transplanting, is hardy very little beyond the northern border of Florida. It does well as a pot plant and is a bit more tolerant of soil leaning toward neutral than are the other species of this genus.

Pycnodoria bahamensis can be transplanted, preferably to pockets in eroded limestone or to crevices in a wall that has been built with lime mortar. This species is not hardy outside of extreme southern Florida and is not recommended for transplanting outside that area. In common with all other species in this genus, with the exception of *P. cretica,* it needs a decided alkaline reaction.

Pycnodoria multifida follows much the same range as *Pycnodoria vittata* except that it does not seem to occur farther south than the center of the Florida peninsula. It transplants readily under conditions similar to those prescribed for *P. vittata.* For use as a pot plant it is much more desirable than any of the others in the genus.   Like *P. vittata* it requires soil with an alkaline reaction.

Pycnodoria vittata, a much larger plant than the other species of the genus, is hardy throughout the lower coastal plain.   It transplants quite readily either to open ground, to pots or to crevices in walls, but does best in some shade and needs soil with an alkaline reaction.

Sphenomeris clavata, a very unusual species and quite unlike any of our other ferns, is native only in extreme southern Florida and is not adapted to transplanting outside that area.   Even within its range it is a difficult subject.   It is a decided calciphile and should be planted in the eroded lime rock to which it is addicted in nature.

Tectaria heracleifolia, the larger halberd-fern, is the only member of the genus that is advisable for transplanting outside extreme southern Florida.   Even this species is not advised for out-of-doors beyond the northern portion of the Florida peninsula.   It transplants easily to lime rock in its native area and is also desirable as a pot plant, but should have some lime rock fragments mixed with the potting soil.

Thelypteris normalis is not only one of the commonest and most abundant of the ferns of Florida and the lower coastal plain but it seems to be at home under a greater variety of conditions than any other species in its area.   It transplants readily to almost any imaginable conditions but, being affected by cold even in its native area, it is not an especially desirable species for transplanting.

Thelypteris noveboracensis, the New York fern, a native of the northern portion of our area, is fairly desirable for transplanting to somewhat dry woods where, with its creeping rootstock, it often forms an almost solid ground cover.   It can be lifted almost like sod where so growing.   One rather objectionable feature applies to it, however— that being the fact that its fronds turn brown and wither much earlier than do most wood-ferns.

Thelypteris panamensis, one of the handsomest species of its type, is, unfortunately, extremely sensitive to cold and for that reason is not advised for transplanting except in southern Florida and even there it should have some protection during cold spells.   So sensitive is this fern that a near approach to frost will injure it and actual freezing temperatures will occasionally completely kill plants even in the protection of the deep swamps where it is native.   However, it is such an unusually attractive fern that it deserves to be placed in cultivation under glass.

Thelypteris Thelypteris is native in the same area as *Thelypteris noveboracensis,* but also extends south well into Florida.   It likes conditions quite the opposite to those where the New York fern is found, however, its favorite locations being in damp to extremely wet soil in marshes, meadows, etc., in the open sun, and along the edges of hammocks and swamps in partial shade. It is not an especially desirable species for transplanting.

Trichomanes Boschianum; transplant like *Trichomanes Petersii* and *T. punctatum*. As this species and practically all others in the genus grow in mats on faces of perpendicular rock walls or cliffs, any specimens removed either for transplanting or for herbarium specimens should be taken from the *bottom* edge of the mats, not from the center or top.

Trichomanes Krausii can be transplanted in mats as with *Trichomanes punctatum* but should be given a tree as a host rather than lime rock. It should have rather deep shade and a humid atmosphere and, if transplanted out-of-doors, should be placed on the trunk of a leaning tree, near the ground, where the bark always carries some moisture on its surface.

Trichomanes Petersii is hardy to the northern limits of our range where it grows in mats as do the more tropical species. It can be transplanted as with the other species but *not* to limestone. It requires decidedly acid conditions and should be placed on damp sandstone, in shade, where strongly acid water is available. Like all the filmy-ferns this species is extremely delicate and fragile and can be successfully transplanted only under the most favorable conditions.

Trichomanes punctatum can be transplanted without protection only within its range in extreme southern Florida. Growing in rather extensive sheets as it does, somewhat as do many mosses, it can be lifted and transplanted to porous limestone. It will require considerable moisture and shade to become established. Transplanting outside its natural range is not advised except with protection from cold, preferably under glass. If planted in a greenhouse it should not be subjected to direct, strong light.

Trichomanes sphenoides; transplant like *Trichomanes punctatum*.

Trichomanes lineolatum; transplant like *Trichomanes punctatum*.

Vittaria lineata grows as an epiphyte, usually on cabbage trees, almost throughout Florida, and is a common associate of the serpent fern (*Phlebodium aureum*). It is probably not hardy much north of Florida. It can be transplanted to palm trees but small plants are much better for this purpose than larger ones. They should be firmly placed in the fibrous matter at the base of the leaf stems. It does not take to potting as readily as some of the other epiphytic species but its unusual character, totally unlike any of our other ferns, makes it especially desirable. If small specimens which are sometimes found in rotting logs can be secured, they are preferable to larger ones. If none such are available, a larger plant may be removed from the trunk of a palm by means of a sharp spade or trowel. If properly done the entire plant can be detached with the roots concentrated in a plate or sheet of wood fibre. This "plate" may then be placed in a wire basket or other receptacle which has been lined with moss and filled with a mixture of soil and decayed wood. By attaching the receptacle to a wall or suspending it from a bracket in such a way that the surface hangs at an angle of about 45 degrees, the fronds will hang about as they do in nature. Unless they do so hang the fern will not show to advantage.

Woodsia obtusa is a good plant for use about rockeries but preferably in such positions as have some shade. This species grows well enough in the open sun but maintains a much more attractive appearance where it is given at least partial shade.

Woodsia scopulina, a much rarer species in our area than the preceding one, is a lower growing, more compact plant and is more desirable for use about a rockery or in crevices in a wall. It is most attractive when given some shade under not too dry conditions. Its soil preference seems to be at least slightly on the acid side.

TAXONOMIC LIST, WITH CITATIONS[1]

FILICALES

HYMENOPHYLLACEAE

TRICHOMANES L. Sp. Pl. 1097. 1753.
Trichomanes Petersii A. Gray, Am. Jour. Sci. II. 15: 326. 1853.
  Microgonium Petersii Bosch, Hym. Jav. 7. 1861.
  Hemiphlebium Petersii Bosch; Prantl, Hym. 46. 1875.
Trichomanes punctatum Poir. in Lam. Encyc. 8: 64. 1808.
  Didymoglossum punctatum Desv. Mém. Soc. Linn. Paris 6: 330. 1827.
  Hemiphlebium punctatum Bosch, Hym. Jav. 6. 1861.
  Trichomanes sphenoides A. A. Eaton, Bull. Torrey Club 33: 460.
    1906. Not *T. sphenoides* Kunze, 1834.
Trichomanes sphenoides Kunze, Linnaea 9: 102. 1834.
  Didymoglossum sphenoides Presl, Abh. Böhm. Ges. Wiss. V. 3: 115.
    1843.
  Hemiphlebium sphenoides Bosch; Prantl, Hym. 46. 1875.
Trichomanes lineolatum (Bosch) Hook.; Hook. & Baker, Syn. Fil. 73.
    1867.
  Didymoglossum lineolatum Bosch, Nederl. Kruidk. Arch. 5: 136
    [308]. 1863.
  Hemiphlebium lineolatum Bosch; Salomon, Nom. 191. 1883.
Trichomanes Krausii Hook. & Grev. Ic. Fil. *pl. 149.* 1829.
  Didymoglossum Krausii Presl. Abh. Böhm. Ges. Wiss. V. 3: 115.
    1843.
  Hemiphlebium Krausii Bosch; Prantl, Hym. 46. 1875.
Trichomanes Boschianum Sturm; Bosch, Nederl. Kruidk. Arch. 5: 160.
    1861.
  Trichomanes radicans A. Gray, Am. Jour. Sci. II. 15: 325. 1853.
  Not *T. radicans* Sw. 1801.

POLYPODIACEAE

STENOCHLAENA J. Smith, Jour. Bot. Hook. 3: 401; 4: 149. 1841.
Stenochlaena Kunzeana (Presl) Underw. Bull. Torrey Club 33: 196.
    1906.
  Olfersia Kunzeana Presl, Tent. Pterid. 235, hyponym. 1836.
Stenochlaena tenuifolia (Desv.) Moore, Gard. Chron. 1856: 193. 1856.
  Lomaria tenuifolia Desv. Ges. Nat. Freunde Berlin Mag. 5: 326.
    1811.
  Lomariobotrys tenuifolia Fée, Gen. Fil. 46. 1852.
  Polybotrya tenuifolia Kuhn, Fil. Agr. 52. 1868.
  Acrostichum tenuifolium Baker; Hook. & Baker, Syn. Fil. 412. 1868.
  Lomariopsis tenuifolia Christ, Farnkr. Erde 42. 1897.

[1] Contributed by JOHN HENDLEY BARNHART.

ACROSTICHUM L. Sp. Pl. 1067. 1753.
Acrostichum aureum L. Sp. Pl. 1069. 1753.
   Chrysodium aureum Mett. Fil. Lips. 21. 1856.
Acrostichum danaeaefolium Langsd. & Fisch. Ic. Fil. 5. 1810.
   Chrysodium danaeaefolium Fée, Mém. Foug. 2: 101. 1845.
   Chrysodium lomarioides Jenman, Timehri 4: 314. 1885.
   Acrostichum lomarioides Jenman, Bull. Bot. Dep. Jam. 5: 154. 1898.
      Not *A. lomarioides* Bory, 1833; nor *A. lomarioides* Christ, 1895.
   Acrostichum excelsum Maxon, Proc. Biol. Soc. Wash. 18: 224. 1905.

POLYPODIUM [Tourn.] L. Sp. Pl. 1082. 1753.
Polypodium virginianum L. Sp. Pl. 1085. 1753.
   Polypodium vulgare Michx. Fl. Bor. Am. 2: 271. 1803. Not *P. vulgare* L. 1753.
   Polypodium vulgare acuminatum Gilbert, Fern Bull. 10: 13. 1902.
   Polypodium vulgare f. *deltoideum* Gilbert, Fern Bull. 14: 37. 1906.
   Polypodium virginianum f. *acuminatum* Fernald, Rhodora 24: 141. 1922.
   Polypodium virginianum f. *deltoideum* Fernald, Rhodora 24: 141. 1922.
   Polypodium virginianum f. *cambricoides* F. W. Gray, Am. Fern. Jour. 14: 5. 1924.
Polypodium Plumula Humb. & Bonpl.; Willd. Sp. Pl. 5: 178. 1810.
   Ctenopteris Plumula J. Smith, Hist. Fil. 185. 1875.
Polypodium pectinatum L. Sp. Pl. 1085. 1753.
   Goniophlebium pectinatum J. Smith, Jour. Bot. Hook. 4: 57. 1841.

MARGINARIA Bory, Dict. Class. Hist. Nat. 6: 587. 1824; 10: 176. 1826.
Marginaria polypodioides (L.) Tidestrom, Torreya 5: 171. 1905.
   Acrostichum polypodioides L. Sp. Pl. 1068. 1753.
   Polypodium incanum Sw. Prodr. 131. 1788.
   Polypodium ceteraccinum Michx. Fl. Bor. Am. 2: 271. 1803.
   Marginaria incana Presl, Tent. Pterid. 188. 1836.
   Goniophlebium incanum J. Smith, Jour. Bot. Hook. 4: 56. 1841.
   Lepicystis incana J. Smith, Lond. Jour. Bot. 1: 195. 1842.
   Polypodium polypodioides Watt, Can. Nat. II. 13: 158. 1867.

GONIOPHLEBIUM Presl, Tent. Pterid. 185. 1836.
Goniophlebium brasiliense (Poir.) Farwell, Am. Midl. Nat. 12: 295. 1931.
   Polypodium brasiliense Poir. in Lam. Encyc. 5: 525. 1804.

PHLEBODIUM (R. Br.) J. Smith, Jour. Bot. Hook. 4: 58. 1841.
Phlebodium aureum (L.) J. Smith, Jour. Bot. Hook. 4: 59. 1841.
   Polypodium aureum L. Sp. Pl. 1087. 1753.
   Pleopeltis aurea Presl, Tent. Pterid. 193. 1836.
   Chrysopteris aurea Link, Fil. Sp. 121. 1841.

CAMPYLONEURUM Presl, Tent. Pterid. 189. 1836.
Campyloneurum angustifolium (Sw.) Fée, Gen. Fl. 257. 1852.

Polypodium angustifolium Sw. Prodr. 130. 1788.
Marginaria angustifolia Presl, Tent. Pterid. 188. 1836.
Grammitis angustifolia Heward, Mag. Nat. Hist. II. 2: 458. 1838.
Cyrtophlebium angustifolium J. Smith, Bot. Mag. 72: Comp. 12. 1846.
Goniophlebium angustifolium Brack. U. S. Expl. Exp. Fil. 33. 1855.
Campyloneurum Phyllitidis (L.) Presl, Tent. Pterid. 190. 1836.
Polypodium Phyllitidis L. Sp. Pl. 1083. 1753.
Cyrtophlebium Phyllitidis J. Smith, Jour. Bot. Hook. 4: 58. 1841.
Campyloneurum latum Moore, Index Fil. 225. 1861.
Polypodium Phyllitidis latum Hook. Sp. Fil. 5: 38. 1863.
Polypodium latum Sodiro, Crypt. Vasc. Quit. 371. 1893.
Campyloneurum costatum (Kunze) Presl, Tent. Pterid. 190. 1836.
Polypodium costatum Kunze, Linnaea 9: 38. 1834.
Cyrtophlebium costatum J. Smith, Lond. Jour. Bot. 1: 196. 1842.

PHYMATODES Presl, Tent. Pterid. 195. 1836.
Phymatodes heterophyllum (L.) Small, Ferns Fla. 81. 1932.
Polypodium heterophyllum L. Sp. Pl. 1083. 1753.
Polypodium serpens Sw. Prodr. 131. 1788. Not *P. serpens* Forst. 1786.
Marginaria serpens Presl, Tent. Pterid. 188. 1836.
Polypodium exiguum Heward, Mag. Nat. Hist. II. 2: 458. 1838.
Phlebodium serpens J. Smith, Jour. Bot. Hook. 4: 59. 1841.
Craspedaria serpens Fée, Gen. Fil. 264. 1852.
Anapeltis serpens J. Smith, Cat. Cult. Ferns 5. 1857.
Polypodium Swartzii Baker; Hook. & Baker, Syn. Fil. 357. 1868.
Phymatodes Swartzii Underw. Our Nat. Ferns ed. 6. 84. 1900.
Phymatodes exiguum Underw. Torreya 3: 18. 1903.

PITYROGRAMMA Link, Handb. 3: 19. 1833.
Pityrogramma calomelanos (L.) Link, Handb. 3: 20. 1833.
Acrostichum calomelanos L. Sp. Pl. 1072. 1753.
Gymnogramma calomelanos Kaulf. Enum. Fil. 76. 1824.
Ceropteris calomelaena Link, Fil. Sp. 141. 1841.
Neurogramma calomelanos Diels, in E. & P. Nat. Pfl. 1⁴: 264. 1899.
Ceropteris calomelanos Underw. Bull. Torrey Club 29: 632. 1902.

VITTARIA Smith, Mém. Acad. Turin 5: 413 1793.
Vittaria lineata (L.) Sw. Jour. Bot. Schrad. 1800²: 72. 1801.
Pteris lineata L. Sp. Pl. 1073. 1753.
Vittaria angustifrons Michx. Fl. Bor. Am. 2: 261. 1803.
Taeniopsis lineata J. Smith, Jour. Bot. Hook. 4: 67. 1841.
Haplopteris lineata J. Smith, Ferns Brit. & For. 132. 1866.
Oetosis lineata Greene, Pittonia 4: 106. 1900.

PALTONIUM Presl, Epim. Bot. 156. 1851.
Paltonium lanceolatum (L.) Presl, Epim. Bot. 156. 1851.
Pteris lanceolata L. Sp. Pl. 1073. 1753.
Taenitis lanceolata Kaulf. Enum. Fil. 130. 1824.
Pteropsis lanceolata Desv. Mém. Soc. Linn. Paris 6: 218. 1827.

Drymoglossum lanceolatum J. Smith, Jour. Bot. Hook. **4**: 66. 1841.
Neurodium lanceolatum Fée, Mém. Foug. 3–4: 28. 1852.
Vittaria lanceolata Baker, in Mart. Fl. Bras. **1**²: 544. 1870. Not
     V. lanceolata Sw. 1799.
Elaphoglossum lanceolatum Keyserl. Polyp. Cyath. Herb. Bung. 37.
     1873.
Oetosis lanceolata Kuntze, Rev. Gen. 817. 1891.
Heteropteris lanceolata Diels, in E. & P. Nat. Pfl. **1**⁴: 305. 1899.
Cheilogramma lanceolata Underw. Our Nat. Ferns ed. 6. 88. 1900.

PYCNODORIA Presl, Epim. Bot. 100. 1851.
Pycnodoria bahamensis (Ag.) Small, Ferns SE. 100. 1938.
   Pteris diversifolia bahamensis Ag. Recens. Pter. 6. 1839.
   Pteris bahamensis Fée, Gen. Fil. 125. 1852.
   Pteris longifolia bahamensis Hieron. Hedwigia 54: 289. 1914.
   Pycnodoria pinetorum Small, Ferns Trop. Fla. 31. 1918.
Pycnodoria vittata (L.) Small, Ferns Fla. 89. 1932.
   Pteris vittata L. Sp. Pl. 1074. 1753.
Pycnodoria cretica (L.) Small, Ferns Fla. 91. 1932.
   Pteris cretica L. Mant. 130. 1767.
   Pteris cretica albolineata Hook. Bot. Mag. *pl. 5194.* 1860.
Pycnodoria multifida (Poir.) Small, Ferns SE. 104. 1938.
   Pteris serrulata L. f. Suppl. 445, in part. 1781. Not *P. serrulata*
     Forsk. 1775.
   Pteris multifida Poir. in Lam. Encyc. 5: 714. 1804.

PTERIS L. Sp. Pl. 1073. 1753.
Pteris latiuscula Desv. Mém. Soc. Linn. Paris 6: 303. 1827.
   Pteris aquilina Michx. Fl. Bor. Am. 2: 262, in part. 1803. Not
     P. aquilina L. 1753.
   Pteris aquilina lanuginosa Bong. Mém. Acad. St.-Pétersb. VI. 2: 176.
     1832. Not *P. lanuginosa* Bory, 1810.
   Pteridium aquilinum Kuhn, in Decken, Reisen Ost-Afrika 3³: Bot. 11,
     in part. 1879.
   Pteris aquilina pseudocaudata Clute, Fern Bull. 8: 39. 1900.
   Pteridium latiusculum Hieron.; R. E. Fries, Wiss. Ergebn. Schwed.
     Rhod.-Kongo-Exp. 1: 7. 1914.
   Pteris latiuscula pseudocaudata St. John fr. Am. Fern Jour. **25**:
     40. 1935.
   Pteris latiuscula lanuginosa Small, Ferns N. Y. 37. 1935.
Pteris caudata L. Sp. Pl. 1075. 1753.
   Allosorus caudatus Presl, Tent. Pterid. 154. 1836.
   Pteris aquilina caudata Hook. Sp. Fl. 2: 196. 1858.
   Ornithopteris caudata J. Smith, Hist. Fil. 298. 1875.
   Pteridium caudatum Maxon, Proc. U. S. Nat. Mus. **23**: 631. 1901.

LITOBROCHIA Presl, Tent. Pterid. 148. 1836.
Litobrochia tripartita (Sw.) Presl, Tent. Pterid. 150. 1836.
   Pteris tripartita Sw. Jour. Bot. Schrad. 1800²: 67. 1801.

ADIANTUM [Tourn.] L. Sp. Pl. 1094. 1753.
Adiantum pedatum L. Sp. Pl. 1095. 1753.

Adiantum melanoleucum Willd. Sp. Pl. 5: 443. 1810.
Adiantum hispidulum Sw. Jour. Bot. Schrad. 1800². 82. 1801.
Adiantum Capillus-Veneris L. Sp. Pl. 1096. 1753.
   Adiantum Capillus Sw. Jour. Bot. Schrad. 1800². 83. 1801.
Adiantum tenerum Sw. Prodr. 135. 1788.

HYPOLEPIS Bernh. Neues Jour. Bot. Schrad. 1²: 34. 1806.
Hypolepis repens (L.) Presl, Tent. Pterid. 162. 1836.
   Lonchitis repens L. Sp. Pl. 1078. 1753.
   Cheilanthes repens Kaulf. Enum. Fil. 215. 1824.

CHEILANTHES Sw. Syn. Fil. 126. 1806.
Cheilanthes tomentosa Link, Hort. Berol. 2: 42. 1833.
   Notholaena tomentosa Keyserl. Polyp. Cyath. Herb. Bung. 28. 1873.
   Not *N. tomentosa* J. Smith, 1841.
   Myriopteris tomentosa Fée, Gen. Fil. 149. 1852.
Cheilanthes lanosa (Michx.) D.C. Eaton, Bot. Mex. Bound. Surv.
   234. 1859.
   Nephrodium lanosum Michx. Fl. Bor. Am. 2: 270. 1803.
   Adiantum vestitum Spreng. Anl. 3: 122. 1804.
   Polypodium lanosum Poir. in Lam. Encyc. 5: 538. 1804.
   Aspidium lanosum Sw. Syn. Fil. 58. 1806.
   Cheilanthes vestita Sw. Syn. Fil. 128. 1806.
   Cincinalis vestita Desv. Ges. Nat. Freunde Berlin Mag. 5: 312.
   1811.
   Notholaena vestita Desv. Jour. de Bot. Desv. II. 1: 93. 1813.
   Myriopteris vestita J. Smith, Cat. Cult. Ferns 29. 1857.
Cheilanthes alabamensis (Buckl.) Kunze, Linnaea 20: 4. 1847.
   Pteris alabamensis Buckl. Am. Jour. Sci. 45: 177. 1843.
   Pellaea alabamensis Baker; Hook. & Baker, Syn. Fil. 148. 1867.
   Allosorus alabamensis Kuntze, Rev. Gen. 806. 1891.
Cheilanthes microphylla Sw. Syn. Fil. 127. 1806.
   Adiantum microphyllum Sw. Prodr. 135. 1788.
   Allosorus microphyllus Liebm. Danske Vid. Selsk. Skr. V. 1: 219.
   1849.
   Notholaena microphylla Keyserl. Polyp. Cyath. Herb. Bung. 28.
   1873.

PELLAEA Link. Fil. Sp. 59. 1841.
Pellaea atropurpurea (L.) Link, Fil. Sp. 59. 1841.
   Pteris atropurpurea L. Sp. Pl. 1076. 1753.
   Asplenium atropurpureum Bernh. Neues Jour. Bot. Schrad. 1²: 10.
   1806.
   Allosorus atropurpureus Kunze; Presl, Tent. Pterid. 153. 1836.
   Platyloma atropurpurea J. Smith, Jour. Bot. Hook. 4: 160. 1841.
   Notholaena atropurpurea Keyserl. Polyp. Cyath. Herb. Bung. 30.
   1873.
Pellaea glabella Mett.; Kuhn, Linnaea 36: 87. 1869.
   Pellaea atropurpurea Bushii Mackenzie; Mackenzie & Bush, Man.
   Fl. Jackson Co. 5. 1902.

BLECHNUM L. Sp. Pl. 1077. 1753.
Blechnum occidentale L. Sp. Pl. ed. 2. 1524. 1763.
  Blechnum "orientale" (in error) L. Sp. Pl. 1077. 1753.
  Spicanta occidentalis Kuntze, Rev. Gen. 822. 1891.
Blechnum serrulatum Rich. Act. Soc. Hist. Nat. Paris 1: 114. 1792.
  Blechnopsis serrulata Presl, Epim. Bot. 119. 1851.
  Spicanta serrulata Kuntze, Rev. Gen. 822. 1891.

WOODWARDIA Smith, Mém. Acad. Turin 5: 411. 1793.
Woodwardia radicans (L.) Smith, Mém. Acad. Turin 5: 412. 1793.
  Blechnum radicans L. Mant. 307. 1771.

ANCHISTEA Presl, Epim. Bot. 71. 1851.
Anchistea virginica (L.) Presl, Epim. Bot. 71. 1851.
  Blechnum virginicum L. Mant. 307. 1771.
  Blechnum carolinianum Walt. Fl. Car. 257. 1788.
  Woodwardia virginica Smith, Mém. Acad. Turin 5: 412. 1793.
  Woodwardia Banisteriana Michx. Fl. Bor. Am. 2: 263. 1803.
  Doodia virginica Presl, Tent. Pterid. 99. 1836.

LORINSERIA Presl, Epim. Bot. 72. 1851.
Lorinseria areolata (L.) Presl, Epim. Bot. 72. 1851.
  Acrostichum areolatum L. Sp. Pl. 1069. 1753.
  Woodwardia angustifolia Smith, Mém. Acad. Turin 5: 411. 1793.
  Woodwardia floridana Schkuhr, Krypt. Gen. 1: 103. 1809.
  Woodwardia onocleoides Willd. Sp. Pl. 5: 416. 1810.
  Woodwardia areolata Moore, Index Fil. xlv. 1857.

PHYLLITIS Ludwig, Inst. ed. 2. 142. 1757.
Phyllitis Scolopendrium (L.) Newman, Hist. Brit. Ferns ed. 2. 10.
    1844.
  Asplenium Scolopendrium L. Sp. Pl. 1079. 1753.
  Scolopendrium vulgare Smith, Mém. Acad. Turin 5: 421. 1793.
  Scolopendrium phyllitis Roth, Fl. Germ. 3: 47. 1799.
  Scolopendrium officinarum Sw. Jour. Bot. Schrad. 1800²: 61. 1801.
  Scolopendrium officinale DC. Fl. Fr. 2: 552. 1805.
  Scolopendrium Scolopendrium Karst. Deuts. Fl. 278. 1881.
  Phyllitis vulgaris Bubani, Fl. Pyr. 4: 423. 1901.
  Phyllitis Scolopendrium americana Fernald, Rhodora 37: 220. 1935.

ASPLENIUM L. Sp. Pl. 1078. 1753.
Asplenium serratum L. Sp. Pl. 1079. 1753.
Asplenium pinnatifidum Nutt. Gen. 2: 251. 1818.
  Antigramma pinnatifida Wood, Class-Book ed. 1861. 822. 1861.
  Camptosorus pinnatifidus Wood, Bot. & Fl. 373. 1870.
  Scolopendrium pinnatifidum Diels, in E. & P. Nat. Pfl. 1⁴: 231.
    1899.
Asplenium abscissum Willd. Sp. Pl. 5: 321. 1810.
  Asplenium firmum Kunze, Bot. Zeit. 3: 283. 1845.

Asplenium dentatum L. Sp. Pl. 1080. 1753.

Asplenium auritum Sw. Jour. Bot. Schrad. 1800²: 52. 1801.

Asplenium erosum Maxon, in Small, Fl. SE. U.S. ed. 2. 16. 1913. Not *A. erosum* L. 1759.

Asplenium verecundum Chapm.; Fourn. Pl. Mex. Crypt. 111, hyponym. 1872; Underw. Bull. Torrey Club **33**: 193. 1906.

Asplenium myriophyllum Chapm. Fl. S. U.S. 593. 1860. Not *A. myriophyllum* Presl, 1825.

Asplenium subtile E. St. John; Small, Ferns SE. 164. 1938.

Asplenium biscaynianum (D. C. Eaton) A. A. Eaton, Fern Bull. **12**: 45. 1904.

Asplenium rhizophyllum biscaynianum D. C. Eaton, Bull. Torrey Club **14**: 97. 1887.

Asplenium scalifolium E. St. John; Small Ferns SE. 167. 1938.

Asplenium suave E. St. John; Small, Ferns SE. 169. 1938.

Asplenium Curtissii Underw. Bull. Torrey Club **33**: 194. 1906.

Asplenium cristatum Lam. Encyc. **2**: 310. 1786.

Asplenium cicutarium Sw. Prodr. 130. 1788.

Caenopteris cicutaria Thunb. Nova Acta Petrop. **9**: 158. 1795.

Darea cicutaria Willd. Sp. Pl. **5**: 300. 1810.

Asplenium plenum E. St. John; Small, Ferns SE. 173. 1938.

Asplenium pumilum Sw. Prodr. 129. 1788.

Tarachia pumila Presl, Epim. Bot. 75. 1851.

Asplenium Trudelli Wherry, Am. Fern Jour. **15**: 47. 1925.

Asplenium montanum Willd. Sp. Pl. **5**: 342. 1810.

Asplenium cryptolepis Fernald, Rhodora **30**: 41. 1928.

Asplenium Ruta-muraria Michx. Fl. Bor. Am. **2**: 266. 1803. Not *A. Ruta-muraria* L. 1753.

Asplenium ebenoides R. R. Scott, Gard. Mo. **7**: 267. 1865.

Asplenosorus ebenoides Wherry, Am. Fern Jour. **27**: 56. 1937.

Asplenium Trichomanes L. Sp. Pl. 1080. 1753.

Asplenium melanocaulon Willd. Enum. 1072. 1809.

Asplenium heterochroum Kunze, Linnaea **9**: 67. 1834.

Asplenium muticum Gilbert, Am. Bot. **4**: 86. 1903.

Asplenium resiliens Kunze, Linnaea **18**: 331. 1844.

Asplenium parvulum Mart. & Gal. Mém. Acad. Brux. 15⁵: 60. 1842. Not *A. parvulum* Hook. 1840.

Asplenium platyneuron (L.) Oakes; D. C. Eaton, Ferns N. Am. **1**: 24. 1878.

Acrostichum platyneuros L. Sp. Pl. 1069. 1753.

Asplenium ebeneum Ait. Hort. Kew. **3**: 462. 1789.

Asplenium ebeneum incisum E. C. Howe; Peck, Ann. Rep. N. Y. State Cab. **22**: 104. 1869.

Asplenium ebeneum bacculum-rubrum Featherman, Rep. Bot. Surv. La. (1870). 75. 1871.

Asplenium ebeneum serratum E. S. Miller, Bull. Torrey Club **4**: 41. 1873.

Asplenium platyneuron serratum B.S.P. Prel. Cat. N. Y. 73. 1888.

Asplenium ebeneum Hortonae Davenp. Rhodora **3**: 1. 1901.

Asplenium platyneuron incisum B. L. Robinson, Rhodora **10**: 29. 1908.
Asplenium platyneuron f. *Hortonae* L. B. Smith, Rhodora **30**: 14. 1928.
Asplenium platyneuron euroaustrinum Fernald, Rhodora **37**: 382. 1935.
Asplenium platyneuron bacculum-rubrum Fernald, Rhodora **38**: 304. 1936.
Asplenium Bradleyi D. C. Eaton, Bull. Torrey Club **4**: 11. 1873.

ATHYRIUM Roth, Fl. Germ. Bot. 3^1: 58. 1799.
Athyrium asplenioides (Michx.) Eaton, Man. 122. 1817.
Nephrodium asplenioides Michx. Fl. Bor. Am. **2**: 268. 1803.
Asplenium Athyrium Spreng. Anl. **3**: 113. 1804.
Aspidium asplenioides Sw. Syn. Fil. 60. 1806.
Asplenium asplenioides D. C. Eaton, in Chapm. Fl. S. U.S. 593. 1860.
Athyrium angustum (Willd.) Pr 1, Rel. Haenk. **1**: 39. 1825.
Polypodium Filix-foemina Michx. Fl. Bor. Am. **2**: 268. 1803. Not *P. Filix-foemina* L. 1753.
Aspidium angustum Willd. Sp. Pl. **5**: 277. 1810.
Aspidium Filix-foemina Pursh, Fl. Am. Sept. 664. 1814. Not *A. Filix-foemina* Sw. 1801.
Asplenium elatius Link, Fil. Sp. 94. 1841.
Asplenium Filix-foemina Wood, Class-Book 161. 1845. Not *A. Filix-foemina* Bernh. 1806.
Athyrium Filix-foemina rubellum Gilbert, List 35. 1901.
Athyrium angustum elatius Butters, Rhodora **19**: 191. 1917.
Athyrium angustum rubellum Butters, Rhodora **19**: 193. 1917.

DIPLAZIUM Sw. Jour. Bot. Schrad. 1800^2: 61. 1801.
Diplazium acrostichoides (Sw.) Butters, Rhodora **19**: 178. 1917.
Asplenium acrostichoides Sw. Jour. Bot. Schrad. 1800^2: 54. 1801.
Asplenium thelypteroides Michx. Fl. Bor. Am. **2**: 265. 1803.
Athyrium thelypteroides Desv. Mém. Soc. Linn. Paris **6**: 266. 1827.
Diplazium thelypteroides Presl, Tent. Pterid. 114. 1836.
Athyrium acrostichoides Diels, in E. & P. Nat. Pfl. 1^2: 223. 1899.

HOMALOSORUS Small, Ferns N. Y. 80. 1935.
Homalosorus pycnocarpus (Spreng.) Small, Ferns N. Y. 80. 1935.
Asplenium angustifolium Michx. Fl. Bor. Am. **2**: 265. 1803. Not *A. angustifolium* Jacq. 1786.
Asplenium pycnocarpum Spreng. Anl. **3**: 112. 1804.
Athyrium angustifolium Milde, Bot. Zeit. **24**: 376. 1866.
Athyrium pycnocarpum Tidestrom, Elys. Marianum Ferns 36. 1906.
Diplazium angustifolium Butters, Rhodora **19**: 178. 1917.

CAMPTOSORUS Link, Hort. Berol. **2**: 69. 1833.
Camptosorus rhizophyllus (L.) Link, Hort. Berol. **2**: 69. 1833.
Asplenium rhizophylla L. Sp. Pl. 1078. 1753.
Antigramma rhizophylla J. Smith, Jour. Bot. Hook. **4**: 176. 1841.

TECTARIA Cav. Anal. Hist. Nat. **1**: 115. 1799.
Tectaria heracleifolia (Willd.) Underw. Bull. Torrey Club **33**: 200. 1906.
  Aspidium heracleifolium Willd. Sp. Pl. **5**: 217. 1810.
  Aspidium trifoliatum D. C. Eaton, Bull. Torrey Club **8**: 99. 1881. Not *A. trifoliatum* Sw. 1801.
Tectaria minima Underw. Bull. Torrey Club **33**: 199. 1906.
Tectaria Amesiana A. A. Eaton, Bull. Torrey Club **33**: 479. 1906.
Tectaria coriandrifolia (Sw.) Underw. Bull. Torrey Club **33**: 200. 1906.
  Aspidium coriandrifolium Sw. Jour. Bot. Schrad. **1800**²: 36. 1801.

CYRTOMIUM Presl, Tent. Pterid. 86. 1836.
Cyrtomium falcatum (L.f.) Presl, Tent. Pterid. 86. 1836.
  Polypodium falcatum L.f. Suppl. 446. 1781.
  Polypodium japonicum Houtt. Nat. Hist. **14**: 167. 1783.
  Aspidium falcatum Sw. Jour. Bot. Schrad. **1800**²: 31. 1801.
  Dryopteris falcata Kuntze, Rev. Gen. 812. 1891.
  Polystichum falcatum Diels, in E. & P. Nat. Pfl. **1**⁴: 194. 1899.

MENISCIUM Schreb. Gen. 757. 1791.
Meniscium reticulatum (L.) Sw. Jour. Bot. Schrad. **1800**²: 16. 1801.
  Polypodium reticulatum L. Syst. Nat. ed. 10. 1325. 1759.
  Phegopteris reticulata Mett. Fil. Lechl. **2**: 24. 1859.
  Nephrodium reticulatum Keyserl. Polyp. Cyath. Herb. Bung. 49. 1873.
  Dryopteris reticulata Urban, Symb. Ant. **4**: 22. 1903.
Meniscium serratum Cav. Descr. 548. 1803.
  Phegopteris serrata Mett. Ann. Sci. Nat. V. **2**: 243. 1864.
  Nephrodium serratum Keyserl. Polyp. Cyath. Herb. Bung. 49. 1873. Not *N. serratum* Presl, 1825; nor *N. serratum* Desv. 1827.
  Dryopteris serrata C. Chr. Index Fil. 291. 1905.

GONIOPTERIS Presl, Tent. Pterid. 181. 1836.
Goniopteris reptans (J. F. Gmel.) Presl, Tent. Pterid. 182. 1836.
  Polypodium reptans J. F. Gmel. Syst. Nat. **2**: 1309. 1791.
  Polypodium repens Sw. Prodr. 132. 1788. Not *P. repens* Sw. Prodr. 130. 1788.
  Phegopteris reptans D. C. Eaton, Bull. Torrey Club **10**: 101. 1883.
  Nephrodium reptans Diels, in E. & P. Nat. Pfl. **1**⁴: 168. 1899.
  Dryopteris reptans C. Chr. Index Fil. 288. 1905.
  Dryopteris radicans Maxon, Contr. U. S. Nat. Herb. **10**: 490. 1908.

THELYPTERIS Schmidel, Ic. Pl. 45. 1762.
Thelypteris panamensis (Presl) E. St. John, Am. Fern Jour. **26**: 44. 1936.
  Nephrodium panamense Presl, Rel. Haenk. **1**: 35. 1825.
  Polypodium litigiosum Liebm. Danske Vid. Selsk. Skr. V. **1**: 205. 1849.
  Nephrodium caribaeum Jenman, Jour. Bot. **24**: 270. 1886.

Dryopteris caribaea C. Chr. Index Fil. 257. 1905.
Dryopteris panamensis C. Chr. Danske Vid. Selsk. Skr. VII. 4: 292. 1907.
Dryopteris litigiosa C. Chr.; Christ, Bull. Herb. Boiss. II. 7: 263. 1907.

Thelypteris noveboracensis (L.) Nieuwl. Am. Midl. Nat. 1: 226. 1910.
Polypodium noveboracense L. Sp. Pl. 1091. 1753.
Aspidium noveboracense Sw. Jour. Bot. Schrad. 1800²: 38. 1801.
Dryopteris noveboracensis A. Gray, Man. 630. 1848.
Aspidium conterminum strigosum D. C. Eaton, Bull. Torrey Club 7: 62. 1880.
Dryopteris contermina strigosa Underw. Our Nat. Ferns ed. 4. 113. 1898.

Thelypteris Thelypteris (L.) Nieuwl. Am. Midl. Nat. 1: 226. 1910.
Acrostichum Thelypteris L. Sp. Pl. 1071. 1753.
Polypodium Thelypteris Weiss, Pl. Crypt. Gott. 307. 1770.
Polypodium palustre Salisb. Prodr. 403. 1796.
Polystichum Thelypteris Roth, Fl. Germ. 3: 77. 1799.
Aspidium Thelypteris Sw. Jour. Bot. Schrad. 1800²: 40. 1801.
Athyrium Thelypteris Spreng. Anl. 3: 134. 1804.
Aspidium palustre S. F. Gray, Nat. Arr. Brit. Pl. 2: 9. 1821.
Nephrodium Thelypteris Strempel, Fil. Berol. Syn. 32. 1822.
Dryopteris Thelypteris pubescens A. R. Prince; Weatherby, Am. Fern Jour. 26: 95. 1836.
Lastraea Thelypteris Bory, Dict. Class. 9: 233. 1826.
Thelypteris palustris Schott, Gen. Fil. [under *pl. 10*]. 1934.
Dryopteris Thelypteris A. Gray, Man. 630. 1848.
Hemestheum Thelypteris Newman, Phytologist 4: App. xxii. 1851.
Lastraea palustris J. Smith, Cat. Cult. Ferns 56. 1857.
Lastraea Thelypteris pubescens Lawson, Edinb. New Phil. Jour. II. 19: 277. 1864.
Thelypteris palustris pubescens Fernald, Rhodora 31: 34. 1929.

Thelypteris macilenta E. St. John, Am. Fern Jour. 26: 50. 1936.

Thelypteris simulata (Davenp.) Nieuwl. Am. Midl. Nat. 1: 226. 1910.
Aspidium simulatum Davenp. Bot. Gaz. 19: 495. 1894.
Dryopteris simulata Davenp. Bot. Gaz. 19: 497. 1894.
Nephrodium simulatum Davenp. Bot. Gaz. 19: 497. 1894.
Lastrea simulata Davenp. Bot. Gaz. 19: 497. 1894.

Thelypteris ovata R. St. John, in Small, Ferns SE. 230. 1938.

Thelypteris ovata Harperi (C. Chr.) R. St. John, in Small, Ferns SE. 233. 1938.
Dryopteris normalis Harperi C. Chr. Danske Vid. Selsk. Skr. VII. 10: 182. 1913.

Thelypteris normalis (C. Chr.) Moxley, Bull. So. Calif. Acad. 19: 57. 1920.
Aspidium patens D. C. Eaton, Ferns N. Am. 2: 181. 1880. Not *A. patens* Sw. 1801.
Nephrodium patens Jenman, Bull. Bot. Dep. Jam. II. 3: 165. 1896.
Dryopteris normalis C. Chr. Ark. Bot. 9¹¹: 31. 1910.

Thelypteris saxatilis R. St. John, in Small, Ferns SE. 236. 1938.
Thelypteris augescens (Link) Munz & Johnston, Am. Fern Jour. 12: 75. 1922.
  Aspidium augescens Link, Fil. Sp. 103. 1841.
  Dryopteris augescens C. Chr. Danske Vid. Selsk. Skr. VII. 10: 182. 1913.
  Nephrodium augescens J. Smith, Bot. Mag. 72: Comp. 32. 1846.
  Lastraea augescens J. Smith, Cat. Cult. Ferns 56. 1857.
Thelypteris augescens Lindheimeri (A. Br.) R. St. John, in Small Ferns SE. 241. 1938.
  Dryopteris normalis Lindheimeri C. Chr. Danske Vid. Selsk. Skr. VII. 10: 182. 1913.
  Aspidium Lindheimeri A. Br.; C. Chr. Danske Vid. Selsk. Skr. VII. 10: 182, as syn. 1913.
Thelypteris Serra (Sw.) R. St. John, in Small, Ferns SE. 241. 1938.
  Polypodium Serra Sw. Prodr. 132. 1788.
  Aspidium Serra Sw. Jour. Bot. Schrad. 1800^2: 33. 1801.
  Nephrodium Serra Desv. Mém. Soc. Linn. Paris 6: 253. 1827.
  Lastraea Serra Presl, Tent. Pterid. 75. 1836.
  Dryopteris Serra Kuntze, Rev. Gen. 813. 1891.
Thelypteris patens (Sw.) Small, Ferns SE. 243. 1938.
  Polypodium patens Sw. Prodr. 133. 1788.
  Aspidium patens Sw. Jour. Bot. Schrad. 1800^2: 34. 1801.
  Aspidium stipulare Willd. Sp. Pl. 5: 239. 1810.
  Nephrodium stipulare Desv. Mém. Soc. Linn. Paris 6: 256. 1827.
  Nephrodium patens Desv. Mém. Soc. Linn. Paris 6: 258. 1827.
  Polystichum patens Gaud. Voy. Freyc. Bot. 329. 1828.
  Lastraea patens Presl, Tent. Pterid. 75. 1836.
  Dryopteris patens Kuntze, Rev. Gen. 813. 1791.
  Dryopteris stipularis Maxon; Underw. Bull. Torrey Club 33: 198. 1906.
Thelypteris unca R. St. John, in Small, Ferns SE. 246. 1938.
Thelypteris gongylodes (Schkuhr) Small, Ferns SE. 348. 1938.
  Polypodium unitum L. Syst. Nat. ed. 10. 1326, in part. 1759.
  Aspidium gongylodes ("goggilodus") Schkuhr, Krypt. Gew. 1: 193. 1809.
  Nephrodium unitum R. Br. Prodr. 148. 1810.
  Polystichum gongylodes ("goggilodus") Gaud. Voy. Freyc. Bot. 326. 1828.
  Cyclosorus gongylodes Link, Hort. Berol. 2: 128. 1833.
  Nephrodium gongylodes ("gongyloides") Schott, Gen. Fil. [under pl. 10.] 1834.
  Aspidium unitum glabrum Mett. Ann. Mus. Lugd.-Bot. 1: 230. 1864.
  Dryopteris gongylodes Kuntze, Rev. Gen. 811. 1891.
  Dryopteris unita glabra Underw. Our. Nat. Ferns ed. 4. 114. 1893.
  Nephrodium unitum glabrum Davenp.; Gilbert, List 17. 1901.
  Dryopteris gongylodes glabra C. Chr. Danske Vid. Selsk. Skr. VII. 10: 193. 1913.
Thelypteris versicolor R. St. John, in Small, Ferns SE. 250. 1938.
Thelypteris dentata (Forsk.) E. St. John, Am. Fern Jour. 26: 44. 1936.

Polypodium dentatum Forsk. Fl. Aegypt.-Arab. 185. 1775.

Polypodium molle Jacq. Coll. 3: 188. 1789. Not *P. molle* Schreb. 1771; nor *P. molle* All. 1785.

Dryopteris mollis Hieron. Hedwigia 46: 348. 1907.

Dryopteris dentata C. Chr. Danske Vid. Selsk. Skr. VIII. 6: 24. 1920.

Nephrodium dentatum Kümmerle, Magyar Bot. Lap. 32: 60. 1933.

Thelypteris reducta Small, Ferns SE. 254. 1938.

Thelypteris tetragona (Sw.) Small, Ferns SE. 256. 1938.

Polypodium tetragonum Sw. Prodr. 132. 1788.

Aspidium tetragonum Sw. Jour. Bot. Schrad. 1800^2: 33. 1801.

Polypodium subtetragonum Link, Hort. Berol. 2: 105. 1833.

Goniopteris tetragona Presl, Tent. Pterid. 183. 1836.

Phegopteris tetragona Mett. Fil. Lips. 84. 1856.

Nephrodium tetragonum Keyserl. Polyp. Cyath. Herb. Bung. 49. 1873. Not. *N. tetragonum* Presl, 1825.

Dryopteris tetragona Urban, Symb. Ant. 4: 20. 1903. Not *D. tetragona* Kuntze, 1891.

Dryopteris subtetragona Maxon, Sci. Surv. Porto Rico 6: 473. 1926.

Thelypteris subtetragona E. St. John, Am. Fern Jour. 26: 44. 1936.

Thelypteris submarginalis (Langsd. & Fisch.) Small, Ferns SE. 258. 1938.

Polypodium submarginale Langsd. & Fisch. Ic. Fil. 12. 1810.

Phegopteris submarginalis J. Smith, Cat. 16. 1857.

Dryopteris submarginalis C. Chr. Index Fil. 296. 1905.

DRYOPTERIS Adans. Fam. Pl. 2: 20, 551. 1763.

Dryopteris marginalis (L.) A. Gray, Man. 632. 1848.

Polypodium marginale L. Sp. Pl. 1901. 1753.

Aspidium marginale Sw. Jour. Bot. Schrad. 1800^2: 35. 1801.

Nephrodium marginale Michx. Fl. Bor. Am. 2: 267. 1803.

Thelypteris marginalis Nieuwl. Am. Midl. Nat. 1: 226. 1910.

Dryopteris cristata (L.) A. Gray, Man. 631. 1848.

Polypodium cristatum L. Sp. Pl. 1090. 1753.

Aspidium cristatum Sw. Jour. Bot. Schrad. 1800^2: 37. 1801.

Nephrodium cristatum Michx. Fl. Bor. Am. 2: 269. 1803.

Thelypteris cristata Nieuwl. Am. Midl. Nat. 1: 226. 1910.

Dryopteris Boottii (Tuckerm.) Underw. Our Nat. Ferns ed. 4. 117. 1893.

Aspidium Boottii Tuckerm. Mag. Hort. 9: 145. 1843.

Aspidium spinulosum Boottii A. Gray, Man. ed. 2. 598. 1856.

Thelypteris Boottii Nieuwl. Am. Midl. Nat. 1: 226. 1910.

Dryopteris Clintoniana (D. C. Eaton) Dowell, Proc. Staten Id. Assoc. 1: 64. 1906.

Aspidium cristatum Clintonianum D. C. Eaton, in A. Gray, Man. ed. 5. 665. 1867.

Dryopteris cristata Clintoniana Underw. Our. Nat. Ferns ed. 4. 115. 1893.

Thelypteris cristata Clintoniana Weatherby, Rhodora 21: 177. 1919.

Thelypteris Clintoniana House, N. Y. State Mus. Bull. 233–234: 69. 1922.

Dryopteris celsa (W. Palmer) Knowlton, Palmer & Pollard, Proc. Biol. Soc. Wash. **13**: 202. 1900.

Dryopteris Goldiana celsa W. Palmer, Proc. Biol. Soc. Wash. **13**: 65. 1899.

Dryopteris atropalustris Small, Ferns SE. 274. 1938.

Dryopteris Goldiana (Hook.) A. Gray, Man. 631. 1848.

Aspidium Goldianum Hook. Edinb. Phil. Jour. 6: 333. 1822.

Nephrodium Goldianum Hook. & Grev. Ic. Fil. *pl. 102.* 1829.

Lastraea Goldiana Presl, Tent. Pterid. 76. 1836.

Thelypteris Goldiana Nieuwl. Am. Midl. Nat. 1: 226. 1910.

Dryopteris Goldiana Goldiana W. Palmer, Proc. Biol. Soc. Wash. 13: 65. 1899.

Dryopteris australis (Wherry) Small, Ferns SE. 279. 1938.

Dryopteris Clintoniana australis Wherry, Am. Fern Jour. **27**: 1. 1937.

Dryopteris ludoviciana (Kunze) Small, Ferns SE. 281. 1938.

Aspidium ludovicianum Kunze, Am. Jour. Sci. II. 6: 84. 1848.

Nephrodium floridanum Hook. Fil. Exot. *pl. 99.* 1859.

Aspidium floridanum D. C. Eaton, in Chapm. Fl. S. U.S. 595. 1860.

Lastraea floridana J. Smith, Ferns Brit. & For. ed. 2. 306. 1877.

Dryopteris floridana Kuntze, Rev. Gen. 812. 1891.

Dryopteris separabilis Small, Ferns SE. 284. 1938.

Dryopteris intermedia (Muhl.) A. Gray, Man. 630. 1848.

Aspidium intermedium Muhl.; Willd. Sp. Pl. 5: 262. 1810.

Polypodium intermedium Muhl.: Willd. Sp. Pl. 5: 262, as syn. 1810.

Nephrodium intermedium Presl, Rel. Haenk. 1: 38. 1825.

Lastraea intermedia Presl, Tent. Pterid. 77. 1836.

Aspidium spinulosum intermedium D. C. Eaton, in A. Gray, Man. ed. 5. 665. 1867.

Dryopteris spinulosa intermedia Underw. Our Nat. Ferns ed. 4. 116. 1893.

Thelypteris spinulosa intermedia **Weatherby, Rhodora 21: 178.** 1919.

Thelypteris intermedia House, N. Y. State Mus. Bull. 233–234: 69. 1922.

Dryopteris spinulosa (Muell.) Watt, Can. Nat. II. **13**: 159, 403. 1867; Kuntze, Rev. Gen. 813. 1891.

Polypodium spinulosum Muell. Fl. Dan. 12: 5. **1777.**

Polystichum spinosum Roth, Fl. Germ. 3¹: 91. 1799.

Aspidium spinulosum Sw. Jour. Bot. Schrad. 1800²: 38. 1801.

Polystichum spinulosum DC. Fl. Fr. 2: 561. 1805.

Thelypteris spinulosa Nieuwl. Am. Midl. Nat. 1: 226. 1910.

Dryopteris campyloptera (Kunze) Clarkson, Am. Fern Jour. **20**: 118. 1930.

Aspidium spinulosum dilatatum Link, Fil. Sp. 106. 1841.

Aspidium spinulosum americanum Fischer; Kunze, Am. Jour. Sci. II. 6: 84. 1848.

Aspidium campylopterum Kunze, Am. Jour. Sci. II. 6: 84. 1848.

31

Dryopteris dilatata A. Gray, Man. 631, in part. 1848.
Dryopteris spinulosa dilatata Watt, Can. Nat. II. 13: 159. 1867;
Underw. Our. Nat. Ferns ed. 4. 116. 1893.
Dryopteris dilatata americana Benedict, Am. Fern Jour. 6: 34.
1916.
Dryopteris spinulosa americana Fernald, Rhodora 17: 48. 1915.
Thelypteris spinulosa americana Weatherby, Rhodora 21: 178. 1919.
Thelypteris dilatata americana House, N. Y. State Mus. Bull. 233–
234: 69. 1922.
Dryopteris ampla (Humb. & Bonpl.) Kuntze, Rev. Gen. 812. 1891.
Polypodium amplum Humb. & Bonpl.; Willd. Sp. Pl. 5: 207. 1810.
Phegopteris ampla Fée, Gen. Fil. 243. 1852.
Aspidium amplum Mett. Abh. Senck. Nat. Ges. 2: 238. 1858.
Nephrodium amplum Baker; Hook. & Baker, Syn. Fil. 285. 1867.
Lastrea ampla Moore, Index Fil. 85. 1858. Not *N. amplum* Bory,
1833.
Dryopteris setigera (Blume) Kuntze, Rev. Gen. 813. 1891.
Cheilanthes setigera Blume, Enum. 138. 1828.
Hypolepis setigera Hook. Sp. Fil. 2: 62. 1852.
Nephrodium setigerum Baker, Syn. Fil. 284. 1867. Not *N. seti-
gerum* Presl, 1825.
Aspidium setigerum Kuhn, Verh. Zool.-bot. Ges. Wien 19: 578.
1869.

POLYSTICHUM Roth, Fil. Germ. 3¹: 69. 1799.
Polystichum acrostichoides (Michx.) Schott, Gen. Fil. [under *pl. 9.*]
1834.
Nephrodium acrostichoides Michx. Fl. Bor. Am. 2: 267. 1803.
Aspidium acrostichoides Sw. Syn. Fil. 44. 1806.
Aspidium Schweinitzii Beck, Bot. U. S. 449. 1833.
Polystichum acrostichoides incisum A. Gray, Man. 632. 1848.
Aspidium acrostichoides incisum A. Gray, Man. ed. 2. 599. 1856.
Dryopteris acrostichoides Kuntze, Rev. Gen. 812. 1891.
Dryopteris acrostichoides incisum Underw. Our. Nat. Ferns. ed. 4.
111. 1893.
Polystichum acrostichoides Schweinitzii Small, Bull. Torrey Club
20: 464. 1893.

PHEGOPTERIS Fée, Gen. Fil. 242. 1853.
Phegopteris hexagonoptera (Michx.) Fée, Gen. Fil. 243. 1853.
Polypodium hexagonopterum Michx. Fl. Bor. Am. 2: 271. 1803.
Nephrodium hexagonopterum Diels, in E. & P. Nat. Pfl. 1⁴: 169.
1899.
Dryopteris hexagonoptera C. Chr. Index Fil. 270. 1905.
Thelypteris hexagonoptera Weatherby, Rhodora 21: 179. 1919.
Phegopteris Phegopteris (L.) Keyserl. Polyp. Cyath. Herb. Bung.
50. 1873.
Polypodium Phegopteris L. Sp. Pl. 1089. 1753.
Gymnocarpium Phegopteris Newman, Phytologist 4: App. xxiii.
1851.

Phegopteris polypodioides Fée, Gen. Fil. 243. 1853.
Nephrodium Phegopteris Prantl, Exc.-fl. Baiern 23. 1884.
Dryopteris Phegopteris C. Chr. Index Fil. 284. 1905.
Thelypteris Phegopteris Slosson, in Rydb. Fl. Rocky Mts. 1043.
  1917.

NEPHROLEPIS Schott, Gen. Fil. [under *pl. 3.*] 1834.
Nephrolepis exaltata (L.) Schott, Gen. Fil. [under *pl. 3.*] 1834.
  Polypodium exaltatum L. Syst. ed. 10. 1326. 1759.
  Aspidium exaltatum Sw. Jour. Bot. Schrad. 1800^2: 32. 1801.
  Nephrodium exaltatum R. Br. Prodr. 1: 148. 1810.
Nephrolepis cordifolia (L.) Presl, Tent. Pterid. 79. 1836.
  Polypodium cordifolium L. Sp. Pl. 1089. 1753.
  Aspidium cordifolium Sw. Jour. Bot. Schrad. 1800^2: 32. 1801.
  Aspidium tuberosum Bory; Willd. Sp. Pl. 5: 234. 1810.
  Nephrodium tuberosum Desv. Mém. Soc. Linn. Paris 6: 252. 1827.
  Nephrolepis tuberosa Presl, Tent. Pterid. 79. 1836.
Nephrolepis biserrata (Sw.) Schott, Gen. Fil. [under *pl. 3.*] 1834.
  Aspidium biserratum Sw. Jour. Bot. Schrad. 1800^2: 32. 1801.
  Nephrodium biserratum Presl, Rel. Haenk. 1: 31. 1825.
  Hypopeltis biserrata Bory, Voy. Bél. Bot. 2: 65. 1833.
  Lepidoneuron biserratum Fée, Gen. Fil. 301. 1852.

CYSTOPTERIS Bernh. Neues Jour. Bot. Schrad. 1^2: 26. 1806.
Cystopteris fragilis (L.) Bernh. Neues Jour. Bot. Schrad. 1^2: 27.
  1806.
  Polypodium fragile L. Sp. Pl. 1091. 1753.
  Filix fragilis Underw. Our Nat. Ferns ed. 6. 119. 1900.
  Cystopteris fragilis Mackeyi, Lamson, Fern Fl. Can. 233. 1889.
  Cystopteris fragilis protrusa Weatherby, Rhodora 37: 373. 1935.
Cystopteris bulbifera (L.) Bernh. Neues Jour. Bot. Schrad. 1^2: 10.
  1806.
  Polypodium bulbiferum L. Sp. Pl. 1091. 1753.
  Cystea bulbifera Watt, Can. Nat. II. 13: 160. 1867.
  Filix bulbifera Underw. Our Nat. Ferns ed. 6. 119. 1900.

WOODSIA R. Br. Prodr. 1: 158. 1810 (*"Woodia"*); Trans. Linn.
  Soc. 11: 170. 1813.
Woodsia ilvensis (L.) R. Br. Trans. Linn. Soc. 11: 173. 1813.
  Acrostichum ilvense L. Sp. Pl. 1071. 1753.
Woodsia scopulina D. C. Eaton, Can. Nat. 2: 91. 1865.
  Physematium scopulinum Trevisan, Nuovo Giorn. Bot. Ital. 7: 161.
  1875.
Woodsia obtusa (Spreng.) Torr. Cat. Pl. Geol. Rep. N. Y. 195. 1840.
  Polypodium obtusum Spreng. Anl. 3: 93. 1804.
  Aspidium obtusum Sw. Syn. Fil. 420. 1806.
  Hypopeltis obtusa Torr. Comp. 380. 1826.
  Cystopteris obtusa Presl, Tent. Pterid. 93. 1836.
  Physematium obtusum Hook. Fl. Bor. Am. 2: 259. 1840.

SPHENOMERIS Maxon, Jour. Wash. Acad. 3: 144. 1913.
Sphenomeris clavata (L.) Maxon, Jour. Wash. Acad. 3: 144. 1913.
  Adiantum clavatum L. Sp. Pl. 1096. 1753.
  Davallia clavata Smith, Mém. Acad. Turin 5: 415. 1790.
  Stenoloma clavatum Fée, Gen. Fil. 330. 1852.
  Lindsaya clavata Mett. Ann. Sci. Nat. IV. 15: 64. 1861.
  Odontosoria clavata J. Smith, Hist. Fil. 264. 1875.
  Schizoloma clavatum Kuhn, Chaetopt. 346. 1882.

DENNSTAEDTIA Bernh. Jour. Bot. Schrad. 1800²: 124. 1801.
Dennstaedtia punctilobula (Michx.) Moore, Index Fil. xcvii. 1857.
  Nephrodium punctilobulum Michx. Fl. Bor. Am. 2: 268. 1803.
  Dicksonia pilosiuscula Willd. Enum. 1076. 1809.
  Dicksonia punctilobula A. Gray, Man. 628. 1848.
Dennstaedtia adiantoides (Humb. & Bonpl.) Moore, Index Fil.
  xcvii. 1857.
  Dicksonia adiantoides Humb. & Bonpl.; Willd. Sp. Pl. 5: 488. 1810.
  Sitolobium adiantoides J. Smith, Lond. Jour. Bot. 1: 434. 1842.

ONOCLEA L. Sp. Pl. 1062. 1753.
Onoclea sensibilis L. Sp. Pl. 1062. 1753.
  Onoclea obtusilobata Schkuhr, Krypt. Gew. 1: 95. 1809.
  Onoclea sensibilis obtusilobata Torr. Fl. N. Y. 2: 499. 1843.

CERATOPTERIDACEAE

CERATOPTERIS Brongn. Bull. Soc. Philom. 1821: 186. 1821.
Ceratopteris pteridoides (Hook.) Hieron. Bot. Jahrb. 34: 561.
  1905.
  Parkeria pteridoides Hook. Exot. Fl. *pl. 147.* 1825.
  Ceratopteris Parkeria J. Smith, Jour. Bot. Hook. 4: 70. 1841.
  Ceratopteris thalictroides Hook. Sp. Fil. 2: 235, in part. 1858.
    Not *C. thalictroides* Brongn. 1821.
Ceratopteris deltoidea Benedict, Bull. Torrey Club 36: 472. 1909.

GLEICHENIACEAE

DICRANOPTERIS Bernh. Neues Jour. Bot. Schrad. 1²: 38. 1806.
Dicranopteris flexuosa (Schrad.) Underw. Bull. Torrey Club 34:
  254. 1907.
  Mertensia flexuosa Schrad. Gott. Gel. Anz. 1824: 863. 1824.
  Gleichenia dichotoma Hook. Sp. Fil. 1: 12, in part. 1844.
  Gleichenia flexuosa Mett. Ann. Lugd. Bat. 1: 50. 1863.

SCHIZAEACEAE

ACTINOSTACHYS Wall.; Hook. Gen. Fil. *pl. 111.* 1842.
Actinostachys Germani Fée, Mém. Foug. 11: 123. 1866.
  Schizaea Germani Prantl, Schiz. 132. 1881.

ANEMIA Sw. Syn. Fil. 155. 1806.
Anemia adiantifolia (L.) Sw. Syn. Fil. 157. 1806.
  Osmunda adiantifolia L. Sp. Pl. 1065. 1753.
  Ornithopteris adiantifolia Bernh. Neues Jour. Bot. Schrad. 1²: 50.
    1806.
LYGODIUM Sw. Jour. Bot. Schrad. 1800²: 106. 1801.
Lygodium palmatum (Bernh.) Sw. Syn. Fil. 154. 1806.
  Gisopteris palmata Bernh. Jour. Bot. Schrad. 1800²: 129. 1801.
  Hydroglossum palmatum Willd. Schr. Akad. Erfurt **1802**: 25.
    1802.
  Cteisium paniculatum Michx. Fl. Bor. Am. 2: 275. 1803.
Lygodium japonicum (Thunb.) Sw. Jour. Bot. Schrad. 1800²: 106.
    1801.
  Ophioglossum japonicum Thunb. Fl. Jap. 328. 1784.

OSMUNDACEAE

OSMUNDA [Tourn.] L. Sp. Pl. 1063. 1753.
Osmunda regalis L. Sp. Pl. 1065. 1753.
  Osmunda spectabilis Willd. Sp. Pl. 5: 98. 1810.
  Osmunda regalis spectabilis A. Gray, Man. ed. 2. 600. 1856.
Osmunda cinnamomea L. Sp. Pl. 1066. 1753.
  Osmunda cinnamomea frondosa A. Gray, Man. 635. 1848.
  Osmunda cinnamomea incisa Huntington, Fern Bull. 7: 12. 1899.
  Osmunda cinnamomea glandulosa Waters, Fern Bull. 10: 21. 1902.
Osmunda Claytoniana L. Sp. Pl. 1066. 1753.
  Osmunda interrupta Michx. Fl. Bor. Am. 2: 273. 1803.

OPHIOGLOSSALES

OPHIOGLOSSACEAE

OPHIOGLOSSUM [Tourn.] L. Sp. Pl. 1062. 1753.
Ophioglossum Engelmanni Prantl, Ber. Deuts. Bot. Ges. 1: 351.
    1883.
Ophioglossum vulgatum L. Sp. Pl. 1062. 1753.
  Ophioglossum Grayi Beck, Bot. U. S. 458. 1833.
  Ophioglossum vulgatum minus Moore, Ferns Gr. Brit. under *pl.*
    51B. 1856.
Ophioglossum tenerum Mett.; Prantl, Ber. Deuts. Bot. Ges. 1: 352.
    1883.
  Ophioglossum pusillum Nutt. Gen. 2: 248. 1818.
  Ophioglossum vulgatum nudicaule D. C. Eaton, in Chapm. Fl. S.
    U.S. 599, excl. syn. 1860.
  Ophioglossum nudicaule Garber, Bot. Gaz. 3: 85. 1878. Not *O.
    nudicaule* L.f. 1781.
Ophioglossum crotalophoroides Walt. Fl. Car. 256. 1788.
  Ophioglossum bulbosum Michx. Fl. Bor. Am. 2: 276. 1803.
  Ophioglossum vulgatum crotalophoroides D. C. Eaton, in Chapm. Fl.
    S. U.S. 599. 1860.

Ophioglossum floridanum E. St. John, Am. Fern Jour. **26**: 52. 1936.
Ophioglossum floridanum f. *favosum* E. St. John, Am. Fern Jour.
  26: 52. 1936.
Ophioglossum floridanum f. *reticulosum* E. St. John, Am. Fern Jour.
  26: 52. 1936.
Ophioglossum Pumilio E. St. John, in Small, Ferns SE. 361. 1938.
Ophioglossum dendroneuron E. St. John, in Small, Ferns SE. 364.
  1938.
Ophioglossum mononeuron E. St. John, in Small, Ferns SE. 364. 1938.

CHEIROGLOSSA Presl, Suppl. Tent. Pterid. 56. 1845.
Cheiroglossa palmata (L.) Presl, Suppl. Tent. Pterid. 57. 1845.
Ophioglossum palmatum L. Sp. Pl. 1063. 1753.

BOTRYCHIUM Sw. Jour. Bot. Schrad. 1800²: 8, 110. 1801.
Botrychium biternatum (Savigny) Underw. Bot. Gaz. **22**: 407.
  1896.
Osmunda biternata Savigny, in Lam. Encyc. 4: 650. 1797.
Botrypus lunaroides Michx. Fl. Bor. Am. 2: 274. 1803.
Botrychium obliquum Muhl.; Willd. Sp. Pl. 5: 63. 1810.
Botrychium lunarioides obliquum A. Gray, Man. 635. 1848.
Botrychium ternatum Hook. & Baker, Syn. Fil. 448, in part. 1868.
  Not *B. ternatum* Sw. 1801.
Botrychium ternatum obliquum D. C. Eaton, Ferns N. Am. **1**: 149.
  1878.
Botrychium ternatum oneidense Gilbert, Fern Bull. **9**: 27. 1901.
Botrychium dissectum obliquum Clute, Fern Bull. **10**: 76. 1902.
Botrychium dissectum oneidense Clute, Fern Bull. **10**: 76. 1902.
Botrychium tenuifolium Underw. Bull. Torrey Club 30: 52. 1903.
Botrychium obliquum oneidense Waters, Ferns 334. 1903.
Sceptridium obliquum Lyon, Bot. Gaz. **40**: 458. 1905.
Sceptridium obliquum oneidense Lyon, Bot. Gaz. **40**: 458. 1905.
Botrychium dissectum Spreng. Anl. 3: 172. 1804.
Botrychium funarioides dissectum Oakes, in Z. Thompson, Hist. Ver-
  mont. 207. 1842.
Botrychium lunarioides dissectum A. Gray, Man. 635. 1848.
Botrychium ternatum dissectum D. C. Eaton, Ferns N. Am. **1**: 150.
  1878.
Botrychium obliquum dissectum Prantl, Jahrb. Bot. Gart. Berlin **3**:
  342. 1884.
Sceptridium dissectum Lyon, Bot. Gaz. **40**: 457. 1905.
Sceptridium ternatum dissectum Clute, Fern Bull. **14**: 48. 1906.
Botrychium alabamense Maxon, Proc. Biol. Soc. Wash. **19**: 23.
  1906.

OSMUNDOPTERIS (Milde) Small, Ferns SE. 377. 1938.
Botrychium § *Osmundopteris* Milde, Fil. Eur. 209. 1867.
Osmundopteris virginiana (L.) Small, Ferns SE. 377. 1938.
Osmunda virginiana L. Sp. Pl. 1064. 1753.
Osmunda virginica L. Syst. Nat. ed. 12. 2: 685. 1767.
Botrychium virginianum Sw. Jour. Bot. Schrad. 1800²: 111. 1801.

Botrychium virginicum Willd. Sp. Pl. **5**: 64. 1810.
Botrychium gracile Pursh, Fl. Am. Sept. 656. 1814.

SALVINIALES

MARSILEACEAE

MARSILEA L. Sp. Pl. 1099. 1753.
Marsilea vestita Hook. & Grev. Ic. Fil. *pl. 159.* 1831.
 Zaluzianskya vestita Kuntze, Rev. Gen. 823. 1891.
Marsilea uncinata A. Br. Flora 22: 304, hyponym. 1839; Am. Jour.
 Sci. II. 3: 55. 1847.
 Marsilea vestita uncinata Baker, Handb. Fern All. 143. 1887.

PILULARIA L. Sp. Pl. 1100. 1753.
Pilularia americana A. Br. Monatsb. Akad. Berlin **1863**: 435. 1864.
 Calamistrum americanum Kuntze, Rev. Gen. 822. 1891.

SALVINIACEAE

AZOLLA Lam. Encyc. **1**: 343. 1783.
Azolla caroliniana Willd. Sp. Pl. **5**: 541. 1810.

SALVINIA Adans. Fam. Pl. **2**: 15. 1763.
Salvinia auriculata Aubl. Pl. Guian. 969. 1775.
 Salvinia natans Pursh, Fl. Am. Sept. 672. 1814. Not *S. natans*
 All. 1785.
 Salvinia auriculata Olfersiana Klotzsch; Baker, Handb. Fern-All.
 136. 1887.

EQUISETALES

EQUISETACEAE

EQUISETUM [Tourn.] L. Sp. Pl. 1061. 1753.
Equisetum arvense L. Sp. Pl. 1061. 1753.
 Equisetum arvense serotinum G. Meyer, Chlor. Hanov. 666. 1836.
Equisetum laevigatum A. Br. Am. Jour. Sci. 46: 87. 1844.
 Equisetum hyemale intermedium A. A. Eaton, Fern Bull. **11**: 108.
 1903.
Equisetum praealtum Raf. Fl. Ludov. 13. 1817. (''prealtum.'')
 Equisetum hiemale Pursh, Fl. Am. Sept. 652. 1814. Not *E.
 hyemale* L. 1753.
 Equisetum robustum A. Br. Am. Jour. Sci. 46: 88. 1844.
 Equisetum robustum affine Engelm.; A. Br. Am. Jour. Sci. 46: 88.
 1844.
 Equisetum variegatum Jesupi A. A. Eaton; Gilbert, List 9, 27.
 1901.
 Equisetum hiemale affine A. A. Eaton, Fern Bull. **11**: 75. 111.
 1903.
 Equisetum hiemale robustum Clute, Fern Allies 256. 1905.

LYCOPODIALES

PSILOTACEAE

PSILOTUM Sw. Jour. Bot. Schrad. 1800²: 8, 109. 1801.
Psilotum nudum (L.) Griseb. Veg. Kar. 130. 1857.
Lycopodium nudum L. Sp. Pl. 1100. 1753.
Hoffmannia aphylla Willd. Mag. Bot. 6: 17. 1789.
Psilotum triquetrum Sw. Jour. Bot. Schrad. 1800²: 109. 1801.
Psilotum floridanum Michx. Fl. Bor. Am. 2: 281. 1803.

LYCOPODIACEAE

LYCOPODIUM [Dill.] L. Sp. Pl. 1100. 1753.
Lycopodium Selago L. Sp. Pl. 1102. 1753.
Plananthus Selago Beauv. Prodr. Aethiog. 112. 1805.
Lycopodium Selago appressum Desv. Mém. Soc. Linn. Paris 6: 180. 1827.
Lycopodium appressum Petrov, Fl. Iakut, 37. 1930.
Lycopodium porophilum Lloyd & Underw. Bull. Torrey Club 27: 150. 1900.
Lycopodium lucidulum porophilum Clute, Fern Allies 262. 1905.
Lycopodium lucidulum Michx. Fl. Bor. Am. 2: 284. 1803.
Lycopodium Selago patens Desv. Mém. Soc. Linn. Paris 6: 180. 1827.
Lycopodium reflexum Willd. Sp. Pl. 5: 52. 1810.
Plananthus patens Beauv. Prodr. Aethiog. 111. 1805.
Lycopodium dichotomum Jacq. Enum. Stirp. Vind. 314. 1762.
Plananthus dichotomus Beauv. Prodr. Aethiog. 111. 1805.
Urostachys dichotomus Herter, Beih. Bot. Centr. 39²: 249. 1922.
Lycopodium appressum (Chapm.) Lloyd & Underw. Bull. Torrey Club 27: 153. 1900. (*L. "adpressum."*)
Lycopodium inundatum Bigelovii Tuckerm. Am. Jour. Sci. 45: 47. 1843.
Lycopodium inundatum appressum Chapm. Bot. Gaz. 3: 20. 1878.
Lycopodium inundatum elongatum Chapm. Bot. Gaz. 3: 21. 1878.
Lycopodium alopecuroides adpressum Chapm. Fl. S. U.S. ed. 3. 638. 1897.
Lycopodium alopecuroides elongatum Chapm. Fl. S. U.S. ed. 3. 638. 1897.
Lycopodium Chapmani Underw.; Maxon, Proc. U.S. Nat. Mus. 23: 646. 1901.
Lycopodium alopecuroides L. Sp. Pl. 1102. 1753.
Plananthus alopecuroides Beauv. Prodr. Aethiog. 111. 1805.
Lycopodium inundatum alopecuroides Tuckerm. Am. Jour. Sci. 45: 47. 1843.
Lycopodium prostratum Harper, Bull. Torrey Club 33: 229. 1906.
Lycopodium inundatum pinnatum Chapm. Fl. S. U.S. 600. 1860.

Lycopodium pinnatum Lloyd & Underw. Bull. Torrey Club 27: 155.
1900. Not *L. pinnatum* Lam. 1791.
Lycopodium carolinianum L. Sp. Pl. 1104. 1753.
Lepidotis caroliniana Beauv. Prodr. Aethiog. 108. 1805.
Lycopodium obscurum L. Sp. Pl. 1102. 1753.
Lycopodium dendroideum Michx. Fl. Bor. Am. 2: 282. 1803.
Lepidotis dendroidea Beauv. Prodr. Aethiog. 108. 1805.
Lycopodium obscurum dendroideum D. C. Eaton, in A. Gray, Man.
ed. 6. 696. 1890.
Lycopodium clavatum L. Sp. Pl. 1101. 1753.
Lepidotis clavata Beauv. Prodr. Aethiog. 108. 1805.
Lycopodium clavatum monostachyon B. L. Robinson, Rhodora 3: 237.
1901. Not *L. clavatum monostachyon* Hook. & Grev. 1831.
Lycopodium clavatum megastachyum Fernald & Bissell, Rhodora
12: 53. 1910.
Lycopodium flabelliforme (Fernald) Blanchard, Rhodora 13: 168.
1911.
Lycopodium complanatum L. Sp. Pl. 1104, in part. 1753.
Lycopodium complanatum flabelliforme Fernald, Rhodora 3: 280.
1901.
Lycopodium tristachyum Pursh Fl. Am. Sept. 653. 1814.
Lycopodium Chamaecyparissus A. Br.; Döll, Rhein. Fl. 36. 1843.
Lycopodium complanatum Chamaecyparissus D. C. Eaton, in A. Gray,
Man. ed. 6. 697. 1890.
Lycopodium cernuum L. Sp. Pl. 1103. 1753.
Lepidotis cernua Beauv. Prodr. Aethiog. 108. 1805.

SELAGINELLACEAE

DIPLOSTACHYUM Beauv. Prodr. Aetheog. 104. 1805.
Diplostachyum Eatoni (Hieron.) Small, Ferns SE. 422. 1938.
Selaginella Eatoni Hieron.; Small, Ferns Trop. Fla. 67. 1918.
Diplostachyum ludovicianum (A. Br.) Small, Ferns SE. 1937.
Selaginella ludoviciana A. Br. Ann. Sci. Nat. IV. 13: 58. 1860.
Selaginella apoda (*"apus"*) *denticulata* Spring, Mém. Acad. Belg.
24: 77. 1850.
Diplostachyum apodum (L.) Beauv. Prodr. Aethiog. 107. 1805.
Lycopodium apodum L. Sp. Pl. 1105. 1753.
Selaginella apoda Spring, in Mart. Fl. Bras. 1²: 119. 1840. (*S.
"apus."*)

SELAGINELLA Beauv. Prodr. Aethiog. 101. 1805.
Selaginella rupestris (L.) Spring, Flora 21: 149, 182. 1838.
Lycopodium rupestre L. Sp. Pl. 1101. 1753.
Stachygynandrum rupestre Beauv. Prodr. Aethiog. 113. 1803.
Selaginella tortipila A. Br. Ann. Sci. Nat. V. 3: 271. 1865.
Selaginella rupestris tortipila Underw. Our Nat. Ferns ed. 3. 140.
1888.
Selaginella Sherwoodii Underw. Torreya 2: 172. 1902.
Selaginella rupestris Sherwoodii Clute, Fern Allies 264. 1905.

Selaginella acanthonota Underw. Torreya 2: 172. 1902.
  Selaginella rupestris acanthonota Clute, Fern Allies 264. 1905.
Selaginella arenicola Underw. Bull. Torrey Club 25: 541. 1898.
  Selaginella arenaria Underw. Bull. Torrey Club 25: 129. 1898. Not
    S. arenaria Baker. 1883.
  Selaginella funiformis Van Eseltine, Proc. Biol. Soc. Wash. 30: 161.
    1917.
  Selaginella humifusa Van Eseltine, Contr. U.S. Nat. Herb. 20: 165.
    1918. Not *S. humifusa* Hieron. 1912.
  Selaginella floridana Maxon, Am. Fern Jour. 11: 1. 1921.

ISOETALES

ISOETACEAE

ISOETES L. Sp. Pl. 1100. 1753.
Isoetes flaccida Shuttlw.; A. Br. Flora 29: 178. 1846.
  Calamaria flaccida Kuntze, Rev. Gen. 828. 1891.
Isoetes flaccida Chapmani Engelm. Trans. Acad. St. Louis 4: 386.
    1882.
  Isoetes Chapmani Small, Ferns Fla. 22. 1932.
Isoetes flaccida alata N. Pfeiffer, Ann. Mo. Bot. Gard. 9: 137. 1922.
  Isoetes alata Small, Ferns Fla. 22. 1932.
Isoetes melanospora Engelm. Trans. Acad. St. Louis 3: 395. 1878.
  Calamaria melanospora Kuntze, Rev. Gen. 828. 1891.
Isoetes Butleri Engelm. Bot. Gaz. 3: 1. 1878.
  Isoetes Butleri immaculata Engelm. Trans. Acad. St. Louis 4: 388.
    1882.
  Calamaria Butleri Kuntze, Rev. Gen. 828. 1891.
Isoetes Engelmanni A. Br. Flora 29: 178. 1846.
  Isoetes Engelmanni gracilis Engelm. in A. Gray, Man. ed. 5. 677.
    1867.
  Isoetes Engelmanni valida Engelm. in A. Gray, ed. 5. 677. 1867.
  Calamaria Engelmanni Kuntze, Rev. Gen. 828. 1891.
  Isoetes Engelmanni georgiana Engelm. Trans. Acad. St. Louis 4:
    384. 1882.
Isoetes Engelmanni caroliniana A.A. Eaton, Fern Bull. 8: 60. 1900.
  Isoetes valida Clute, Fern All. 236. 1905.

AUTHORITIES CITED IN THIS WORK[1]

ADANSON, MICHEL, 1727–1806.—(Adans.)
AGARDH, CARL ADOLF, 1785–1859.—(Ag.)
AITON, WILLIAM, 1731–1793.—(Ait.)
ALLIONI, CARLO, 1728–1804.—(All.)
ÅNGSTRÖM, JOHAN, 1813–1879.—(Angstr.)
ASCHERSON, PAUL FRIEDRICH AUGUST, 1834–1913.—(Asch.)
AUBLET, JEAN BAPTISTE CHRISTOPHE FUSÉE, 1720–1778.—(Aubl.)

BAKER, JOHN GILBERT, 1834–1930.—(Baker)
BEAUVOIS, see PALISOT DE BEAUVOIS
BECK, LEWIS CALEB, 1798–1853.—(Beck)
BEDDOME, RICHARD HENRY, 1830–1911.—(Bedd.)
BENEDICT, RALPH CURTISS, 1883–   .—(Benedict)
BERNHARDI, JOHANN JACOB, 1774–1850.—(Bernh.)
BLANCHARD, WILLIAM HENRY, 1850–1922.—(Blanchard)
BLUME, CARL LUDWIG VON, 1796–1892.—(Blume)
BONGARD, AUGUST GUSTAV HEINRICH, 1786–1839.—(Bong.)
BORY DE SAINT-VINCENT, JEAN BAPTISTE GEORGES MARCELLIN, 1778–
    1846.—(Bory)
BOSCH, ROELOF BENJAMIN VAN DEN, 1810–1862.—(Bosch)
BRACKENRIDGE, WILLIAM DUNLOP, 1810–1893.—(Brack.)
BRAUN, ALEXANDER CARL HEINRICH, 1805–1877.—(A. Br.)
BRITTON, ELIZABETH GERTRUDE (KNIGHT), 1858–1934.—(E. G. Britton)
BRITTON, NATHANIEL LORD, 1859–1934.—(Britton)
BRITTON, NATHANIEL LORD, 1859–1934; BROWN, ADDISON, 1830–1913.
    —(Britt. & Br.)
BRITTON, NATHANIEL LORD, 1859–1934; STERNS, EMERSON ELLICK,
    1846–1926; POGGENBURG, JUSTUS FERDINAND, 1840–1893.—(B.S.P.)
BRONGNIART, ADOLPHE THEODORE, 1801–1876.—(Brongn.)
BROWN, ROBERT, 1773–1858.—(R. Br.)
BUBANI, PIETRO, 1806–1888.—(Bubani)
BUCKLEY, SAMUEL BOTSFORD, 1809–1884.—(Buckl.)
BUTTERS, FREDERIC KING, 1878–   .—(Butters)

CAVANILLES, ANTONIO JOSÉ, 1745–1804.—(Cav.)
CHAPMAN, ALVAN WENTWORTH, 1809–1899.—(Chapm.)
CHRIST, KONRAD HERMANN HEINRICH, 1833–1933.—(Christ)

[1] Contributed by JOHN HENDLEY BARNHART.

487

CHRISTENSEN, CARL FREDERIK ALBERT, 1872.——(C. Chr.)
CLARKSON, EDWARD HALE, 1866–1934.—(Clarkson)
CLUTE, WILLARD NELSON, 1869–   .—(Clute)

DAVENPORT, GEORGE EDWARD, 1833–1907.—(Davenp.)
DESVAUX, NIÇAISE AUGUSTE, 1784–1856.—(Desv.)
DIELS, FRIEDRICH LUDWIG EMIL, 1874–   .—(Diels)
DILLENIUS, JOHANN JACOB, 1684–1747.—(Dill.)
DODGE, RAYNAL, 1844–1918.—(Dodge)
DÖLL, JOHANN CHRISTOPH, 1808–1885.—(Döll)
DOWELL, PHILIP, 1864–1936.—(Dowell)
DURIEU DE MAISONNEUVE, MICHEL CHARLES, 1797–1878.—(Durieu)

EATON, ALVAH AUGUSTUS, 1865–1908.—(A. A. Eaton)
EATON, AMOS, 1776–1842.—(Eaton)
EATON, DANIEL CADY, 1834–1895.—(D. C. Eaton)
EGGLESTON, WILLARD WEBSTER, 1863–1935.—(Eggl.)
EHRHART, FRIEDRICH, 1742–1795.—(Ehrh.)
ENGELMANN, GEORGE, 1809–1884.—(Engelm.)

FARWELL, OLIVER ATKINS, 1867–   .—(Farwell)
FEATHERMAN, AMERICUS, 1822–?.—(Featherman)
FÉE, ANTOINE LAURENT APOLLINAIRE, 1789–1874.—(Fée)
FERNALD, MERRITT LYNDON, 1873–   .—(Fernald)
FERNALD, MERRITT LYNDON, 1873–   ; BISSELL, CHARLES HUMPHREY,
    1857–1925.—(Fernald & Bissell)
FISCHER, FRIEDRICH ERNST LUDWIG VON, 1782–1854.—(Fischer)
FORSKÅL, PEHR, 1732–1763.—(Forsk.)
FRIES, KLAS ROBERT ELIAS, 1876–.—(R. E. Fries)

GALEOTTI, HENRI GUILLAUME, 1814–1858.—(Galeotti)
GARBER, ABRAM PASCHAL, 1858–1881.—(Garber)
GAUDICHAUD-BEAUPRÉ, CHARLES, 1787–1854.—(Gaud.)
GAY, JACQUES ETIENNE, 1786–1864; DURIEU DE MAISONNEUVE, MICHEL
    CHARLES, 1797–1878.—(Gay & Durieu)
GILBERT, BENJAMIN DAVIS, 1835–1907.—(Gilbert)
GMELIN, JOHANN FRIEDRICH, 1748–1804.—(J. F. Gmel.)
GMELIN, SAMUEL GOTTLIEB, 1745–1774.—(S. G. Gmel.)
GRAY, ASA, 1819–1888.—(A. Gray)
GRAY, FREDERICK WILLIAM, 1878–   .—(F. W. Gray)
GRAY, SAMUEL FREDERICK, 1766–1836.—(S. F. Gray)

GREENE, EDWARD LEE, 1842–1915.—(Greene)

GRISEBACH, AUGUST HEINRICH RUDOLF, 1814–1879.—(Griseb.)

HARPER, ROLAND MCMILLAN, 1878– .—(Harper)

HERTER, WILHELM, 1884– .—(Herter)

HEWARD, ROBERT, 1791–1877.—(Heward)

HIERONYMUS, GEORG HANS EMMO WOLFGANG, 1846–1921.—(Hieron.)

HITCHCOCK, ALBERT SPEAR, 1865–1935.—(Hitchc.)

HITCHCOCK, EDWARD, 1793–1864.—(E. Hitchc.)

HOFFMAN, GEORG FRANZ, 1761–1826.—(Hoffm.)

HOOKER, WILLIAM JACKSON, 1785–1865.—(Hook.)

HOOKER, WILLIAM JACKSON, 1785–1865; BAKER, JOHN GILBERT, 1834–1920.—(Hook. & Baker)

HOOKER, WILLIAM JACKSON, 1785–1865; GREVILLE, ROBERT KAYE, 1794–1866.—(Hook. & Grev.)

HOUSE, HOMER DOLIVER, 1878– .—(House)

HOUTTUYN, MARTIN.—(Houtt.)

HOWE, ELLIOT CALVIN, 1828–1899.—(E. C. Howe)

HUMBOLDT, FRIEDRICH WILHELM HEINRICH ALEXANDER VON, 1769–1859; BONPLAND, AIMÉ JACQUES ALEXANDRE, 1773–1858.—(Humb. & Bonpl.)

HUMBOLDT, FRIEDRICH WILHELM HEINRICH ALEXANDRE VON, 1769–1859; BONPLAND, AIMÉ JACQUES ALEXANDER, 1773–1858; KUNTH, CARL SIGISMUND, 1788–1850.—(H.B.K.)

HUNTINGTON, JOHN WARREN, 1853– .—(Huntington)

JACQUIN, NIKOLAUS JOSEPH VON, 1727–1817.—(Jacq.)

JENMAN, GEORGE SAMUEL, 1845–1902.—(Jenman)

KARSTEN, GUSTAV KARL WILHELM HERMANN, 1817–1908.—(Karst.)

KAULFUSS, GEORG FRIEDRICH, 1786–1830.—(Kaulf.)

KEYSERLING, ALEXANDER FRIEDRICH MICHEL LEBERECHT ARTHUR VON, 1815–1891.—(Keyserl.)

KLOTZSCH, JOHANN FRIEDRICH, 1805–1860.—(Klotzsch)

KOCH, WILHELM DANIEL JOSEPH, 1771–1849.—(Koch)

KÜHLWEIN, PAUL EDUARD, 1798–1870.—(Kühl.)

KUHN, MAXIMILIAN FRIEDRICH ADALBERT, 1842–1894.—(Kuhn)

KÜMMERLE, JENÖ BÉLA, 1876–1931.—(Kümmerle)

KUNTZE, CARL ERNST OTTO, 1843–1907.—(Kuntze)

KUNZE, GUSTAV, 1793–1851.—(Kunze)

LAMARCK, JEAN BAPTISTE ANTOINE PIERRE MONNET DE, 1744–1829.—
(Lam.)
LANGSDORFF, GEORG HEINRICH VON, 1774–1852; FISCHER, FRIEDRICH
ERNST LUDWIG VON, 1782–1854.—(Langsd. & Fisch.)
LAWSON, GEORGE, 1827–1895.—(Lawson)
LIEBMANN, FREDERIK MICHAEL, 1813–1856.—(Liebm.)
LINK, JOHANN HEINRICH FRIEDRICH, 1767–1851.—(Link)
LINNAEUS, CARL, 1707–1778.—(L.)
LINNÉ, CARL VON, 1741–1783.—(L.f.)
LLOYD, FRANCIS ERNEST, 1868–   ; UNDERWOOD, LUCIEN MARCUS,
1853–1907.—(Lloyd & Underw.)
LOWE, EDWARD JOSEPH, 1825–1900.—(Lowe)
LUDWIG, CHRISTIAN GOTTLIEB, 1709–1773.—(Ludwig)
LYON, HAROLD LLOYD, 1879–   .—(Lyon)

MACKENZIE, KENNETH KENT, 1877–1934.—(Mackenzie)
MARIE-VICTORIN [KIROUAC, CONRAD], 1885–   .—(Victorin)
MARTENS, MARTIN, 1797–1863.—(Martens)
MARTENS, MARTIN, 1797–1863; GALEOTTI, HENRI GUILLAUME, 1814–
1858.—(Mart. & Gal.)
MAXON, WILLIAM RALPH, 1877–   .—(Maxon)
METTENIUS, GEORG HEINRICH, 1823–1866.—(Mett.)
MEYER, GEORG FRIEDRICH WILHELM, 1782–1856.—(G. Meyer)
MICHAUX, ANDRÉ, 1746–1802.—(Michx.)
MILDE, CARL AUGUST JULIUS, 1824–1871.—(Milde)
MILLER, ELIHU SANFORD, 1848–   .—(E. S. Miller)
MIRBEL, CHARLES FRANÇOIS BRISSEAU, 1776–1854.—(Mirb.)
MOORE, THOMAS, 1821–1887.—(Moore)
MOXLEY, GEORGE LOUCKS, 1871–   .—(Moxley)
MÜLLER, OTTO FRIEDRICH, 1730–1784.—(Müll.)
MUHLENBERG, GOTTHILF HENRY ERNST, 1753–1815.—(Muhl.)
MUNZ, PHILIP ALEXANDER, 1892–   ; JOHNSTON, IVAN MURRAY,
1898–   .—(Munz & Johnston)

NEWMAN, EDWARD, 1801–1876.—(Newman)
NIEUWLAND, JULIUS ALOYSIUS ARTHUR, 1878–1936.—(Nieuwl.)
NUTTALL, THOMAS, 1786–1859.—(Nutt.)

OAKES, WILLIAM, 1799–1848.—(Oakes)

PALISOT DE BEAUVOIS, AMBROISE MARIE FRANÇOIS JOSEPH, 1752–1820. —(Beauv.)

PALMER, THEODORE SHERMAN, 1868–   ; KNOWLTON, FRANK HALL, 1860–1926; POLLARD, CHARLES LOUIS, 1872–   .—(Palmer, Knowlton, & Pollard)

PALMER, WILLIAM, 1859–1921.—(W. Palmer)

PEASE, ARTHUR STANLEY, 1881–   ; MOORE, ALBERT HANFORD, 1883–   .—(Pease & Moore)

PETROV, VSEVOLOD ALEXEEVICH, 1896–   .—(Petrov)

PFEIFFER, NORMA ETTA, 1889–   .—(Pfeiffer)

POIRET, JEAN LOUIS MARIE, 1755–1834.—(Poir.)

PRANTL, KARL ANTON EUGEN, 1849–1893.—(Prantl)

PRESL, KAREL BOŘIWOG, 1794–1852.—(Presl)

PRINCE, ARTHUR REGINALD, 1900–   .—(A. R. Prince)

PURSH, FREDERICK TRAUGOTT, 1774–1820.—(Pursh)

RAFINESQUE, CONSTANTINE SAMUEL, 1783–1840.—(Raf.)

RICHARD, LOUIS CLAUDE MARIE, 1754–1821.—(Rich.)

ROBINSON, BENJAMIN LINCOLN, 1864–1935.—(B. L. Robinson)

ROBINSON, BENJAMIN LINCOLN, 1864–1935; FERNALD, MERRITT LYNDON, 1873–   .—(Rob. & Fern.)

ROTH, ALBRECHT WILHELM, 1757–1834.—(Roth)

RUPRECHT, FRANZ JOSEF, 1814–1870.—(Rupr.)

RYDBERG, PER AXEL, 1860–1931.—(Rydb.)

ST. JOHN, EDWARD PORTER, 1866–   .—(E. St. John)

ST. JOHN, ROBERT PORTER, 1869–   .—(R. St. John)

SALISBURY, RICHARD ANTHONY, 1761–1829.—(Salisb.)

SAVIGNY, MARIE JULES CÉSAR LELORGNE DE, 1777–1867.—(Sav.)

SCHAFFNER, JOHN HENRY, 1866–   .—(J. H. Schaffn.)

SCHKUHR, CHRISTIAN, 1741–1811.—(Schkuhr)

SCHLEICHER, JOHANN CHRISTOPH, 1768–1834.—(Schleich.)

SCHMIDEL, CASIMIR CHRISTOPH, 1718–1792.—(Schmidel)

SCHOTT, HEINRICH WILHELM, 1794–1865.—(Schott)

SCHRADER, HEINRICH ADOLPH, 1767–1836.—(Schrad.)

SCHREBER, JOHANN CHRISTIAN DANIEL VON, 1739–1810.—(Schreb.)

SCOTT, ROBERT ROBINSON, 1827–1877.—(R. R. Scott)

SHUTTLEWORTH, ROBERT JAMES, 1810–1874.—(Shuttl.)

SLOSSON, MARGARET, 1874?–   .—(Slosson)

SMALL, JOHN KUNKEL, 1869–1938.—(Small)

SMITH, JAMES EDWARD, 1759–1828.—(Smith)

SMITH, JOHN, 1798–1888.—(J. Smith)

SMITH, LYMAN BRADFORD, 1904–   .—(L. B. Smith)

SODIRO, LUIS, 1836–1909.—(Sodiro)

SPENNER, FRIDOLIN CARL LEOPOLD, 1798–1841.—(Spenner)

SPRENGEL, CURT POLYCARP JOACHIM, 1766–1833.—(Spreng.)

SPRING, ANTON FRIEDRICH, 1814–1872.—(Spring)

STREMPEL, JOHANNES CARL FRIEDRICH, 1800–1872.—(Strempel)

STURM, JACOB, 1771–1848.—(Sturm)

SWARTZ, OLOF PETER, 1760–1818.—(Sw.)

THUNBERG, CARL PETER, 1743–1828.—(Thunb.)

TIDESTROM, IVAR, 1865–   .—(Tidestrom)

TODARO, AGOSTINO, 1818–1892.—(Todaro)

TORREY, JOHN, 1796–1873.—(Torr.)

TOURNEFORT, JOSEPH PITTON DE, 1656–1708.—(Tourn.)

TREVISAN DE SAINT-LEON, VITTORE BENEDETTO ANTONIO, 1818–1897.—
    (Trevisan)

TUCKERMAN, EDWARD, 1817–1886.—(Tuckerm.)

UNDERWOOD, LUCIEN MARCUS, 1853–1907.—(Underw.)

URBAN, IGNATZ, 1848–1931.—(Urban)

VAN ESELTINE, GLEN PARKER, 1888–   .—(Van Eselt.)

VICTORIN, MARIE [KIROUAC, CONRAD], 1885–   .—(Victorin)

WALLICH, NATHANIEL, 1786–1854.—(Wall.)

WALTER, THOMAS, 1740–1788.—(Walt.)

WATERS, CAMPBELL EASTER, 1872–   .—(Waters)

WATT, DAVID ALLAN POE, 1830–1917.—(Watt)

WEATHERBY, CHARLES ALFRED, 1875–   .—(Weatherby)

WEISS, FRIEDRICH WILHELM, 1744–?.—(Weiss)

WHERRY, EDGAR THEODORE, 1885–   .—(Wherry)

WILLDENOW, CARL LUDWIG, 1765–1812.—(Willd.)

WOOD, ALPHONSO, 1810–1881.—(Wood)

GLOSSARY

ABAXIAL. The side or face away from the axis.

ABBERANT. Departing from type.

ACICULAR. Needle-shaped.

ACUMINATE. Tapering to the end.

ACUTE. Ending in a sharp angle.

ADAXIAL. The side or face next to axils.

ADNATE. United, used in reference to the union of parts of different organs.

AMPHIBIOUS. Living both on land and in water.

ANASTOMOSE. To run together or to unite.

ANNUAL. Having one season's duration.

ANNULUS. The elastic ring of cells in the sporangia.

ANTERIOR. Forward, away from the point of attachment, distal.

ANTHERIDIUM. The organ in ferns, corresponding to an anther in flowering plants.

ANTHEROZOID. A minute organ developed in an antheridium.

ANTRORSELY. Directed upwards.

APICULATE. Ending in a short pointed tip.

AQUATIC. Living in water.

ARCHEGONIUM. The organ in ferns, corresponding to the pistil in flowering plants.

ARCUATE. Bowed or arched.

ARENICOLOUS. Living in sand.

AREOLA. A space marked out by veins or veinlets.

ARTICULATE. Jointed.

ASSURGENT. Abruptly ascending.

ATTENUATE. Slenderly tapering.

AURICLE. An ear-shaped appendage.

AURICULATE. With ear-shaped appendages.

AWL-SHAPED. Tapering from a base to a slender tip.

AWN. A bristle-like appendage.

AXIL. The angle formed by a branch, or a leaf, with the stem from which it arises.

BIENNIAL. Having two seasons' duration.

BIPINNATIFID. Twice pinnately cleft.

BLADE. The dilated part of a leaf.

493

BRACT. A leaf, often much reduced, subtending an organ.

BULBLET. A small bulb.

CADUCOUS. Early-dropping.

CAMPANULATE. Bell-shaped.

CANESCENT. Growing gray.

CARINA. A keel-like process or fold.

CAUDATE. With a tail-like appendage.

CAUDEX. The persistent base of perennial herbaceous plants.

CAULINE. Belonging to the stem.

CELL. The smallest element in the structure of a living organism.

CENTRUM. The central air-space in a stem, as in *Equisetum*.

CESPITOSE. Growing in tufts.

CHAFF. A scale, usually dry and membranous.

CHANNELED. Grooved longitudinally.

CHARTACEOUS. Papery.

CHLOROPHYLL. The green coloring matter in plants.

CILIA. Slender hairs, often marginal.

CLAVATE. Club-shaped.

COALESCENT. United, used in reference to the union of parts or organs of the same kind.

COMMISSURAL. Pertaining to the line of union between two parts.

COMPOUND. Having two or more similar parts.

CONCOLOROUS. Of similar color.

CONE. A structure with imbricated scales around an elongate axis.

CONFLUENT. Running into each other.

CONFORM. Similar in form to the other members of its group.

CONIFEROUS. Cone-bearing.

CORDATE. Having two lobes and a sinus at the base.

CORIACEOUS. Leathery in texture.

CORM. The swollen base of a stem; like a bulb, but solid.

COSTA. A midvein of leaflets or segments.

CREEPING. Lying on the ground and rooting at the nodes.

CRENATE. Dentate with rounded teeth.

CRENULATE. Having small rounded teeth.

CRISPED. Curled.

CROZIER. The coiled end of a young fern leaf.

CUNEATE. Wedge-shaped.

CYLINDRIC. Roller-shaped.

DECIDUOUS. Not evergreen; not persistent.

DECOMPOUND. More than once compound.

DECUMBENT. Reclining or procumbent but with the tip ascending.

DECURRENT. Extending down below the point of insertion.

DEFLEXED. Bent or turned abruptly downward.

DEHISCENT. Opening regularly.

DELTOID. Shaped like the Greek letter delta; triangular.

DENTATE. Toothed, with the teeth directed outward.

DENTICULATE. Finely dentate.

DIAPHRAGM. A partition.

DICHOTOMOUS. Forking regularly by pairs.

DIFFUSE. Loosely or widely spreading.

DIMORPHIC. Occurring in two forms.

DIOECIOUS. With the sexes on different plants.

DISSECTED. Lobed to the base.

DISTAL. Remote from the point of attachment or the point of view.

DISTICHOUS. In two vertical ranks.

DORSAL. Relating to the back of an organ.

DORSIVENTRAL. With distinction of upper and lower surfaces.

ECOLOGICAL. Concerning the relation of plants to their surroundings.

ELATER. One of the four filamentous appendages of the spores in *Equisetum*.

ELLIPSOID. A solid body, elliptic in section.

ELLIPTIC. Having the outline of an ellipse; oval.

EMARGINATE. Having a shallow notch at the apex.

EMERSED. Standing out of the water or rising above it.

ENDOPHYTIC. Growing within a plant, usually parasitic.

ENTIRE. Without toothing or lobing.

EPIDERMAL. Pertaining to the superficial layer of cells.

EPIPHYTIC. Growing attached to other plants; but not parasitic.

EROSE. Uneven, as if gnawed.

EVANESCENT. Fleeting.

FALCATE. Scythe-shaped.

FASCICULATE. Bunched or bundled together.

FIBROUS. Resembling or consisting of fibers.

FILAMENTOSE. Having thread-like structures.

FILIFORM. Thread-shaped.

FIMBRIATE. Fringed.

FLABELLATE. Fan-shaped.

FLACCID. Lax and weak.

FLEXUOUS. Zigzag.

FOLIAR. Leaf-like.

FOLIOLATE. Having leaflets.

FOVEA. A pit, containing the sporangium, at the leaf-base in *Isoetes*.

FREE. Said of veins in a leaf that are simple or forked, but whose branches do not unite.

FRONDS. Leaves of ferns.

FUGACIOUS. Falling away early.

FUSIFORM. Spindle-shaped.

GAMETOPHYTE. The phase of a fern that produces the sexual organs.

GEMMA. Bud.

GEMMIPAROUS. Producing gemmae.

GLABROUS. Without hairs.

GLANDULAR. Bearing glands.

GLAUCOUS. Covered with a white or pale bloom.

GLOBOSE. Spherical.

GREGARIOUS. Growing in groups or colonies.

GROTTO. An area of fantastically eroded rock.

HABIT. (1) Appearance. (2) Characteristic adaptations to environment.

HABITAT. Adaptations to environment. The preferred natural environment.

HAMMOCK. Forest of broad-leaved trees.

HASTATE. Shaped like an arrow-head with the basal lobes directed outward.

HIRSUTE. Bearing stiff or coarse hairs.

HISPIDULOSE. Minutely beset with rough hairs.

HYALINE. Transparent or transluscent.

HYBRID. A cross between two species.

IMBRICATE. Overlapping.

INCISED. Sharply and deeply cut.

INDUSIUM. The covering of the sorus of a fern.

INFERIOR. Lower or below.

INSERTION. Attachment.

INTERNODE. Part of a stem between two nodes.

INTRORSE. Turned inward.

KEY. Florida Keys, rocky islands; Everglade Keys, rocky elevations surrounded by lowland or marsh.

LABYRINTHIFORM. Having complicated curved lines.

LACINIATE.

LANATE. Woolly.

LANCEOLATE. Shaped like a lance-head.

LEAFLET. A division of a compound leaf.

LIGULE. In *Isoetes,* a narrow membranous acuminate projection above the fovea.

LIME-SINK. A depression caused by a subsidence of lime-rock and often containing water.

LINEAR. Long and narrow, with parallel sides.

LIP-CELLS. The line of cells between which the sporangia dehisce.

LOBE. A segment, usually rounded.

LOBED. Having rounded segments.

LOBULE. A small lobe.

LUMEN. A bounded space, especially when translucent.

LUNATE. Crescent or halfmoon-shaped.

MEGASPORANGIUM. The envelope in which megaspores are developed or contained.

MEGASPORE. The larger kind of a spore if there are two kinds.

MICROSPORANGIUM. The receptacle in which the microspores are developed.

MICROSPORE. The smaller kind of a spore if there are two kinds.

MIDRIB. The main vein of a leaf or of a leaflet.

MIDVEIN. The central rib of a leaf or leaflet.

MONOECIOUS. With both sexes on the same plant.

MUCRONATE. Ending in a small abrupt tip.

MURICATE. Rough with short excrescences.

MYCORRHIZA. A fungus mycelium which invests or inhabits the roots or root-hairs of a plant.

NERVE. A simple thread of fibro-vascular tissue.

NODE. Point on a stem which normally bears a leaf or a whorl of leaves.

OB-. In combination, meaning inversion.

OBLANCEOLATE. Inverted lance-shaped.

OBLIQUE. Slanting.

OBLONG. Longer than broad with nearly parallel sides.

OBOVOID. Inverted egg-shaped.

OBTUSE. Blunt or rounded.

ORBICULAR. Circular.

OVAL. Broadly elliptic.

OVATE. Egg-shaped in outline.

OVOID. Shaped like a hen's egg.

PALMATE. Radiately lobed or divided.

PALUDAL. Of or pertaining to a marsh or a swamp.

PANICLE. A loose compound sporophyl with pedicellate sporangia.

PAPILLOSE. Having minute nipple-shaped projections.

PECTINATE. Pinnatifid with segments like the teeth of a comb.

PEDATE. Radiately lobed or compound with the lateral lobes or parts
cleft.

PEDUNCLE. A primary stalk.

PELTATE. Shield-shaped, with an attachment on the lower surface.

PENDULOUS. Hanging.

PENICILLATE. Tipped with fine hairs.

PENTAGONAL. Five-angled.

PERENNIAL. Having several or many years' duration.

PERSISTENT. Evergreen.

PETIOLE. The stalk of a leaf.

PETIOLULE. A secondary petiole.

PILOSE. Hairy, with soft hairs.

PINNA. A leaflet; a secondary or tertiary division of a pinnate leaf.

PINNATE. Compound and with the leaflets arranged on each side of a
common rachis.

PINNATIFID. Pinnately cleft.

PINNULE. A secondary pinna.

PRAIRIE. Low flat ground devoid of trees but covered with vegetation
and subject to flooding much of the year (Local S. E.)

PROCUMBENT. Lying on the ground, but not rooting.

PROLIFEROUS. Producing young from off-shoots.

PROTHALLUS. A usually flat and thallus-like growth, resulting from
the germination of a spore. Upon this are developed sexual organs
or new plants.

PROXIMAL. Posterior, nearer the point of attachment or the point of
view.

PUBESCENT. Bearing hairs.

PUNCTATE. Marked with depressions or internal glands.

PUNGENTLY. With rigid, sharp point.

PYRIFORM. Pear-shaped.

RACHIS. The axis of a compound leaf or of an inflorescence.

RAPHE. A ridge-like line on the sporocarp in Marsilea.

RECEPTACLE. An expanded structure that bears other organs.

REFLEXED. Bent abruptly downward.

RENIFORM. Kidney-shaped.

RETICULATE. Like a net-work.

REVOLUTE. Rolled backward from the margin or apex.

RHOMB. An equilateral parallelogram having oblique angles.

RING. Same as annulus.

ROOTSTOCK. A subterranean stem.

SALIENT. Projecting outwardly.

SCALE. A more or less flattened trichome borne on various parts of a fern.

SCANDENT. Climbing.

SCARIOUS. Thin, dry, and not green.

SEGMENT. A part of a cleft or pinnatifid leaf or leaflet-blade.

SEPTATE. Divided by partitions.

SEPTUM. A partition.

SERRATE. With sharp teeth pointing forward.

SERRULATE. Diminutive of serrate.

SESSILE. Without a stalk.

SETACEOUS. Bristle-like.

SHEATH. A tubular or funnelform envelope.

SILEX. A white or colorless, extremely hard crystalline mineral substance.

SIMPLE. Of one piece, as distinguished from compound.

SINK. A surface depression caused by the collapse of a subterranean cavity or by drainage into it.

SINUATE. With a strongly wavy margin.

SINUS. The recess between two lobes.

SORUS. A heap or cluster, as of spores.

SPATULATE. Gradually dilated upward to a rounded apex.

SPERMATOZOID. The motile male reproductive cell.

SPIKE. A form of sporophyl with the sporangia sessile on a common rachis.

SPINULOSE. Diminutive of spinose. Having small spines.

SPORANGIUM. A spore-sac.

SPORE. An asexual reproductive cell.

SPORELING. A young plant developed from a spore.

SPOROCARP. A capsular organ containing spores or sporangia.

SPOROPHYL. A leaf bearing spores.

SPOROPHYTE. A phase of a plant that bears the asexual spores.

SPUR. A sac-like or tubular extension, usually hollow.

STELLATE. Star-shaped.

STERILE. Unproductive; not bearing spores.

STOLON. A runner from the base of a plant.

STOMA. An orifice in the epidermis of a leaf or stem.

STRAMINEOUS. Straw-colored.

STROBILE. A structure with imbricate scales shaped like a cone.

SUB.–. Latin prefix, signifying slightly or somewhat.

SUBMERGED. Covered with water.

SUBULATE. Awl-shaped.

SUCCULENT. Fleshy.

SYMBIOSIS. The living together of dissimilar organisms with mutual or individual benefit.

TERETE. Circular in cross-section.

TERNATE. In threes.

TERRESTRIAL. Growing on the ground.

TETRAHEDRAL. Having the form of a tetrahedron, *i.e.*, a solid with four triangular faces.

THALLOID. Resembling a thallus.

THALLUS. In ferns, cellular expansion taking the place of the stem and leaves in higher plants.

TOMENTUM. Densely matted wool.

TORTUOUS. Twisted.

TRI–. Latin prefix, signifying three or thrice.

TRICHOMA. Any hair-like outgrowth of the epidermis.

TRIQUETROUS. Having three salient angles.

TRUNCATE. Abrupt, as if cut off transversely.

TUBERCLE. A small tuber or tuber-like body.

TUBEROUS. Tuber-like.

TUMID. Swollen.

TURGID. Swollen, as if by pressure from within.

ULIGINOUS. Living in mud.

UNDULATE. Having a wavy edge.

URCEOLATE. Urn-shaped.

VALLECULAR. Of or near a groove.

VALVE. One of the pieces into which a conceptacle or capsule splits.

VASCULAR. Having vessels or ducts.

VAULTED. Is used where a sorus, mainly on one side of a vein, is curved over to the opposite side.

VEIN. A thread of fibro-vascular tissue in a leaf, usually branching.

VEINLETS. Branches of veins.

VELUM. An indusium-like membrane in *Isoetes*.

VENATION. The arrangement of the veins.

VERNATION. The arrangement of the leaves in a bud.

VERTICILLATE. Disposed in a whorl.

VILLOUS. Bearing long soft hairs.

WHORL. Arrangement of leaves or branches in a circle around a node.

WING. A membranous expansion running along a stem

XEROPHILUS. Able to endure scarcity of moisture.

INDEX